Sustainable Production of Pulses in Diverse Agro-ecosystems

Vol. 1. Strategies for enhancing production

About Editors

Narendra Kumar, completed his Ph.D. from Indian Agricultural Research Institute, New Delhi and joined Agricultural Research Service (ARS) of ICAR in 2003. Dr. Kumar started his career as scientist at ICAR-VPKAS, Almora and developed technologies for crop diversification with off-season vegetables and pulses, intercropping, relay cropping, protected agriculture, weed management and resource conservation practices. He is associated in release of 18 varieties of pulses and oilseeds for different zones of country. He is recipient of Dr. P.S. Deshmukh Young Agronomist Award 2009 and Associateship Award 2016 by Indian Society of Agronomy. He is Fellow of Indian Society of Pulses Research. He has published > 100 research papers in international as well as national journals. Dr. Kumar is presently Head, Division of Crop Production at ICAR-Indian Institute of Pulses Research, Kanpur and involved in research activities related to crop diversification, resource conservation technology and weed management in pulse based cropping systems.

Dr. C.P. Nath, obtained M.Sc. from GBPUA&T (Pantnagar) and Ph.D. from IARI (New Delhi). Dr. Nath has contributed immensely on Conservation Agriculture, Weed Science, Carbon Sequestration and Pulse based Crop Diversification. Dr. Nath has received the DST-INSPIRE Fellowship from Ministry of Science and Technology, Government of India. He has been conferred with the Indian Science Congress Association-Young Scientist Award for the year 2017-18. He has published 71 research articles in national and international reputed journal, 4 review articles, and many book chapters till date. In recognition of his research contribution in agronomy, Dr. Nath also received the 'Indian Society of Agronomy Best Ph.D. Thesis Award 2016'.

Dr. C.S. Praharaj, obtained M.Sc. & Ph.D. from PAU, Ludhiana and now serving as Director, ICAR - Directorate of Groundnut Research (Junagadh). Dr. Praharaj significantly contributed in water management with resource conservation technologies (RCTs), Integrated Plant Nutrient System (IPNS) in cropping system with climate change perspectives and farmers' participatory research / technology assessment and refinement. He has published >100 research articles, 20 review articles, 40 books/chapters and 20 bulletins/manuals. He has also delivered 25 talks in TV/Radio-talks and presented 70 lead/oral in National/ International Conferences. For contribution in Agronomy, he was conferred with Fellow and Gold Medal of the Indian Society of Agronomy, New Delhi.

Dr. Uma Sah, is earned her Master and Doctoral degrees from ICAR-National Dairy Research Institute, Karnal with University gold medal during 1994-99. She is now contributing as Principal Scientist (Agricultural Extension) and Head, Division of Social Sciences, ICAR-Indian Institute of Pulses Research, Kanpur. Previously she served as scientist at CPRI regional station, Shillong for more than six years. Since 2006, she has been actively contributing to extension research at IIPR, Kanpur. She has implemented total 25 research projects, which includes 12 externally funded projects from external agencies like DBT, DST, NATP, ICSSR, BMGF, ICAR and UPCAR. She has been instrumental in providing incubation support to potential entrepreneurs in identified areas of pulse technologies. She has more than 170 publications to her credit which include research papers, technical articles, books, book chapters, technical bulletins and extension literatures.

Dr. N.P. Singh obtained Ph.D. from IARI, New Delhi and now serving as Vice-Chancellor, Banda University of Agriculture and Technology, Banda (U.P.). He is an eminent pulse geneticist served as Director of ICAR-IIPR, Kanpur. Previously, Dr. Singh was coordinating and guiding national chickpea research programme as Project Coordinator (Chickpea). Dr. Singh acquired advanced training in early days of his career in the area of molecular biology and genetic transformation from some of the leading biotechnology laboratories in India and abroad. He also served as visiting scientist at WA Biotechnology Centre, Murdoch University, Perth, Australia, and the Plant Biotechnology Institute, NRC, Saskatoon, Canada. Dr. Singh has published over 150 research/conference papers in national and international journals of repute.

Sustainable Production of Pulses in Diverse Agro-ecosystems

Vol. 1. Strategies for enhancing production

Narendra Kumar
Ph.D., ARS.
Pr. Scientist (Agronomy) & Head
Division of Crop Production
ICAR-Indian Institute of Pulses Research
Kanpur – 208 024 (U.P.), India

C.P. Nath
Ph.D., ARS. Scientist (Agronomy)
Division of Crop Production
ICAR-Indian Institute of Pulses Research
Kanpur – 208 024 (U.P.), India

C.S. Praharaj
Director
ICAR-Directorate of Groundnut Research
Junagadh – 362 001 (Gujarat), India

Uma Sah
Ph.D., ARS.
Pr. Scientist (Agric. Extension) & Head
Division of Social Sciences
ICAR-Indian Institute of Pulses Research
Kanpur – 208 024 (U.P.), India

N.P. Singh
Vice Chancellor
Banda University of Agriculture and Technology
Banda – 210 001 (U.P.), India

SCIENTIFIC PUBLISHERS

Published by
SCIENTIFIC PUBLISHERS (INDIA)
5 A, New Pali Road, P.O. Box 91
Jodhpur 342 001 (INDIA)
E-mail: info@scientificpub.com
Website: http://www.scientificpub.com

ISBN : **978-93-90749-95-9** HB (Vol 1)

EISBN : 978-93-90749-11-9 (Vol 1)

ISBN : **978-93-90749-77-5** HB (SET)

ISBN : 978-93-90749-19-5 HB (Vol 2)

Printed in India

सत्यमेव जयते
त्रिलोचन महापात्र, पीएच.डी.
सचिव, एवं महानिदेशक
TRILOCHAN MOHAPATRA, Ph.D.
SECRETARY & DIRECTOR GENERAL

भारत सरकार
कृषि अनुसंधान और शिक्षा विभाग एवं
भारतीय कृषि अनुसंधान परिषद
कृषि एवं किसान कल्याण मंत्रालय, कृषि भवन, नई दिल्ली 110 001
GOVERNMENT OF INDIA
DEPARTMENT OF AGRICULTURAL RESEARCH & EDUCATION
AND
INDIAN COUNCIL OF AGRICULTURAL RESEARCH
MINISTRY OF AGRICULTURE AND FARMERS WELFARE
KRISHI BHAVAN, NEW DELHI 110 001
Tel.: 23382629; 23386711 Fax: 91-11-23384773
E-mail: dg.icar@nic.in

Foreword

Sugarcane is the second important industrial crop of the country and contributing significantly to rural economy. This crop is emerging as a multipurpose crop involved in the production of sugar, ethanol, electricity, paper and allied products. The area under this crop is not likely to increase and therefore, it is important to enhance the sugarcane production by growth in productivity and sugar recovery to meet increasing demand.

National level institutes, namely Sugarcane Breeding Institute, Coimbatore, Indian Institute of Sugarcane Research, Lucknow and National Sugar Institute, Kanpur besides All India Coordinated Sugarcane Improvement Project are contributing immensely by developing modern technologies of sugarcane production. With a view to provide ready access to the stakeholders, the information on technologies has been compiled in the form of a book "Modern Technologies of Sugarcane Cultivation". This publication has been developed under the able guidance of Dr. Shankar Lal, Former Director, Indian Institute Pulses Research, Kanpur.

I am sure, this document will add value to available literature and benefit the sugarcane growers, extension workers and sugar industry.

(T. Mohapatra)

Date: 22nd September, 2021
Place: New Delhi - 110001

PREFACE

Pulses are an important group of food legumes, which are grown in diverse agro-ecosystems of the world. They have been an integral part of agriculture since time immemorial. These crops are widely acknowledged as super foods with double the protein in wheat and three-fold that in rice. Besides, they are also rich in complex carbohydrates, micro-nutrients, protein and B-vitamins and minerals like folate, iron, calcium, magnesium, zinc and potassium. Pulses are important crops for food security, combating malnutrition, alleviating poverty, improving human health and enhancing agricultural sustainability. By virtue of their ability to improve soil health and being rich in protein, pulses offer one of the viable options for crop diversification. Considering the importance of pulses, Food and Agricultural Organization (FAO) has declared year 2016 as 'International Year of Pulses' and 10th February as 'World Pulse Day'. Despite these, pulses could not received due attention by Indian farmers and continue to be primarily grown on marginal rainfed land with poor management.

Pulses have far greater role than the traditionally acknowledged role in 'nitrogen fixation' and 'insect-pest break' in the modern agriculture. Their role to reverse the negative effects of continuous following of cereal-cereal cropping systems and in conservation agriculture is well established. Also, they can be used as cash crops, green /brown manuring, cover crop and to control weeds. India is the largest producer and consumer of pulses in the world contributing around 24-28% of the total global production. At present India is near to the self sufficiency in pulses with production level of about 25 Mt. However, to fulfill the demand of ever increasing population of India, there is need to produce 39 Mt of pulses by 2050 A.D. at an annual growth rate of 2.2%. To achieve the target, for every 5-year interval, productivity needs to be enhanced by an average of about 80 kg/ha to achieve a final productivity rate of 1,335 kg/ha by the end of 2050 A.D. following inclusion of about 4 million ha additional area under pulses cultivation. Therefore, concerted efforts are required to develop new & advance production technology to achieve the target.

The present book is outcome of valuable contributions made by various scientists and researchers working on pulse crops in diverse agro-ecosystems of the country. This book has comprehensive coverage of advanced production technologies related to abiotic stress management and livelihood security in the form of 18 chapters that provided the technological back-up to make the country self-sufficient in pulses production. This book would serve as an information source for all R&D personnel involved in promotion of pulses in the country. The editors are sincerely thankful to all the contributors for their valuable chapters to this book, thereby sharing their experiences with the readers.

Editors

CONTENTS

1. Pulses production in India: An overview — 1–14
   –Narendra Kumar, C.P. Nath, C.S. Praharaj, Asik Dutta and N.P. Singh
2. Alternative cropping systems of rice-wheat involving faboid legume crops for crop diversification and sustainability — 15–32
   –Jagmohan Kaur and Satpal S. Paalli
3. Intercropping of pulses in sugarcane for crop diversification and livelihood security — 33–54
   –Om Prakash, A.K. Singh, Brahm Prakash, A.D. Pathak and Pallavi Yadav
4. Potential of pigeonpea intercropping systems in NEH region — 55–66
   –Lowrence Kithan
5. Sustainable intensification of cereal based cropping systems with summer mungbean in Indo-Gangetic Plains — 67–80
   – C.P. Nath, Narendra Kumar, Debarati Datta, T.K. Das, Asik Dutta, K.K. Hazra and C.S. Praharaj
6. Tillage management in pulse crops under diverse agricultural production systems — 81–98
   – Bishal Mukherjee, Purabi Banerjee, Rajib Nath, V. Visha Kumari and Mousumi Ghose
7. Management strategies for enhancing phosphorus use efficiency in pulse crops — 99–122
   –Asik Dutta, Narendra Kumar, C.P. Nath, K.K. Hazra and C.S. Praharaj
8. Response of pulse crops to zinc application — 123–142
   –Dharmendra Singh Yashona and Satish Bhagwatrao Aher
9. Management strategies for micronutrients deficiency in pulses — 143–156
   –Ranabir Chakraborty, Abhishek Das and Asik Dutta
10. Nutrient and weed management in summer pulses in IGP — 157–172
    –Harpreet Kaur Virk and Guriqbal Singh
11. Precision water management for higher crop and water productivity in pulse crops — 173–190
    –C.S. Praharaj, N. Kumar, C.P. Nath, K.K. Hazra and Prasoon Verma
12. Biofertilizers for sustainable pulse production in India — 191–208
    –K. Das, Narendra Kumar and M. Senthilkumar

13. Weed management in pulse-based conservation agriculture system 209–228
– *C.P. Nath, Narendra Kumar, Debarati Datta, T.K. Das, Asik Dutta, K.K. Hazra and C.S. Praharaj*

14. Retrospect and prospects of grass pea cultivation in Central India 229–240
–*Mangla Parikh, S.K. Nair, Deepak Chandrakar and Ritu R. Saxena*

15. Technological interventions for enhancing pulses production under rice fallows in India 241–262
–*Narendra Kumar, C.P. Nath, C.S. Praharaj, K.K. Hazra and Asik Dutta*

16. Role of pulse crop green manuring on soil health and agricultural sustainability 263–282
– *M.A. Ansari, Anup Das, M.H. Ansari, S.K. Sharma, S.S. Roy and Narendra Kumar*

17. Mechanization in pulses production systems in India: Status and way forward 283–293
–*M.K. Singh*

CHAPTER 1

Pulses production in India: An overview

Narendra Kumar*, C.P. Nath, C.S. Praharaj, Asik Dutta and N.P. Singh

ICAR-Indian Institute of Pulses Research, Kanpur – 208024, Uttar Pradesh

*Corresponding author email: nkumar.icar@gmail.com

Abstract

Pulses occupy 96.7 M ha area with total production of 94.99 Mt in the world. The major countries which produce pulses are India, Myanmar, Canada, Nigeria and Brazil. India is the largest producer as well as consumer of pulses in the world. India share in area and production of total pulses in the world is 37.69 and 26.75 per cent, respectively. However, its production in the country has been stagnant till 2010 at around 14 Mt per annum. Due to increase in population, the per capita availability of pulses decreased from 69 g/day from 1961 to 29.1 g/day in 2003. The gap of demand and supply is being bridged through pulses import (4-6 Mt) with a value of 28523 crores during 2016-17. However during 2017-18, India has produced remarkable all time highest pulses of 25.23 Mt which has shown a sign to become self sufficiency in pulses production. The climatic conditions of country favour for cultivation of large numbers of pulses throughout year. The major pulses grown in country are chickpea, pigeonpea, urdbean, mungbean, lentil and pea. The major pulses producing states are Madhya Pradesh, Rajasthan, Maharashtra, Uttar Pradesh, Karnataka and Andhra Pradesh which together share about 80% of total pulse production of the country. But, to meet the future demand of burgeoning population, concerted research efforts will be needed to increase its productivity apart from favourable government policy.

Keywords: Area, Export, Geographical shift, Import, Nutritional value, Statistics, Yield

1. INTRODUCTION

Pulses or grain legumes are the second most important group of crops after cereals in the world. They are important food crops for nutritional security, soil health and sustainable agriculture. Consequently, these crops remained an internal component of Indian agriculture especially in rainfed areas since time immemorial. Pulses are among the ancient food crops with evidence of their cultivation for over 8,000 years. About three-fourth of global pulse production is contributed by developing countries. India, Canada, Myanmar, China, Brazil, Ethiopia and Australia are the major pulse producing countries with relative share of 26.7%, 6.7%, 6.5%, 5.3%, 3.1, 2.9% and 2.1%, respectively (FAOSTAT, 2020). In 2018, the global pulses production was 94.99 million tonnes (Mt) from an area of 96.70 million hectare (M ha) with an average yield of 982 kg/ha. India is the largest producer and consumer of pulses in the world contributing around 24-28% of the total global production. Pulse crops have remained as a mainstay of Indian agriculture for centuries. This is because of their inherent capacity to fix large quantity of atmospheric nitrogen with symbiotic association with *Rhizobium* bacteria. This has helped in maintaining soil health as well as agricultural sustainability. The other unique feature of pulse crops is their deep root systems which enable them to utilize the limited available soil moisture more efficiently than many other field crops, and also contribute substantially to loosening up of soil. In general, pulses are more drought tolerant than any cereal crop, hence fit for rainfed agriculture. Pulses form an essential component of daily diet of Indians who are predominantly vegetarian. The combination of *dal* + *roti* or *dal* + *bhat* (rice) provides all the essential amino acids in requisite amounts and helps eliminate protein-calorie malnutrition.

India can be proud of growing the largest number of pulse crops (grain legumes) in the world. Over a dozen pulse crops including chickpea (*Cicer arietinum*), pigeonpea (*Cajanus cajan*), mungbean (*Vigna radiata*), urdbean (*Vigna mungo*), cowpea (*V. unguiculata*), lentil (*Lens culinaris* ssp. *Culinaris*), lathyrus (*Lathyrus sativus* L.), frenchbean (*Phaseolus vulgaris*), horsegram (*Macrotyloma uniflorum*), field pea (*Pisum sativum*), moth bean (*V. aconitifolium*), *etc.* are grown in one or the other part of the country throughout year (Ali *et al.*, 2016). The latest data (2017-18) indicate that the present production of pulses is 25.23 Mt from an area of 29.99 M ha with productivity of 841 kg/ha (DES, 2019) that led to achieve self-sufficiency in pulses production in the country. In order to ensure demand of growing population, the pulse requirement in the country is projected to be about 39 Mt by 2050 (Fig. 1) which necessitates an annual growth rate of 4.0% (IIPR, 2013).

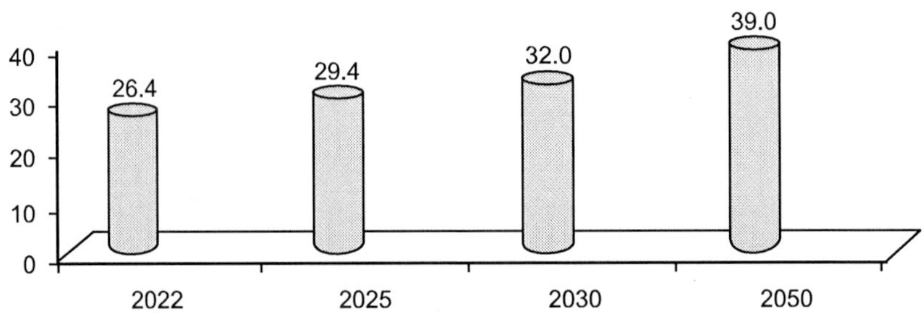

Fig. 1. Estimated target of pulses production in India (Mt)

2. PULSES STATISTICS

2.1 Indian scenario of pulses

During 1950-51, pulses were cultivated in 19.09 M ha area across country with production of 8.41 Mt of grains. The average productivity was only 441 kg/ha. The area under pulses during 2009-10 increased to 23.28 M ha with production of 14.66 Mt and productivity of 630 kg/ha. However, the last one decade was the golden period of pulses in the country in which total pulses production increased to all time highest 25.23 Mt during 2017-18 (Fig. 2). With this achievement, India in now self-sufficient in pulses production. Sometimes, this event is termed as '*Pulses Revolution*' in the country.

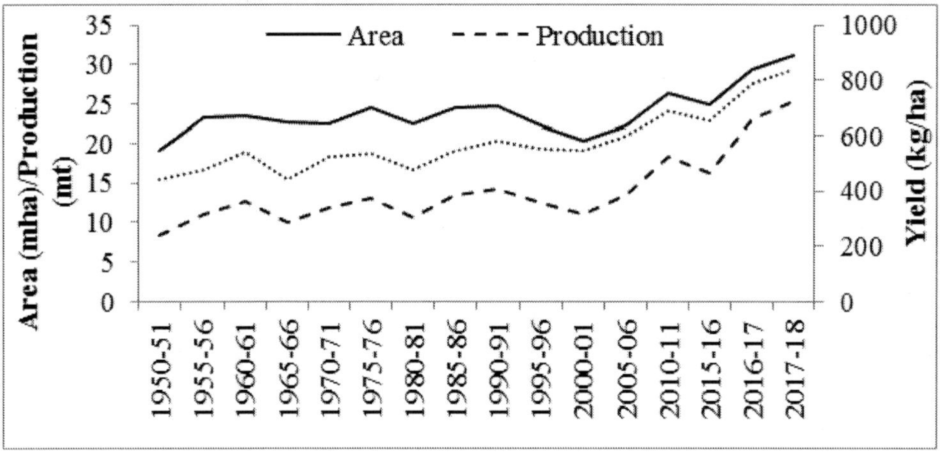

Fig. 2. Area, production and yield trend of total pulses in India

Chickpea continues to be the largest contributor in this complex comprising of 44.5% of the total pulses production from 35.2% pulses area with average productivity of 1063 kg/ha (Table 1). Pigeonpea is the second most important pulse crop with total production of 4.25 Mt from 4.43 M ha area and productivity of 960 g/ha (DES, 2019). The other important pulses grown in India are urdbean (14.12%), mungbean (7.96%), lentil (6.37%) and field pea (3.23%). The contribution of *rabi* pulse crops are more than *kharif* pulse crops in total pulses production in the country. *Rabi* pulses are contributing 62.97% in total pulses production in the country from an area of 159.10 lakh ha (53.05%), whereas *kharif* pulses are contributing 37.03% from an area of 140.83 lakh ha.

Table 1. Season and crop contribution in total pulses in India

Crop	Year: 2017-18		% contribution	
	Area	Production	Area	Production
Chickpea	105.61	112.29	35.21	44.5
Pigeonpea	44.31	42.54	14.47	16.86
Urdbean	54.39	35.62	18.13	14.12
Mungbean	42.57	20.09	14.19	7.96
Lentil	15.54	16.07	5.18	6.37
Other kharif pulses	18.71	8.15	6.25	3.23
Other rabi pulses	34.34	33.65	11.45	13.33
Total kharif pulses	140.83	93.45	46.95	37.03
Total rabi pulses	159.10	158.90	53.05	62.97
Total pulses	299.93	252.35		

**Area-lakh ha, Production-lakh tonnes*

Maximum growth rate per annum of total pulses in the country in area (2.97%), production (6.46%) and yield (2.70%) was recorded during decade period of 2000-01 to 2010-11. Before this period, only during the first decade after independence i.e. 1950-51 to 1960-61, per annum growth rate in area, production and yield was 2.34%, 5.10% and 2.22%, respectively. Whereas, during 1960-61 to 2000-01 (4 decades), there were not much gain observed in area, production and yield of pulses, which has resulted in 3-4 tonnes deficit in demand and supply of pulses in the country. Further during 2010-11 to 2017-18, considerable increase in area (1.94%), production (5.47%) and yield (3.10%) was recorded that has led to the country self-sufficient in pulses production. Pulses are predominantly grown under rainfed condition in different parts of the country. The per cent coverage of pulses area under irrigation during 1950-51 was only 9.43% which increased to 19.87% during 19.87% during 2014-15 (Table 2). The major gain in area under irrigation was recorded in chickpea which increased from 12.48 to 38.60 per cent during same period, whereas majority area (about 95%) is still under rainfed in other pulse crops.

Table 2. Per annum growth rate of area, production and yield of total pulses

Year	Area		Production		Yield		% coverage under irrigation
1950-51	19.09		8.41		441		9.43
1960-61	23.56	2.34	12.70	5.10	539	2.22	8.02
1970-71	22.54	-0.43	11.82	-0.69	524	-0.28	8.75
1980-81	22.46	-0.04	10.63	-1.01	473	-0.97	8.95
1990-91	24.66	0.98	14.26	3.41	578	2.22	10.48
2000-01	20.35	-1.75	11.08	-2.23	544	-0.59	12.64
2010-11	26.40	2.97	18.24	6.46	691	2.70	14.92
2017-18	29.99	1.94	25.23	5.47	841	3.10	19.87#

*Area- M ha, Production- Mt, Yield- kg/ha, Growth rate- Per cent (%); #2014-15

The growth patterns of different pulses between triennium ending 2003 (average of 2000-01 to 2002-03) and 2018 (average of 2015-16 to 2017-18) are given in Table 3. The area under total pulses during the period and production was increased by 33.9% (20.95 to 28.06 M ha) and 82.3% (11.86 to 21.62 Mt). The maximum gain in area (3.69 M ha) and production (4.7 Mt) was recorded in chickpea. Urdbean was the second most important pulse crop with 37.1% gain in area and 95.8% in production followed by mungbean with 36.2 and 92.0 per cent increase in area and production, respectively. The considerable gain in area (31.1%) and production (74.4%) was also observed in pigeonpea. However, lentil area remained almost similar, but the production gain was 38.0% due the increase in yield from 639 kg/ha to 879 kg/ha during TE 2003 to TE 2018. The area under other pulse crops also remained same but the production was increased by 43.5%.

Table 3. Crop wise progress in area and production of pulses

Crop	Area (M ha)			Production (Mt)		
	*TE 2003	TE 2018	% increase	TE 2003	TE 2018	% increase
Chickpea	5.84	9.53	63.2	4.52	9.22	104.0
Pigeonpea	3.44	4.58	33.1	2.23	3.89	74.4
Lentil	1.44	1.43	-0.7	0.92	1.27	38.0
Mungbean	3.04	4.14	36.2	1.00	1.92	92.0
Urdbean	3.29	4.51	37.1	1.42	2.78	95.8
Other pulses	3.90	3.87	-0.8	1.77	2.54	43.5
Total pulses	20.95	28.06	33.9	11.86	21.62	82.3

*Triennium ending 2003

During 1950-51, pulses contribution in the area and production of total foodgrains in the country was 19.62 and 16.55 per cent, respectively. The yield difference in foodgrains and pulses was only 81 kg/ha (Table 4). After 'Green Revolution' (1960s), the area, production and yield of cereal crops (especially rice and wheat) increased drastically in almost all parts of the country. However, pulses crops remained untouched with this event and therefore, area and production of pulses couldn't increase upto the expectations. Thus, the contribution of pulses in total foodgrains production decreased continuously and reached all-time lowest value of 5.63% during 2000-01. Only after 2000-01, little increase in contribution of pulses in total foodgrains area and production was observed and that reached to 23.51% and 8.86%, respectively during 2017-18. The yield gap also increased to a greater extent and it is now only 37.66% of the total foodgrains yield, which was 84.48% during 1950-01. This is mainly because of drastic gains in cereal crops (rice, wheat and maize) yields after 'Green Revolution'.

Table 4. Contribution of pulses to total foodgrains in India

Year	Pulses			Foodgrains			Pulses % to foodgrains		
	A	P	Y	A	P	Y	A	P	Y
1950-51	19.09	8.41	441	97.32	50.82	522	19.62	16.55	84.48
1960-61	23.56	12.70	539	115.58	82.02	710	20.38	15.48	75.92
1970-71	22.54	11.82	524	124.32	108.42	872	18.13	10.90	60.09
1980-81	22.46	10.63	473	126.67	129.59	1023	17.73	8.20	46.24
1990-91	24.66	14.26	578	127.84	176.39	1380	19.29	8.08	41.88
2000-01	20.35	11.08	544	121.05	196.81	1626	16.81	5.63	33.46
2010-11	26.40	18.24	691	126.67	244.49	1930	20.84	7.46	35.80
2011-12	24.46	17.09	699	124.76	259.32	2079	19.61	6.59	33.61
2012-13	23.25	18.34	789	120.77	257.12	2129	19.25	7.13	37.06
2013-14	25.21	19.25	764	125.04	265.04	2120	20.16	7.26	36.03
2014-15	23.10	17.16	743	122.07	252.67	2069	18.92	6.79	35.91
2015-16	24.91	16.35	656	123.22	251.57	2042	20.22	6.50	32.13
2016-17	29.45	23.13	785	129.23	275.11	2129	22.78	8.40	36.88
2017-18	29.99	25.23	841	127.56	284.83	2233	23.51	8.86	37.66

*A- Area (M ha), P- Production (Mt), Y- Yield (kg/ha)

2.2 State-wise trends in area and production of pulses

Madhya Pradesh is major contributor in total pulses production in the country with 32.14% share in production from 24.94% of total pulses area in the country. The second most important pulses producing state is Rajasthan with total share of 13.42% in production from 17.77% area. The 6 major pulses producing states in the country are Madhya Pradesh (32.14%), Rajasthan (13.42%), Maharashtra (13.09%), Uttar Pradesh (8.75%), Karnataka (7.35%) and Andhra Pradesh (4.85%) which together shares about 80% of total pulse production while remaining 20% is contributed mainly by Gujarat, Chhattisgarh, Bihar, Orissa, Jharkhand and Tamil Nadu (Table 5). The 3 states viz., Madhya Pradesh, Gujarat and Jharkhand, where yield levels of pulses are more than 1.0 t/ha. The minimum yield level of pulses (635 kg/ha) during 2017-18 is recorded in Tamil Nadu. The low yield level of pulses in Tamil Nadu is mainly due to low yield of urdbean and mungbean under rainfed rice fallow, which is about 200-300 kg/ha.

Table 5. Area, production and productivity of pulses in India (2017-18)

State	Area (M ha)	% share in area	Production (Mt)	% share in production	Yield (kg/ha)
Madhya Pradesh	7.48	24.94	8.11	32.14	1084
Rajasthan	5.33	17.77	3.39	13.42	635
Maharashtra	4.35	14.51	3.30	13.09	759
Uttar Pradesh	2.27	7.56	2.21	8.75	974
Karnataka	3.02	10.87	1.86	7.35	614
Andhra Pradesh	1.41	4.69	1.22	4.85	870
Gujarat	0.91	3.03	0.93	3.67	1018
Jharkhand	0.79	2.64	0.85	3.35	1065
Tamil Nadu	0.87	2.88	0.55	2.18	635
Chhattisgarh	0.78	2.61	0.54	2.15	693
Telangana	0.57	1.91	0.51	2.01	885
West Bengal	0.46	1.53	0.44	1.76	969
Others	1.75	5.85	1.33	5.28	--
All India	29.99	100.00	25.23	100.00	841

Source: DES (2019)

The progress in area and production of pulses in major pulse growing states during triennium ending 2003 (TE 2003) and TE 2018 was not similar (Table 6). In some of the states area and production increased considerably whereas in other states little progress was observed. Few states in northern India have shown negative trend in area and production of pulses during the period. The maximum increase in area (92.0%) and production (225.0%) during TE 2003and TE 2018 was recorded in Rajasthan. Madhya Pradesh was the second most important state where area and production was increased by 68.9 and 149.8per cent, respectively. Karnataka was the third state with 47.0% increase in area and 101.3 per cent in production. Among major states, negative trend in area (-17.2%) and production (-17.3%) was recorded in Uttar Pradesh. The overall increase in area and production of pulses in the country was 33.9 and 82.3 per cent, respectively during same period.

Table 6. Progress in area and production of pulses in major states

Crop	Area (M ha)			Production (Mt)		
	*TE 2003	TE 2018	% increase	TE 2003	TE 2018	% increase
Madhya Pradesh	3.95	6.67	68.9	2.63	6.57	149.8
Rajasthan	2.51	4.82	92.0	0.88	2.86	225.0
Maharashtra	3.51	4.04	15.1	1.86	2.89	55.4
Uttar Pradesh	2.68	2.22	-17.2	2.25	1.85	-17.8
Karnataka	2.00	2.94	47.0	0.80	1.61	101.3
Andhra Pradesh	1.97	1.42	-27.9	1.08	1.13	4.6
Others	4.33	5.95	37.4	2.36	4.71	99.6
All India	20.95	28.06	33.9	11.86	21.62	82.3

*Triennium ending 2003

Pulses growing districts can be categorized as per area coverage and yield level under different pulse crops. Based on area and production, all districts can be grouped in 4 categories viz., (i) Low Area Low Productivity (LALP), (ii) Low Area High Productivity (LAHP), (iii) High Area Low Productivity (HALP) and (iv) High Area High Productivity (HAHP). Out of 366 districts in the country where chickpea is grown, 36.3% districts categorized under LALP, 32.0% in LAHP, 16.7% in HALP and 15.0% in HAHP (Table 7). Similarly, out of 418 pigeonpea growing districts, majority (45.7%) is categorized under LALP and only 14.6% districts under HAHP, whereas 35.2% districts under are categorized under high productivity (average yield of district > state average yield). In other pulses also, majority of districts categorized under LALP and least under HAHP. In contrast to above, more than 50% districts growing urdbean and horsegram are categorized under high productivity districts. In case of total pulses, 34.8 per cent districts categorized under LALP, 29.0% in LAHP, 20.5% in HALP and 15.6% in HAHP.

Table 7. Crop-wise categorization of districts (%) according to area and productivity

Crop	LALP	LAHP	HALP	HAHP	Total districts
Chickpea	36.3	32.0	16.7	15	366
Pigeonpea	45.7	20.6	19.1	14.6	418
Urdbean	32.3	38.7	14.6	14.6	432
Mungbean	30.4	37.7	16.1	15.8	385
Lentil	47.5	18.4	18.8	15.2	223
Pea	47.9	25.0	11.0	16.1	236
Lathyrus	42.3	25.6	16.7	15.4	78
Horasegram	22.9	43.4	16.0	17.7	175
Total pulses	34.8	29.0	20.5	15.6	551

LALP : Low Area Low Productivity, LAHP : Low Area High Productivity, HALP : High Area High Productivity, HAHP : High Area High Productivity (Source: Tiwari and Shivhare, 2018)

Similar to above, Reddy (2014) categorized districts on the basis of yield level and the changes occurred with time (between 1999 and 2012). The percentage of districts which produces less than 0.5 t/ha yield decreased under chickpea, mungbean and urdbean, whereas it was increased under pigeonpea and lentil (Table 8). Similarly, percentage of districts increased under yield category of 0.5 to 1.0 t/ha for all pulses except lentil. The increasing trend in percentage of districts under yield level of more than 1.0 t/ha was also recorded in given pulses, except pigeonpea in which decreasing trend was observed. The maximum yield gain was recorded in chickpea in which percentage of districts increased from 19 to 66% under more than 1.0 t/ha yield category. Further, majority of pigeonpea and lentil growing districts falls under 0.5 to 1.0 t/ha yield category while in mungbean and urdbean under less than 0.5 t/ha.

Table 8. Distribution of districts by level of yield (% to total districts growing the crops)

Yield level	Chickpea		Pigeonpea		Lentil		Mungbean		Urdbean	
	1999	2012	1999	2012	1999	2012	1999	2012	1999	2012
Less than 0.5 t/ha	13	3	17	27	14	34	74	67	77	47
0.5 to 1.0 t/ha	68	31	46	51	73	48	26	32	28	51
More than 1.0 t/ha	19	66	37	22	13	18	0	1	0.7	2.1
Total	100	100	100	100	100	100	100	100	100	100

Source: Reddy (2015)

2.3 Global scenario of pulses

Pulses are grown in many parts of the world under diverse agro-ecological regions. The major countries which produce pulses are India, Myanmar, Canada, Nigeria, Brazil, China, Russia Federation, Australia, USA and Ethiopia. India ranked first in both area and production of pulses in the world. As per FAOSTAT (2020), India share in area and production of total pulses in the world is 37.69 and 26.75 per cent, respectively. India along with other developing nations together contributes more than three-fourth of world's pulses production. Canada is the second most important country which contributes 6.6% in global pulses production. The area and production of pulses indifferent countries are given in Table 9. Globally during 2018, pulses occupy 96.7 M ha area with total production of 94.99 Mt.

Table 9. Global ranking of major pulses producing countries (2018)

State	Area (M ha)	% share in area	Production (Mt)	% share in production
India	36.451	37.69	25.406	26.75
Myanmar	3.782	3.91	6.184	6.51
Canada	3.244	3.35	6.325	6.66
Nigeria	3.003	3.11	2.676	2.82
Brazil	2.875	2.97	2.930	3.08
China	2.761	2.86	5.027	5.29
Russia Fed.	2.471	2.56	3.143	3.31
Australia	1.858	1.92	2.018	2.12
USA	1.786	1.85	3.406	3.59
Ethiopia	1.491	1.54	2.753	2.90
Others	36.98	38.24	35.119	36.97
World	96.702	100.00	94.987	100.00

Source: FAOSTAT (2020)

Globally, beans are the major pulse crops which occupy 35.246 M ha area with production of 31.772 Mt (Table 10). The share of beans in global pulses area and production is 36.45 and 33.45 per cent, respectively. The second most important pulse crop in the world is chickpea which occupy 17.817 M ha area with total production of 17.08 Mt. The share of chickpea in world pulses area and production is 18.42 and 18.12 per cent, respectively. The other major pulse crops in the world are pea (dry), cowpea, lentil and chickpea with their contribution to global pulses production are 15.85, 7.63, 6.85 and 6.28 per cent, respectively. These six pulse crops together contribute 88.18% to the global pulse basket.

Table 10. Global ranking of different pulse crop (2018)

Crop	Area (M ha)	% share in total area	Production (Mt)	% share in total production
Chickpea	17.817	18.42	17.208	18.12
Lentil	6.168	6.38	6.506	6.85
Pigeonpea	6.993	7.23	5.961	6.28
Pea	8.878	9.18	15.060	15.85
Beans	35.246	36.45	31.772	33.45
Cowpea	12.511	12.94	7.249	7.63
Total pulses	96.702	100.00	94.987	100.00

Source: FAOSTAT (2020)

3. GEOGRAPHICAL SHIFT

The Indo-Gangetic Plain (IGP) is used to be the major pulse basket of the country till the 1970s. Thereafter, a declining trend in area under pulses is observed in this region during last five decades. Due to Green Revolution and increase in area under irrigation in northern India, pulses (mainly chickpea and pigeonpea) were forcibly replaced (about 5.0 M ha area) by HYVs of rice, wheat and maize (Fig 3). However during same period, area under pulses increased from 10.5 M ha to 15.50 M ha in central and southern India. This was mainly because of short duration chickpea and pigeonpea varieties developed by ICAR-SAUs-ICRISAT collaboration which played a key role in expanding the area and productivity of these pulses in central and southern India. Earlier Uttar Pradesh was main contributor to the pulse basket of the country which was later taken up by Andhra Pradesh and Madhya Pradesh. Andhra Pradesh became the leader in total pulse production with an average increase in the yield of two of major pulses, chickpea by about 81-100% during the last two decades (1991-2010). Similarly, the area of lentil increased significantly in Madhya Pradesh, and pigeonpea in Andhra Pradesh and Karnataka. Development and adoption of appropriate varieties led to increase in area, production and yield of lentil in Jharkhand and Rajasthan. On contrary, an increasing trend was observed in the area under mungbean and urdbean in north India which increased to almost double along with a significant increase in productivity. The increase in area of pigeonpea between 1970-13 to 2009-12 was about 280% in Andhra Pradesh and Karnataka, 223% in Maharashtra and 304% in Gujarat whereas in Uttar Pradesh pigeonpea area decreased by 40% and in Bihar by 80%. During same period, pigeonpea production increased by 432% in Andhra Pradesh, 306% in Karnataka, 366% in Maharashtra and 644% in Gujarat, and decreased by 60% in Uttar Pradesh and 65% in Bihar. Similarly during same period, chickpea area increased by

5.29 lakh ha in Andhra Pradesh, 7.64 lakh ha in Karnataka and 9.12 lakh ha in Maharashtra whereas, area under chickpea in Uttar Pradesh declined by 14.07 lakh ha.

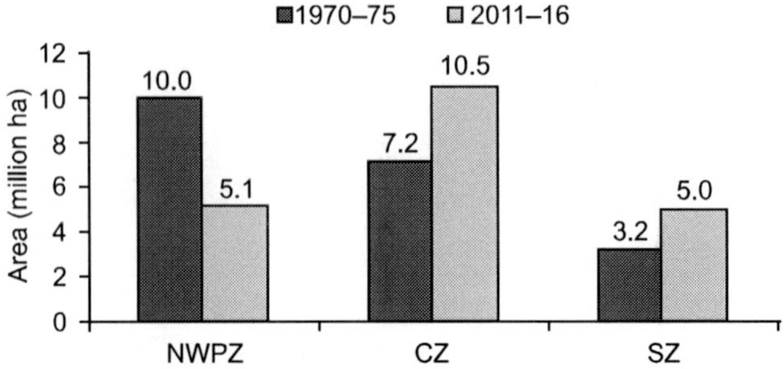

Fig 3. Area shift in total pulses in India

4. AVAILABILITY OF PULSES IN INDIA

After independence during 1951, pulses availability in the country was fairly good (60.7 g/person/day or 22.2 kg/person/yr) which reached to all time high of 69.0 g/capita/day during 1961 (Table 11). Thereafter, as a result of stagnant pulse production and continuous increase in population, the per capita availability of pulses decreased considerably and reached all time low of 30 g/person/day during 2001. The availability of pulses remains 40-43 g/person/day up to 2016. With the increase in pulses production in the country during 2017 onward, further increase in availability of pulses was observed and it reached to 55.9 g/person/day in the year of 2018. It is also expected that the availability of pulses will further increase with time.

Table 11. Per capita net availability of pulses in India

Year	Per capita pulses availability	
	g/day	kg/year
1951	60.7	22.2
1961	69.0	25.2
1971	51.2	18.7
1981	37.5	13.7
1991	41.6	15.2
2001	30.0	10.9
2011	43.0	15.7
2012	41.7	15.2
2013	43.3	15.8
2014	46.4	16.9
2015	43.8	16.0
2016	43.0	15.7
2017	54.7	20.0
2018	55.9	20.4

Source: DES (2019)

5. NUTRITIONAL VALUE

Grains of cereals and pulses remain the major sources of calories and proteins for a large proportion of the world population. Large genotypic variations observed in nutrients content in different pulses (Table 12). Protein content in different pulses varied from 20to 29% in common bean, 15 to 32% in pea, 19 to 30% in lentil, 16 to 28% in chickpea, 16 to 31% in cowpea, 21 to 31% in mungbean and 18 to25% in pigeonpea. Protein content in pulses (18-28%) is generally double than most cereals, but is usually deficient in sulphur containing amino acids, methionine and cystine. On the other hand, cereal-grains contain lower amounts of proteins which are deficient in lysine but have adequate amounts of sulphur containing amino acids. It is often, therefore, emphasized that pulses proteins are the natural supplement to cereal-grain protein in producing an overall essential amino acid balance. The food values of seeds of pulses are high providing 1040 to 1430 kJ of energy per 100 g. The carbohydrate content in pulses is about 60%. Carbohydrate profiles of pulses include prebiotics: raffinose-family oligosaccharides, fructooligo-saccharides, sugar alcohols, and resistant starch that contribute to the low glycemic index (GI<55) and high dietary fibre. Among the sugars, raffinose, stachyose, verbascose, ajugose and pentosans predominate in most of the pulses. These sugars escape digestion in the gut and are fermented in the large bowel and can cause abdominal discomfort and flatulence, if pulses are consumed in abundance. However, soaking pulses overnight in water helps to reduce the content of these sugars. There is significant increase in nutrients in sprouted pulses when compared to their dried embryo. In the process of sprouting, the vitamins, minerals and protein increase substantially. Sprouting of the pulses not only improves nutritive value but also digestibility. Pulses are also good source of minerals like iron, zinc, calcium, magnesium, sodium, etc. The mineral profile of major pulses is described in Table 13.

Pulses are low in fats (1-6%) most of which is provided by poly-unsaturated and mono-unsatured fatty acids. When consumed with the seed coat, pulses are much higher in dietary fibre than those have been dehulled prior to consumption. Pulses are good source of B vitamin folate, which significantly reduces the risk of neural tube defects (NTDs). In addition to the traditional macronutrients, pulses contain a wide variety of antinutritional compounds which vary considerably in their biochemistry. They can be proteins (protease inhibitors, α-amylases, lectins), glycosides (α-galactosides, vicine and convicine) and tannins, saponins as well as alkaloids. They do not appear equally distributed in all legumes, and their physiological effects are diverse. The enzyme inhibitors reduce protein digestibility, and lectins can reduce nutrient absorption. Phytic acid reduces mineral bioavailability. Some phenolic compounds can reduce protein digestibility and mineral bioavailability, and galacto-oligosaccharides may cause flatulence. On the other hand, the same compounds may have health protective effects (for example, as anticarcinogenic, hypocholesterolemic or hypoglycemic agents). Phytic acid exhibits antioxidant activity and protects DNA damage; Lignans and isoflavones have anticarcinogenic, weak oestrogenic, and antioxidant properties. Phenolic compounds, including tannins found mainly in the seed coat have antioxidant activity. Phytoestrogens in pulses may play a role in the prevention of hormone-related cancers, such as breast and prostate cancer; saponins have hypocholesterolaemic effect and anti-cancer activity.

Table 12. Nutritional profile of pulse grains (per 100g)

Pulse crop	Energy (Kcal)	Protein (g)	Fat (g)	Carbohydrate (g)	Total dietary fiber (%)
Chickpea	368	21.0	5.7	61	22.7
Pigeonpea	342	21.7	1.49	62	15.5
Urdbean	347	24.0	1.6	63.4	16.2
Mungbean	345	25.0	1.1	62.6	16.3
Lentil	346	27.2	1.0	60	11.5
Fieldpea	345	25.1	0.8	61.8	13.4
Rajmash	345	23.0	1.3	62.7	17.7
Cowpea	346	28.0	0.3	63.4	18.2
Horsegram	321	23.6	2.3	59.1	15.0
Mothbean	330	24.0	1.5	61.9	--

Table 13. Mineral content of pulse grains (per 100g)

Pulse crop	Iron (mg)	Zinc (mg)	Calcium (mg)	Magnesium (mg)	Potassium (mg)	Sodium (mg)	Selenium (mg)
Chickpea	6.2	3.4	105	115	875	24	8.2
Pigeonpea	5.2	2.7	130	183	1392	17	—
Urdbean	8.4	3.5	110	—	—	—	—
Mungbean	6.7	2.7	132	189	1246	15	8.2
Lentil	7.5	4.7	56	122	955	6	8.2
Fieldpea	4.4	3.0	55	115	981	15	1.6
Rajmash	3.4	1.9	186	188	1316	18	12.9
Cowpea	7.5	3.8	80	250	1450	23	—
Horsegram	7.0	—	287	—	—	—	—
Mothbean	9.6	—	202	—	—	—	—

6. INDIA TRADE OF PULSES

During past decades, because of the persistent deficit in demand and production of pulses, the significant change has been observed in trade of these commodities. The production and consumption data of last decade show an estimated shortage of 3 to 4 Mt of pulses in the country. Due to the liberalization in international trade during early 1990s and thereafter, the import of pulses increased in terms of quantity as well as in value (Table 14). The pattern of import also changed with time. The chickpea which had highest share (about 25%) in pulses import during 2001, underwent a drastic decline to just 4% during 2010, whereas yellow pea import increased more than 17 folds during same period. During 2017-18, India has imported 82.96 lakh tonnes of pulses which cost about 14,462 crore rupees. During 2000, pulses import was mainly from Australia, Canada, Myanmar, Tanzania, Thialand,

Turkey, USA and Uzbekistan. Over the time, the volume of pulses import increased and the India has started importing from additional countries. The newer trade partner includes China, Ethiopia, Indonesia, Malawi, Mozambique and the Russian Federation. The list of top 5 countries from which India has trade of different pulses is given in Table 15.

Table 14. India's import and export of pulses

Year	Import		Export	
	Import quantity (Lakh tonnes)	Import value (Crore rupees)	Import quantity (Lakh tonnes)	Export value (Crore rupees)
2007-08	28.35	5375	1.64	526
2008-09	24.74	6246	1.36	540
2009-10	35.10	9813	1.00	408
2010-11	27.78	7512	2.09	870
2011-12	34.96	9448	1.74	1068
2012-13	40.13	13345	2.03	1285
2013-14	31.78	11037	3.46	1749
2014-15	45.85	17063	2.22	1218
2015-16	57.98	21176	2.56	1553
2016-17	112.82	22160	1.54	1228
2017-18	82.96	14462	1.35	1120

Source: DES (2019)

Table 15. Pulse importing and exporting countries of major pulses (2016-17)

Pulses	Top 5 Export Destinations	Top 5 Import Sources
Peas	Sri Lanka (96.3%), Myanmar (1.6%), Bhutan (1.4%), Nepal (0.5%), UAE (0.09%)	Canada (54.5%), Russia (10.3%), Luthuania (9.0%), France (6.8%), USA (6.4%)
Chickpea	Pakistan (21.6%), UAE (10.6%), Algeria (11.6%), Saudi Arab (9.5%), Sri Lanka (7.3%)	Australia (85.1%), Russia (4.7%), Tanzania (3.8%), USA (1.4%), Canada (0.91%)
Mungbean/ Urdbean	USA (39.96%), Sri Lanka (13.05%), UK (9.86%), Australia (7.77%), Malaysia (7.63%)	Myanmar (70.37%), Kenya (7.43%), Australia (6.32%), Tanzania (3.15%), Uzbekistan (2.60%)
Lentil	Sri Lanka DSR (43.39%), Bangladesh (18.11%), UAE (8.35%), Egypt (3.98%), USA (3.67%)	Canada (89.58%), USA (7.47%), Australia (2.88%), Turkey (0.03%), Mozambique (0.03%)
Pigeonpea	USA (40.79%), UAE (18.28%), Canada (11.28%), UK (10.75%), Singapore (5.11%)	Myanmar (46.35%), Tanzania (18.71%), Mozambique (15.36%), Malawi (12.56%), Sudan (3.36%)

Source: DES (2019)

CONCLUSION

Pulses remained integral part of Indian agriculture since time immemorial. They are main source protein for large vegetarian population of the country. India is the largest producer and consumer of the pulses in the world and contributes 24-28% of the total global production. Diverse group of pulses i.e., more than a dozen pulses area grown in the one or other parts of country throughout year. The major pulses producing states in India area Madhya Pradesh, Rajasthan, Maharashtra, Uttar Pradesh, Karnataka and Andhra Pradesh which together contribute about 80% in the Indian pulse basket. In the recent past, the increasing trend in pulses production observed and the highest production reached to 25.23 Mt in the year 2017-18. But, to fulfill the demand of ever increasing population of India, there is need to produce 39 Mt of pulses by 2050. Thus, there is an urgent need of concerted research effort to increase the productivity and use of new niches, apart from favourable policy to achieve the set target.

REFERENCES

Ali, M., Kumar, N. and Praharaj, C.S. (2016) Agronomic research in pulses in India: Historical perspective, accomplishments and way forward. *Indian Journal of Agronomy* 61 (4th IAC Special Issue), S83-S92.

DES. (2019) Agricultural Statistics At A Glance 2019. Directorate of Economics and Statistics. Department of Agriculture, Cooperation and Farmers Welfare; Ministry of Agriculture and Farmers Welfare, Government of India.

FAOstat. (2020) http://www.fao.org/faostat/en/#data/QC

IIPR. (2013) Vision 2050. Indian Institute of Pulses Research (Indian Council of Agricultural Research), Kanpur.

Reddy, A.A. (2015) Pulses production trends and strategies to become self sufficient. *Indian Farming* 65(6), 2-10.

Tiwari, A.K. and Shivhare, A.K. (2018) Pulses in India: Retrospect and Prospects-2018. Directorate of Pulses Development. Government of India, Bhopal.

CHAPTER 2

Alternative cropping systems of rice-wheat involving faboid legume crops for crop diversification and sustainability

Jagmohan Kaur* and Satpal S. Paalli
Punjab Agricultural University, Ludhiana 141004
*Corresponding author email: kaurjagmohan@pau.edu

Abstract

Rice-wheat is the most predominant cropping system of Indo-Gangetic Plains (IGP) and is the backbone of national food security. This chapter highlights various sustainability issues originated due to monoculture of rice-wheat cropping system and discusses various diversification options mainly involving faboid legume crops (FLCs) which have multifaceted benefits i.e. diversified cropping system, maintaining/ enhancing the system sustainability, less dependence on imports etc. The simplest approach can be inclusion of short duration summer FLCs after harvesting of wheat viz., summer greengram, summer blackgram and cowpea fodder. Green manures like sunhemp, *Sesbania* and cowpea are also suitable for soil health. Second way is to replace the rice or wheat with FLCs. The third approach can be complete replacement of rice-wheat with FLCs and follow alternative cropping systems e.g. maize-potato-summer greengram and soybean-peas-summer greengram. The main message of the chapter is to include FLCs partially or fully as per situation in a particular area.

***Keywords*:** Crop diversification, Faboid legume, Pulses, Rice-wheat system, Sustainability

1. INTRODUCTION

Rice (*Oryza sativa* L.)-wheat (*Triticum aestivum* L.) cropping system is practised on large area of India and has given a foodgrains and nutritional security to the nation. This system occupies an area of about 13.5 M ha in South Asia covering prime agricultural regions of India, Pakistan, Bangladesh and Nepal (Ladha *et al.*, 2003). This system is followed in India over an area of about 10.5 M ha in the IGP. The magnitude of contribution of this system can be adjudged from Punjab alone which covers just 1.54% of geographical area of India and produces about 18% of wheat and 11% of rice, contributing 35-40% and 25-30%, respectively to the central pool of foodgrains during the last one decade (Anonymous, 2020). In spite of being labour, water, capital and energy intensive, this remained the most predominant cropping system of North-West IGP (NWIGP) mainly because of higher productivity, yield stability, assured market price, less risks as compared to other alternative cropping systems and timely availability of cheap fertilizers and irrigation (Singh and Kaur, 2012). A number of problems have cropped up due to continuous cultivation of rice and wheat in a system mode for the last four decades. The NWIGP region has paid a heavy price to earn the status of food bowl. At present, the agronomic technologies responsible for green revolution are loosing their relevance due to emergence of second generation problems associated with this system such as receding groundwater table, deteriorating soil health, declining factor productivity, increasing cultivation costs as well as environmental pollution (Chauhan *et al.*, 2012). Among various approaches to solve the issues of rice-wheat system, growing of leguminous crops is an important management strategy. These crops belong to sub-family 'faboideae' and have been mentioned as 'faboid legume crops' (FLCs). Most of FLCs fix atmospheric N_2 and its incorporation into soil can improve soil structure, promote aeration and avoid the formation of hardpan.

2. CONCEPT OF CROPPING SYSTEM

It represents cropping pattern used on a farm and their interaction with farm resources, other farm enterprises and available technology which determine their make-up. It is an important component of a farming system. This represents a philosophy of maximum crop production per unit land area within a relevant time frame with minimum natural resource degradation.These remain dynamic in time and space. Under irrigated conditions, several cropping systems have been identified, of which rice-wheat (10.5 M ha) is the major contributor, followed by rice-rice (5.9 M ha) and coarse grain based systems (10.8 M ha). At macro level, these are decided by agro-climatic and soil conditions, productivity and profitability of a system and at micro level by the interaction of socio-economic conditions, infrastructural facilities and technological development.

3. SUSTAINABILITY ISSUES WITH RICE-WHEAT SYSTEM

Though, rice-wheat system provides food security to nation, but at the same time, causing a great threat to the natural resource base and deteriorating the other ecosystems also. Therefore, there is a great need to have balanced approach where we protect our resources particularly through the addition of pulses in this system. Major sustainability issues arisen from dominance of rice-wheat system are numerous and are discussed below:

3.1 Depleting aquifers

The ground water is one of the important sources of water for irrigation. Due to demographic pressure, the per capita availability of water in India is receding very fast which was approximately 1700 m^3 per capita/yr in 2011 and is projected to be 1341 m^3 per capita/yr by 2025. The share of water for irrigation also shows the same plight. Rice, a water guzzling crop, consumes 4 to 5 thousand litres of water for production of 1.0 kg of grain. About 11,650 m^3/ha of irrigation water is consumed by this system and out of which 7650 m^3/ha is used by rice alone (Bhatt *et al.*, 2016). Due to dominance of rice-wheat in the NWIGP, covering even the non-ideal rice soils and expansion of tubewells network has resulted in depletion of ground water resources, thus creating an alarming situation. Indian Punjab can depict this situation very well where more than 70% of the area is irrigated by tubewells (2.91 M ha). The net annual groundwater availability is 21.58 BCM against the total annual groundwater draft of 35.78 BCM, thus overdraft of 14.58 BCM is resulting in over-exploitation of ground water. According to Central Ground Water Board and Development of Irrigation, the number of overexploited blocks increased from 53 in 1984 to 109 in 2018 in the state. The average decline in the groundwater table was 0.60 m/yr during 2014-2017. According to NASA (USA), about 13-17 km^3 of groundwater was lost annually from north-western plains of Punjab, Haryana and western Uttar Pradesh (Rodell *et al.*, 2009). Thus, the increased depth of underground water compelled the farmers to replace centrifugal with submersible pumps, increasing overall pumping costs. It also resulted in continuous abatement of quality of water due to intrusion of saline groundwater into good quality water.

3.2 Sodicity and salinity in the command areas

These problems are increasing in the command areas due to excessive accumulation of salts and water logging rendering cultivated soils unproductive particularly in the north western part of India. Punjab, Haryana and Rajasthan suffer from the problem of marginal quality of waters and the irrigation induced salinity seems to intensify in the future (Singh, 2009). According to one estimate, potential monetary losses due to this type of salinity can be as high as Rs. 1669/- million annually in Haryana state, clearly depicting its disastrous effect. In Punjab, soil slope is from north-east to south-west direction and the water also moves in this direction.With the reduction in water table of north-west, there is a risk of poor quality water of south west, deteriorating good quality water of the former, thus further aggravating the threatening situation.

3.3 Groundwater pollution

Groundwater has not only suffered quantitatively but also qualitatively. Due to the excessive use of fertilizers especially nitrogen as well as pesticides, large amount of these enter into groundwater through leaching and cause contamination. Higher nitrate concentration leads to over nourishment of the lakes/water bodies and gives rise to the phenomenon of eutrophication (eu = more, trophication= nutrition). Increased level of nitrate in drinking water (>25 mg/l) can cause serious health hazard "methaemoglobinaemia" also known as "Blue Baby Syndrome", which affects mostly infants even leading to their death. N-nitroso compounds are also very harmful as these are carcinogenic. Fertilizers containing heavy metals as impurities result in heavy metal contamination of water. Groundwater in about 13 states of India has been found to be contaminated with heavy metals. Flouride content of Punjab state is above permissible limit (> 1.5 ppm) and this increased content is also due to the use of excessive phosphatic fertilizers (Gupta and Singh, 2006).

3.4 Diminishing profit-margins

Increased cost of cultivation due to escalating cost of agricultural inputs owing to declining factor productivity is further aggravated by the continuous reduction in subsidies on agro-chemicals. The fertilizer response ratio in intensively irrigated areas has decreased nearly three times from 13.4 in 1970 to 3.7 kg grain/kg nutrient. Tillage costs and overall cost are rising, thus reducing the overall profit margins.

3.5 Depletion of soil fertility

Rice and wheat, both are heavy feeders of nutrients, thus, this cropping system has resulted in excessive mining of nutrients and also created nutrient imbalance. Annual demand of NPK fertilizer was 28 Mt and the actual fertilizer consumption stands at only 18 Mt of NPK, thus creating net negative balance of about 10 Mt of primary nutrients. The ratio of N: P_2O_5: K_2O is also highly skewed which is 25.8:5.8:1 of Punjab and 22.7:6.1:1 of Haryana whereas the average ratio for India is 6.1:2.5:1, against the standard of 4:2:1. The major factor contributing to declining crop response is continuous nutrient mining due to imbalanced nutrient use without replenishing fertility limiting nutrients, leading to deficiencies of multinutrients like P, K, S, Zn, Mn, Fe and B from the soil (Chauhan *et al.*, 2012; Bhatt *et al.*, 2016). Formation of hard impervious soil pan due to puddling in rice also causes hindrance in root growth of the succeeding crops (Kukal and Aggarwal, 2003).

3.6 Burning of crop residue

Residue management is a big challenge in the rice-wheat system which alone contributes one-fourth of the total crop residues produced in India. Rice residue has higher silica content so it is not preferred by animals, and secondly wider C: N ratio (>100:1) causes immobilisation of nitrogen in soil and thus reduces yield. So, farmers adopt easy and cheap method of residue disposal like burning which produces ample of green house gases *viz.*, 70% C on burning straw evolves as CO_2, 7% as CO, 0.66% as CH_4 and 2.09% of N as N_2O. This practice not only causes environmental pollution and global warming but also deteriorates soil health due to loss of nutrients as well as organic matter and killing of beneficial microorganisms from soil.

3.7 Build-up of pests

Pests and disease problems are now more serious than ever before. This situation is the result of monoculture of selected crops leading to build-up of pests and diseases. Carry-over of stem borer (pink borer) and build-up of soil borne pathogens in continuous cereal systems and occurrence of *Phalaris minor* weed in rice-wheat system are examples of such serious problems. There is loss of biodiversity with the widespread use of mono-cropping and varietal diversification is also not that widespread eg. in 1960's, 2.25 lakh ha area of rice was sown in Punjab and cultivated varieties were 37 but now only 3-4 varieties are grown when area has increased to 30 lakh ha.

3.8 Herbicide resistance and weed shift

Continuous growing of rice and wheat in sequence has resulted in dependence on herbicides in 90-95% of area. Constant and excessive use of herbicides resulted in the problems of herbicide resistant biotypes. *Phalaris minor* showed resistance to isoproturon and shift (new entry) to hardy weed flora like *Sphenoclea zaylanica* in rice and *Malva parviflora*, *Rumex retroflexus* in wheat, warranting the use of alternate costly and more potent herbicides. Indiscriminate use of chemicals eliminates the natural enemies and thus resulted in development of resistance in weeds and pests.

3.9 Climate change

Global warming is likely to threaten food security of entire South Asian countries including India as this is located in the strategic geographical position declared as most vulnerable to climate change and agricultural production. In India, 18% of all emissions are from agriculture and the major sources being - flooded paddies, enteric fermentation by ruminants, CO_2 from burning residues and N_2O from nitrogenous fertilizers.

4. CONCEPT OF CROP DIVERSIFICATION

The term 'diversification' originated from the word 'diverge', which means to move or extend in different directions from common phenomena. Thus, it refers to a shift of a crop or cropping system to another crop or cropping system which is more remunerative and sustainable. Traditionally, it was used for subsistence kind of farming, but recently it is used for high-value crops. Currently, our approach should be using the resources in best possible way by changing and modifying the spatial and temporal status in crops or cropping systems. In case of rice-wheat system, diversification is either replacement of less remunerative rice or wheat with more remunerative crops or inclusion of some additional short-duration crops in the existing system. Diversification of cropping systems by inclusion of pulse or legume crops shows an ample scope for maintaining agricultural sustainability (Stagnari *et al.*, 2017) and enhancing the system productivity (Gan *et al.*, 2015). Incorporation of legumes/pulses enhances the sustainability of cropping systems by strengthening its all the four components *viz.*, environmental, economic, social and institutional (Lal *et al.*, 2016; Lal, 2017) as given in Figure 1.

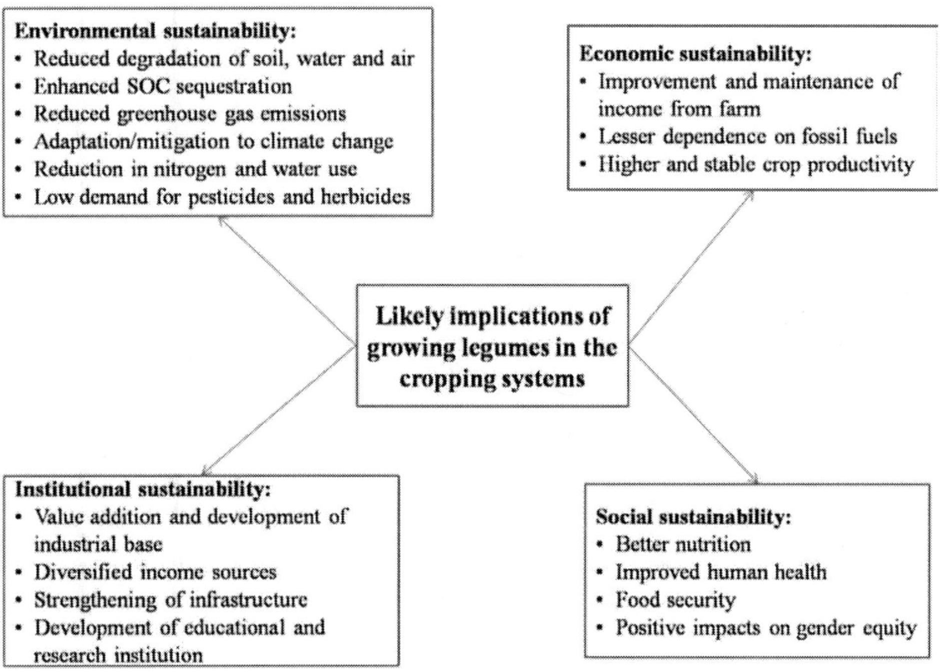

Fig. 1. Implications of growing legumes in the cropping systems

5. APPROACHES TO CROP DIVERSIFICATION

5.1 Horizontal approach

This is a primary approach to crop diversification used in agriculture production systems. In this approach, new high-value crops are added to the existing cropping system or crop substitution where space available between two crops is utilized as a way of improving the overall production. The significance of horizontal diversification increases especially for small land holders for increasing production by adopting high cropping intensities. The multiple cropping systems can increase food production potential many folds by enhanced cropping intensities.

5.2 Vertical approach

In this approach, value is added to the products produced by farmers through various methods such as processing, packaging, regional branding, merchandising etc. This is just complementary to horizontal diversification, which helps to make any production system more remunerative by product diversification and value addition.

6. ALTERATIONS IN RICE-WHEAT SYSTEM

Though, rice-wheat system has created various problems but we cannot ignore it due to food security. Most of the times, farmers' own preference is also important due to problems in marketing of other crops. We can modify this system partially for longer duration by including FLCs. A certain percentage of rice-wheat area can be shifted completely to other crops and there is also a need to have a rotational plan in such a manner that monoculture is avoided. For this, the first approach is to include FLCs in existing rice-wheat system. Second way is to replace rice or wheat by growing faboid legumes and third option is the complete removal of rice-wheat system by FLCs and other crops. The possible reformation of rice-wheat system by including FLCs is given below:

6.1 Include FLCs in the existing rice-wheat system

6.1.1 Rice-wheat-summer greengram

This system is followed in Punjab, Haryana and western Uttar Pradesh. Greengram offers great opportunity for sustainable intensification of cereal based systems through triple benefits *viz*., additional protein rich food, income and enhanced soil fertility. Short duration varieties of summer greengram are available *viz.*,SML1827, TMB 37, SML 668, SML 832, Pusa 9531, Samrat, Pusa Vishal and Virat, which can fit well in the short window period between harvesting of wheat and rice transplanting. Different agro-techniques such as planting methods, sowing time, plant density, nutrient and weed management in summer greengram have been developed. For facilitating combine harvesting of greengram, non-residual herbicide like paraquat can be sprayed for drying of foliage.

Greengram (April–May) inclusion in rice-wheat rotation increased rice grain yield by 10-14% (Ghosh *et al*., 2019). Continuous adoption of rice-wheat-greengram cropping system for four years resulted in improvement in organic C, available N and available P of soil to the tune of 8.8, 7.3 and 3.7%, respectively over the initial soil status in comparison to rice-wheat cropping system (Singh *et al.*, 2011). Rice-wheat followed by summer greengram significantly improved soil organic carbon, available nitrogen, phosphorus, potassium as well as sulphur and zinc over rice-wheat system (Venkatesh *et al.*, 2015). In IGP, the inclusion of summer greengram in rice-wheat system significantly increased very labile carbon fraction from 0.11 to 0.18%, labile carbon from 0.09 to 0.11% and less labile carbon from 0.23 to 0.27% at 0-20 cm soil surface (Ghosh *et al.*, 2012). Incorporation of residues of greengram increases microbial population and nitrogenase activity in roots over dual rice-wheat system without greengram (Tilak, 2004).This system is very useful for the environment in terms of soil health as well as greenhouse gas emissions (Sapkota *et al.*, 2017).

6.1.2 Rice-wheat-cowpea (fodder)

Cowpea is the only arid legume which is spread widely over different continents and is characterized by initial fast growth with drooping leaves which suppress weed growth and is also characterized by good regeneration potential. In IGP, it is cultivated in pockets of Punjab, Haryana, Delhi and western Uttar Pradesh. After wheat harvesting, cowpea is sown following recommended package of practices and vacates the field for timely sowing of the succeeding rice crop. During the lean period, it provides green fodder. Harvesting at 40-45 days generally provides 20-25 t/ha of high feeding value green fodder. Due to higher biomass, the fodder crop assures equal or higher profit as compared to other crops. It also helps in improving the productivity as well as nutrient use efficiency of rice-wheat cropping system, minimizing of leaching of nitrate nitrogen to below ground and reduction in the bulk density of surface (0-15 cm) as well as sub-surface (15-30 and 30-45 cm) soil layers (Dwivedi *et al.*, 2003).

6.1.3 Rice-wheat-green manuring

In rice-wheat system, the window after harvesting of wheat and before transplanting of paddy is quite wide and can be used for green manuring with pre-soaked seed of *Sesbania* (pre-soaked in water for 8 hours) or sunnhemp @ 50 kg seed/ha or cowpea @ 30 kg seed/ ha after heavy pre-sowing irrigation. Six-seven week old green manure crops are buried before flowering and thereafter, transplanting of paddy can be done after one or two days. This can help in saving of nitrogen to the tune of 62.5 kg/ha in rice besides enhancing productivity and maintenance of the soil health. Sunnhemp also helps in reduction of root-knot nematode population (Kimenju *et al.*, 2008). Summer greengram can also act as a green manure crop by burying its stover after picking of pods, and then, transplanting of rice can be done on the next day. About one-third of nitrogen can be saved by this method. Among the various cropping systems, Yadav *et al* (2005) found that the inclusion of *Sesbania* in rice-wheat system gave the highest grain yield as well as land use efficiency as compared to other systems including rice-wheat.

6.2 Include FLCs to replace rice/wheat from the existing rice-wheat system

6.2.1 Groundnut-wheat

One of the main issues in rice-wheat system is the growing of rice on light soils. In this case, groundnut can be sown in *kharif* or summer season followed by wheat. Apart from other practices, P fertilizer may be skipped in groundnut provided it was applied in preceding wheat (Aulakh *et al.*, 2003). Increase in soil organic carbon under groundnut-wheat system was higher than other groundnut based cropping systems (Ghosh *et al.*, 2006).

6.2.2 Soybean/greengram/blackgram/pigeonpea-wheat

Generally soybean is sown in the first fortnight of June and harvested in the early days of November, and thereafter, wheat is sown in the first fortnight of November. Alternate to soybean, *kharif* sown greengram and blackgram can be sown in July. In soybean-wheat rotation, if P was applied at recommended rate to wheat, almost 25% P is reduced for soybean and in wheat crop almost 25% N can be saved due to leguminous nature of soybean. Fertilizer requirement of greengram and blackgram is very less but their contribution towards soil richness is higher.

Pigeonpea-wheat cropping system has emerged as a promising system in Haryana, Punjab, Uttar Pradesh and north Rajasthan. Availability of short-duration varieties of pigeonpea *viz*., Pusa 992, UPAS 120, Manak and ICPL 151 has made this system successful. Sowing of pigeonpea is done in the second fortnight of May for higher yields as well as early maturity of these crops for timely sowing of wheat. Optimum sowing time and plant population, both are important for higher yields. To get rid of the problem of stagnation of water it can be sown on raised beds. Weeds can be successfully controlled by hand weeding or alternatively by spray of pendimethalin. The major constraints in its cultivation is problem of *Fusarium* wilt, sterility mosaic, *Phytophthora* blight and with late monsoon, maturity is delayed. Singh *et al* (2005) observed that replacement of rice with pigeonpea in rice-wheat system reduced nitrate N as well as bulk density and increased carbon sequestration in the soil profile. The root volume (58%) as well as weight (99.5%) of succeeding wheat crop was also improved. Pigeonpea residue (root, stubble, nodule & leaf litter) accounted for total N and P recycling to the tune of 38-42 kg/ha and 3.1-4.2 kg/ha, respectively. In succeeding wheat crop, the N and P fertilizer use efficiency in terms of apparent recovery and agronomic efficiency increased in pigeonpea-wheat cropping system as compared to rice-wheat along with net monetary returns.

6.2.3 Cowpea (fodder)/summer greengram-maize-wheat

Cowpea is a short-duration cover crop, grain legume, fodder, green vegetable as well as a green manure crop. It can be sown from March to mid-July which is a longer period for growing as fodder crop and provide fodder during lean period. Harvesting should be done at pre-flowering stage at 55-65 days after sowing. Thereafter, maize can be sown in June followed by wheat in November. Unlike cowpea fodder, the sowing window for summer greengram is lesser. In case harvesting of previous wheat crop is delayed due to rains, sowing of summer greengram is not a good option. While following this system, selection of variety (early maturing) is very important.

6.2.4 Summer greengram-toria-wheat

Both summer greengram and *toria* (*Brassica rapa* L. *ssp. toria*) are of short duration; therefore, a good fitting is possible having higher cropping intensity. Accomplish the sowing process of summer greengram not later than early April and go for sowing of *toria* in the first week of September. Generally, it takes almost 3 months but we have to select a shorter variety, otherwise the late-sown varieties of wheat are to be selected.

6.2.5 Maize-wheat-green manuring

After harvesting of wheat in April, green manure crops like *Sesbania*, sunnhemp and cowpea can be sown in the end of April. When the crop is of 6-8 weeks, burry it in the soil with implements. A gap of 10-12 days is needed for partial decomposition before the sowing of maize in June. Addition of organic matter by green manures is known to improve soil fertility.

6.2.6 Summer groundnut-potato/toria/pea/late kharif fodder-late wheat

Summer groundnut is sown after the harvest of wheat. This crop vacates the field early, so before the sowing of late wheat, there is possibility of adjustment of any short-duration crop like potato, *toria*, pea, and *kharif* fodders.

6.2.7 Rice-chickpea

Fitting of two crops in a single year is an easy option. It is commonly followed in eastern Uttar Pradesh and various parts of Bihar. This system is known to improve soil fertility. Ghosh *et al* (2012) observed that very labile and labile fractions of carbon (0-20 cm soil layer) were significantly higher in rice-chickpea than rice-wheat system.

6.2.8 Rice-*Brassica* species-summer greengram

Rice crop transplanted in second fortnight of June can be followed by *raya* or *gobhi sarson* (*Brassica napus* L.) sown in the month of October. Both these crops vacate the field by end-March, thus enabling timely sowing of summer greengram. In a field study conducted at New Delhi, it was reported that inclusion of greengram during summer (May-June) in rice–rapeseed-greengram system increased the productivity as well as profitability over rice–wheat system (Sharma and Sharma, 2005).

6.2.9 Rice-chickpea-summer greengram

Rice-chickpea is a popular system but inclusion of summer greengram can add a great value to it. The pulses involving chickpea and greengram are best suited for our family needs, and also improve the soil health. Hazra *et al* (2020) reported that inclusion of legume crops like greengram, blackgram, cowpea, chickpea, lentil, field pea and pigeonpea etc. alternative to rice-wheat system can be popularised to improve soil health and enhanced C-sequestration.

Time of sowing is very important in this system because we are fitting three crops in a year. The most suitable time for rice transplanting in North India is June-July. But in this case, we cannot go for transplanting in July because it will lead to delayed harvesting of rice and thus delay the sowing of subsequent chickpea crop. We may prefer early part of June for transplanting of rice as per recommendation of that area. At the same time, selection of variety is also very important. Harvesting of long-duration varieties of rice is generally done uptill the end of November and it will badly affect the sowing of chickpea. Right time of sowing of chickpea will automatically benefit the sowing of summer greengram. The last irrigation in rice and greengram should be stopped at physiological maturity otherwise these crops may take additional 15-20 days in field.

6.2.10 Rice-potato-summer greengram

Rice-potato-greengram cropping system recorded highest net returns (Rs. 1,61,928/ha) followed by rice-vegetable peas-vegetable frenchbean (Rs. 1,58,192/ha) and rice-potato-vegetable cowpea cropping systems (Rs. 1,52,415/ha) in Dehradun, Uttarakhand (Singh and Kumar 2014). Prasad *et al* (2013) conducted a field experiment at Kanke, Ranchi to evaluate the production potential and resource use efficiency of rice based cropping systems. The maximum net profit (Rs.1,25,000/ha), benefit cost ratio (1.61) and monetary efficiency (Rs. 342.7/ha/day) were recorded in rice-potato-greengram sequence. In this cropping sequence, rice could be planted in mid June to vacate the field for timely sowing of potato crop in the second fortnight of September. Summer greengram should preferably be sown after seed crop of potato in the second or third week of March. Summer greengram after potato does not require any fertilizer application if the preceding potato crop received recommended dose of NPK and FYM.

6.2.11 Rice-potato-groundnut

Rice-potato-groundnut is a highly productive cropping system which produced 1.92 t/ha of wheat equivalent yield (WEY) and productivity of 53.7 kg/ha/day as compared to the existing rice-wheat system with WEY of 1.01 t/ha and productivity of 37.2 kg/ha/day, it also showed improvement in the soil fertility (Katyal *et al.*, 2002)

6.2.12 Basmati rice-berseem (fodder and seed)

This cropping system provides substantial net returns than the existing basmati rice-wheat system. Transplant the basmati rice in mid-July which will vacate the field in mid November. A successful crop of *berseem* for seed production can be grown at the end of November after the harvest of basmati rice. It provides three cuttings of green fodder before leaving the crop for seed production.

6.2.13 Addition of pulses with short-duration rice

Existing rice-wheat cropping system needs to be diversified to short duration rice (IET-1410)-cauliflower-frenchbean which recorded highest rice equivalent yield (REY) of 27.20 t/ha/yr, net return of Rs. 1,05,085/ha/yr and production efficiency of 74.52 kg/ha/day (Thakur *et al.*, 2009).

6.2.14 More possibilities

Basmati rice-celery-*bajra*, Maize/cotton-senji-sugarcane-ratoon I-ratoon II-wheat, Arhar-oat/senji-fodder-sugarcane-ratoon I-ratoon-II-wheat, Groundnut-*toria*-wheat, *Kharif* fodder (cowpea)/green manure/ greengram - autumn sugarcane + raya/ potato/ wheat/ *gobhi sarson*/ cabbage-ratoon I-ratoon II-wheat, Rice-*berseem*, Rice-lentil-summer greengram, and rice-pea (early)-celery.

6.3 Include FLCs to completely replace the existing rice-wheat system

6.3.1 Maize-Brassica species-summer greengram

This cropping system is more productive and remunerative than rice-wheat system and is prevalent in Punjab, Haryana and western Uttar Pradesh. Maize crop sown in the month of May-June takes 95-100 days to mature and high yielding varieties of *raya* or *gobhi sarson* can be sown in the month of October. These crops vacate the field by mid-March and thus summer greengram can easily be adjusted. The summer greengram can also be sown without any preparatory tillage after applying pre-sowing irrigation which helps in reducing cost of cultivation. Maize-*toria*-summer greengram can also be a good option as *toria* sown in mid-September vacates the field upto mid-December and timely sowing of summer greengram can be ensured. According to Mal *et al* (2018), the production efficiency of Maize-*toria*-summer greengram was higher (36.36 kg/ha/day) as compared to rice-wheat system (33.86 kg/ha/day).

6.3.2 Maize-potato-summer greengram

Maize sown in the month of June easily vacates field for timely sowing of potato upto mid-September. Summer greengram sown after harvesting of potato can be sown upto mid-March so it can easily escape early monsoon rains in its growing season unlike the crop preceded by wheat. Also, summer greengram does not require any fertilizer application if it is followed by potato crop supplied with recommended doses of NPK and FYM. In comparison to rice-wheat (12.9 tREY/ha/yr), maize-potato-summer greengram cropping system resulted in 22.9 tREY/ha/yr productivity along with saving of 119.3 cm irrigation water (Walia *et al.*, 2011).

6.3.3 Maize-vegetable pea-spring maize

In this system, maize as a fodder crop should be sown in the first fortnight of June, vegetable pea in the second fortnight of September and spring maize during first fortnight of February. This system is more productive and remunerative as compared to rice-wheat system. It produced higher maize equivalent yield (28.15 t/ha), production efficiency (77.12 kg/ha/day) and net returns (Rs. 2,38,986/ha) as compared to rice-wheat system where the corresponding values were 12.36 t/ha, 33.86 kg/ha/day and Rs 1,10,393/ha, respectively (Mal *et al.*, 2018). For saving of irrigation water, spring maize can be cultivated under drip irrigation system.

6.3.4 Maize-berseem-bajra

In this cropping system, maize is sown in the second week of August and can be harvested 50-60 days after sowing , particularly when the crop is in between milk ripe and dough stage of the grain development process. *Berseem* can be sown in the first or second week of October and about 4-5 cuttings can be taken. *Bajra* sown in second week of June can be harvested 45 to 55 days after sowing i.e. starting of ear initiation stage.

6.3.5 Maize-berseem-maize+cowpea

Both, maize and maize+cowpea as a fodder are harvested in 50-60 days, so in total it takes 4 months. The rest of period can be adjusted for *berseem* by taking 4-5 cuttings. Maize is sown in rainy season followed by *berseem* in *rabi* season and then, mixed cropping of maize + cowpea in the month of June. Thus, maize-based cropping systems can also play an important role in replacing the traditional rice-wheat system.

6.3.6 Soybean-chickpea

There is sufficient time to adjust both the crops in a year. Sowing time for soybean is around June and of chickpea in October-November. Both crops are a good combination for soil and human health. Coumar *et al* (2020) reported that soil organic carbon pool values were higher under soybean-chickpea system than rice-wheat system.

6.3.7 Soybean-peas-summer greengram

Soybean based cropping system involving three crops is more productive and remunerative as compared to rice-wheat and also improves the soil health. Soybean can be sown during first fortnight of June followed by peas sowing in the first fortnight of November and it timely vacates the field for summer greengram cultivation during second fortnight of March.

6.3.8 Groundnut -toria + gobhi sarson

This system is more productive and remunerative than both maize-wheat and rice-wheat cropping systems. Groundnut can be sown in the first fortnight of May followed by *toria* + *gobhi sarson* intercropping in mid September. Both the crops can be sown in alternate rows at 22.5 cm row-row spacing or *toria* can be broadcasted and *gobhi sarson* in rows at 45 cm spacing using 2.5 kg seed rate per hectare for each crop. In this system, harvesting of *toria* can be done near mid-December, while *gobhi sarson* vacates the field in end March.

6.3.9 Summer groundnut-green onion-onion

This groundnut based cropping systems provides oilseed as well as vegetables, so it is highly remunerative and beneficial for meeting household needs. Groundnut can be sown in the second fortnight of May. In separate field, March sown bulbs of onion can be uprooted in the month of June and should be stored in an airy place for sowing purpose. These bulbs can be sown in the field after uprooting of summer groundnut in the second fortnight of September. In the second fortnight of December, the crop can be uprooted and can be consumed as green onions. For next crop, nursery can be transplanted in the first fortnight of January and these *rabi* onions are harvested upto mid-May.

6.3.10 Summer groundnut-peas-sunflower

This cropping system is highly productive and profitable and also improves soil health. Groundnut can be sown during second fortnight of May and peas in the second fortnight of October followed by sunflower in the rotation during first fortnight of February. Since it consists of oilseed crops, it can play an important role in putting a curb on imports of oil for meeting dietary requirements.

6.3.11 Summer groundnut-potato-bajra (fodder)

This system is superior over rice-wheat in terms of water saving, soil health and productivity. Summer groundnut is sown in first week of May followed by potato in first week of October and *bajra* fodder in the first fortnight of March.

6.4 Other options

6.4.1 Multiple cropping systems

Maize-early pea-sunflower, Maize-senji-sugarcane-cotton, Early fodder/*bajra*-raya-summer greengram, Sorghum/*bajra*-chickpea, Maize-chickpea/*berseem*, *Desi* cotton-lentil, Groundnut-lentil, Guara-African sarson, Groundnut/greengram/arhar-African sarson, Maize-rajmash-greengram, Maize-potato/mustard-blackgram, Maize-*toria*-spring maize, Maize -potato-spring maize and Cotton/maize/greengram/blackgram-*berseem*/ senji/oat

6.4.2 Intercropping

Spring sugarcane+summer greengram/summer blackgram, Autumn sugarcane+peas/ chickpea, *kharif* fodder-*toria*+*gobhi sarson*-summer greengram, *Kharif* fodder (cowpea)/ groundnut-*toria*+*gobhi sarson*, Fodder sorghum-chickpea/lentil+mustard, Maize-rajmash + potato, Spring sugarcane + greengram / blackgram.

7. CONSTRAINTS IN CROP DIVERSIFICATION

The major problems in adoption of crop diversification (Gangwar *et al.*, 2016) are as follows:

- More than 60 percent of 141 M ha of the net cultivated area in the country is completely dependent on rainfall.
- Sub-optimal and over-exploitation of resources like land and water resources, causing a negative impact on the environment and sustainability of agriculture.
- Inadequate supply of seeds and plants of improved cultivars.
- Fragmentation of land holding less favoring modernization and mechanization of agriculture.

- Poor basic infrastructure like rural roads, power, transport, communications etc.
- Very weak agro-based industry.
- Weak research - extension - farmer linkages.
- Inadequately trained human resources together with persistent and large scale illiteracy amongst farmers.
- Host of diseases and pests affecting most crop plants.
- Decreased investments in the agricultural sector over the years.
- Lack of policies
- Lack of contract or cooperative farming
- Lack of proper machinery
- Lack of marketing
- Socio-economic problems

8. CONCLUSION

Diversification of the existing rice-wheat cropping system with alternative systems is the need of the hour. It is the option of enhancing productivity, profitability as well as employment generation under diverse agro-climatic conditions of our resource ridden farming community. Inclusion of faboid legume crops in the cropping systems covers all the four aspects of sustainability *viz*., environmental, economic, social and institutional. Fitting of FLCs should be done in a systematic manner. It can be done by adding FLCs to the existing rice-wheat, replacing either rice or wheat from the system and also, by replacing rice-wheat system completely from a certain percentage of area. Thus, against the backdrop of degradation of natural resources and changing climate scenario, incorporation of legumes in the existing cereal based systems following the climate resilient agro-techniques can help in a big way for transition towards intensive crop production and sustainability in the IGP of north-west India.

9. FUTURE OUTLOOK

Identification of efficient management systems based on soil/water/variety, which can play an important role in sustainable intensification of cropping systems involving FLCs for niche areas. Short duration varieties of FLCs especially pulse crops needs to be identified for best fit in cereal based cropping systems.

REFERENCES

Anonymous (2020) Statistics of Punjab Agriculture, Punjab Agricultural University, Ludhiana, Pp 1-58.

Aulakh, M.S., Kabba, B.S., Baddesha, H.S., Bahl, G.S. and Gill, M.P.S. (2003) Crop yields and phosphorus fertilizer transformations after 25 years of applications to a subtropical soil under groundnut–based cropping systems. *Field Crops Research* 83, 283-296.

Bhatt, R., Kukal, S.S., Busari, M.A., Arora, S. and Yadav, M. (2016) Sustainability issues on rice-wheat cropping system. *International Soil and Water Conservation Research* 4, 64-74.

Chauhan, B.S., Mahajan, G., Sardana, V., Timsina, J. and Jat, M.L. (2012) Productivity and sustainability of the rice -wheat cropping system in the Indo-Gangetic Plains of the Indian subcontinent: problems, opportunities, and strategies. *Advances in Agronomy* 117, 316-355.

Coumar, M.V., Kundu, S., Saha, J.K., Rajendiran, S., Dotaniya, M.L., Karthikeyan, K. and Patra, A.K. (2020) Soil carbon dynamics, carbon budget and its relationship with crop yield under different cropping systems in Vertisols of Central India. *Indian Journal of Agricultural Sciences* 90(1), 123-127.

Dwivedi, B.S., Shukla, A.K., Singh, V.K. and Yadav, R.L. (2003) Improving nitrogen and phosphorus use efficiencies through inclusion of forage cowpea in the rice–wheat systems in the Indo-Gangetic Plains of India. *Field Crops Research* 84, 399-418.

Gan, Y., Hamel, C. and O'Donovan, J. (2015) Diversifying crop rotations with pulses enhances system productivity. *Scientific Reports*5,14625. doi:10.1038/srep14625.

Gangwar, B., Ghosh, P.K., Rana, D.S. and Ravisankar, N. (2016) Crop Diversification. In: Rana, D.S., Ghosh, P.K., Shivay, Y.S.and Singh, G. (Eds), Modern Concepts of Agronomy. IARI, New Delhi, India. Pp. 113-145.

Ghosh, P.K., Hazra, K.K., Venkatesh, M.S., Praharaj, C.S., Kumar, N., Nath, C.P., Singh, U. and Singh, S.S. (2019) Grain legume inclusion in cereal–cereal rotation increased base crop productivity in the long run. *Experimental Agriculture* 56(1), 142-158.

Ghosh, P.K., Manna, M.C., Dayal, D. and Wanjari, R.H. (2006) Carbon sequestration potential and sustainable yield index for groundnut-and fallow- based cropping systems. *Journal of Agricultural Science* 144, 249-259.

Ghosh, P.K., Venkatesh, M.S., Hazra, K.K. and Kumar, N. (2012) Long term effect of pulses and nutrient management on soil organic carbon dynamics and sustainability on an inceptisol of Indo-Gangetic plains of India. *Experimental Agriculture* 48,473-487.

Gupta, R.D. and Singh, H. (2006) Indiscriminate use of fertilizer poses health hazards. Farmers' Forum. pp 20-24.

Hazra, K.K., Nath, C.P., Ghosh, P.K. and Swain, D.K. (2020) Inclusion of Legumes in Rice–Wheat Cropping System for Enhancing Carbon Sequestration. In: Ghosh, P., Mahanta, S., Mandal, D., Mandal, B., Ramakrishnan, S. (eds) Carbon Management in Tropical and Sub-Tropical Terrestrial Systems. Springer, Singapore.doi:10.1007/978-981-13-9628-1_2.

Katyal, V., Gangwar, B. and Bhandari, A.L. (2002) Productivity and yield stability of crop sequences in Haryana and Punjab. *Indian Journal of Agricultural Sciences* 72(5), 260-262.

Kimenju, J.W., Kagundu, A.M., Nderitu, J.H., Mambala, F., Mutua, G.K. and Kariuki, G.M. (2008) Incorporation of green manure plants into bean cropping systems contribute to root-knot nematode suppression. *Asian Journal of Plant Sciences* 7(4), 404-408.

Kukal, S.S. and Aggarwal, G.C. (2003) Puddling depth and intensity effects in rice–wheat system on a sandy loam soil. I. Development of subsurface compaction. *Soil and Tillage Research* 72, 1-8.

Ladha, J.K., Dawe, D., Pathak, H., Padre, A.T., Yadav, R.L., Singh, B., Singh, Y., Singh, P., Kundu, A.L., Sakal, R., Ram, N., Regmi, A.P., Gami, S.K., Bhandari, A.L., Amin, R., Yadav, C.R., Bhattarai, E.M., Das, S., Aggarwal, H.P. and Gupta, R.K. (2003) How extensive are yield declines in long-term rice-wheat experiments in Asia? *Field Crops Research* 81, 159-180.

Lal, R. (2017) Improving soil health and human protein nutrition by pulses-based cropping systems. *Advances in Agronomy* 145, 167-204.

Lal, R., Kraybill, D., Hansen, D.O., Singh, B.R., Mosogoya, T. and Eik, L.O. (Eds.). (2016) Climate Change and Multi-Dimensional Sustainability in African Agriculture. Springer, Cham, Switzerland, pp. 717.

Mal, T., Walia, S.S. and Saini, K.S. (2018) Productivity and economics of different cropping systems in relation to tillage, mulching and fertilizer management practices in north-western Indo-Gangetic Plains of India. *Indian Journal of Agricultural Sciences* 88(2), 216-221.

Naresh, R.K., Tomar, S.S., Shahi, U.P., Singh, S.P., Purushottam, Singh, B. and Kumar, P. (2014) Sustainability of maize -wheat cropping system by different legume intercropping and nitrogen level treatments on light distribution, soil temperature and crop productivity. *African Journal of Plant Science* 8(4), 204-213.

Prasad, D., Yadava, M.S. and Singh, C.S. (2013) Diversification of rice (*Oryza sativa*)-based cropping systems for higher productivity, profitability and resource-use efficiency under irrigated ecosystem of Jharkhand. *Indian Journal of Agronomy* 58(3), 264-270.

Rodell, M., Velicigna I. and Famiglietti, J.S. (2009) Satellite-based estimates of groundwater depletion in India. *Nature* 460, 999-1002.

Sapkota, T.B., Shankar, V., Rai, M., Jat, M.L., Stirling, C.M., Singh, L.K., Jat, H.S. and Grewal, M.S. (2017) Reducing global warming potential through sustainable intensification of basmati rice-wheat systems in India. *Sustainability* 9, 1044.

Sharma, S.K. and Sharma, S.N. (2005) Effect of crop diversification of rice-wheat cropping system on productivity and profitability. *Journal of Sustainable Agriculture* 26(1), 39-48.

Singh, A. and Kaur, J. (2012) Impact of conservation tillage on soil properties in rice-wheat cropping system. *Agricultural Science Research Journal* 2(1), 30-41.

Singh, D.K. and Kumar, V. (2014) Influence of diversification of rice (*Oryza sativa*)-wheat (*Triticum aestivum*) system on productivity, energetics and profitability under on-farm conditions. *Indian Journal of Agronomy* 59(2), 200-203.

Singh, G. (2009) Salinity-related desertification and management strategies: Indian experience. *Land Degradation and Development* 20, 367-385.

Singh, R.K., Bohra, J.S., Nath, T., Singh, Y. and Singh, K. (2011) Integrated assessment of diversification of rice-wheat cropping system in Indo-Gangetic plain. *Archives of Agronomy and Soil Science* 57, 489-506.

Singh, V.K., Dwivedi, B.S., Shukla, A.K., Chauhan, Y.S. and Yadav, R.L. (2005) Diversification of rice with pigeonpea in a rice-wheat cropping system on a Typic Ustochrept: Effect on soil fertility, yield and nutrient use efficiency. *Field Crops Research* 92, 85-105.

Stagnari, F., Maggio, A., Galieni, A. and Pisante, M. (2017) Multiple benefits of legumes for agriculture sustainability: An overview. *Chemical and Biological Technologies in Agriculture* 4(2), 1-13.

Thakur, N.P., Kachroo, D., Kumar, J., Kour, M. and Kumar, P. (2009) Diversification of rice-wheat cropping system in subhumid Indo-Gangetic plains of Jammu. *Oryza- An International Journal on Rice* 46(2),108-112.

Tilak, K.V.B.R. (2004) Response of *Sesbania* green manuring and mungbean residue incorporation on microbial activities for sustainability of a rice-wheat cropping system. *Journal of Agriculture and Rural Development in the Tropics and Subtropics* 105(2), 189-96.

Venkatesh, M.S., Hazra, K.K., Singh, J. and Nadarajan, N. (2015) Introducing summer mungbean in cereal based production system. *Indian Farming* 65, 12-13.

Walia, S.S., Gill, M.S., Bhushan, B., Phutela, R.P. and Aulukh, C.S. (2011) Alternate cropping systems to rice (*Oryza sativa*)-wheat (*Triticum aestivum*) for Punjab. *Indian Journal of Agronomy* 56(1), 20-27.

Yadav, M.P., Rai, J., Kushwaha, S. and Singh, G.K. (2005) Production potential and economic analysis of various cropping systems for central plains zone of Uttar Pradesh. *Indian Journal of Agronomy* 50(2), 83-85.

CHAPTER 3

Intercropping of pulses in sugarcane for crop diversification and livelihood security

Om Prakash[1]*, A.K. Singh[2], Brahm Prakash[1], A.D. Pathak[1] and Pallavi Yadav[3]

1. ICAR-Indian Institute of Sugarcane Research, Lucknow (U.P.)

2. Sugarcane Research Institute, Dr RPCAU, Pusa, Samastipur (Bihar)

3. CBG Ag PG College, Bakshi Ka Talab, Lucknow (U.P.)

*Corresponding author email: dromprakashiisrlucknow@gmail.com

Abstract

Crop diversification has witnessed paradigm shift which encompasses several concepts to accommodate the intercrops with sugarcane in space and time for vertical land productivity. In sub-tropical India, sugarcane is planted at narrow spacing of 90 cm in autumn season, 75 cm in spring season and 60 cm row to row spacing in the summer season, while sugarcane is still planted at wider spacing of 120-150 cm to facilitate the mechanization of cultivation operations in tropical India. Being widely spaced, initially slow growing, long duration and one time income generating crop, sugarcane crop provides ample scope for intercropping with short duration, high value and mid-season income generating pulse crops for food, nutritional and livelihood security especially of small and marginal cane growers. Intercropping of pulse crops with sugarcane also offers viable technology for improving the productivity of winter initiated ratoon, which suffers on account of extreme cold and/or frost conditions in sub tropics. Now, a wide cafeteria of intercrops with matching production technology is available for sub-tropical India as well as tropical India which would facilitate in raising the land utilization efficiency, declining the cost of production, economizing the use of market purchased costly inputs and making plant-ratoon system sustainable which ultimately helps in raising the socio-economic status of small and marginal resource constrained farmers and generates plenty of employment opportunities especially for rural women and youths.

Keywords: Additive series, Biological N-fixation, Cowpea, Economics, Lentil, Mungbean, Rajmash, Urdbean

1. INTRODUCTION

Several transformational changes are being noticed in the society. Indian Agriculture also is not an exception to this transformation but the national agricultural research and development support system is facing number of constraints viz., growing population, changing lifestyles, expanding urbanization and accelerating climate changes are creating new challenges for national agricultural research and development. A kind of sequence and arrangement of crops grown on a given area of land over a period of time is known as cropping system. Cropping systems are the outcome of the technological innovations, household needs, reflection of government policies, availability of production inputs, market forces and socio-economic compulsion (Singh *et al.,* 2009). A cropping system which efficiently uses natural resources provides high returns with stability without causing any harm to the ecological balance is treated as an ideal cropping system. Sequential cropping and intercropping are two major category of cropping system. A cropping system may be a regular rotation of different crops in which the crops follow a definite order of appearance on the land or it may consist of only one crop grown year after year on the same area. Inclusion of different crops with definite or planned order in which crops follow one another or growing of two, or several crops mixed together are other types of cropping systems (Singh, 1972). There are more than 250 double cropping systems of primary, secondary and tertiary importance in terms of their spread in the country has been listed. Out of which only 30 systems are of primary importance (Yadav and Prasad, 1997). Among top ten popular cropping systems in the country, only two, *viz*., rice-chickpea and maize-chickpea contain a pulse crop with less than 6% of the total pulse area (Yadav, 1996).

Sugarcane (*Saccharum officinarum*) is an important cash crop playing a pivotal role in agrarian economy and raises the socio-economic status of small and marginal resource constrained farmers. Approximately 0.6 crore farmers, their dependence and large number of farm labourers are engaged in cultivation of such an important agro-industrial crop like sugarcane for their livelihood. Sugarcane occupied 5.11 M ha area during 2018-19 in India, producing about 400 million tonnes of sugarcane with an average productivity of about 78.2 t/ha (DES, 2019). However, there have been fluctuations in area as well as yield over the period of time due to several factors like plateauing yield level, declining factor productivity and increasing production cost. In view of continuously changing market scenario, consumers' preferences and global competitions, new income generating opportunities needs to be created through crop diversification in sugarcane based production system. This would help in increasing the land utilization efficiency, reducing the production cost, economizing the use of market purchased costly inputs and making plant-ratoon system sustainable.

In sub-tropical India, sugarcane occupies 6-8, 70-80 and 10-15 per cent of the total area in autumn, spring and summer season and is planted at 90, 75 and 60 cm row spacing, respectively, while in tropical India, it is planted still at wider spacing of 120-150 cm to facilitate the mechanization of cultivation operations. Although sugarcane was being produced in monocropping for number of centuries but intercropping in sugarcane has assumed importance during past few decades in view of declining land resources, continuously changing market scenario and consumers' preferences with stiff global competitions and new income generating opportunities. Inclusion of short duration high value crops in sugarcane based production system as intercrop holds great promise in increasing the land utilization efficiency and generating additional income. Initial growth of sugarcane is quite slow, as it takes 30-35 days to germinate in spring and even more in autumn season. Thereafter, the crop takes another 100 days for full canopy development. Hence, these 130-135 days can be well utilized for short duration pulse crops. Crop rotation and intercropping makes sugarcane cultivation more remunerative especially for small and marginal growers. Moreover, it reduces the adverse effects of monoculture or continuous cropping of sugarcane on soil and sustains its productivity. Intercropping in sugarcane act as a boon for the marginal farmers as it offers increased land utilization efficiency, judicious use of costly inputs and mid-season income generation (Yadav *et al.*, 2019; Prakash *et al.*, 2020).

In this context, a major research programme on 'Management of Intercrops in Sugarcane' was pursued at ICAR-Indian Institute of Sugarcane Research, Lucknow with the following specific objectives:

- To identify the most compatible, efficient and remunerative intercrops with sugarcane plant and winter initiated ratoon at different locations
- To work out proper moisture environment and nutrient requirement for intercropping systems involving pulse crops in sugarcane for rationalizing irrigation and fertilizer schedules
- To assess the effect of incorporation of intercrops residues on nutrient use efficiency, soil fertility, productivity and sustainability of sugarcane plant-ratoon system
- To investigate the allelopathic effects of intercrops on sugarcane, if any
- To demonstrate the technologies through on-station and on-farm trials
- To develop sugarcane based intercrop models and study the degree of adoption pattern of generated technologies.

Pulses, long considered 'the poor man's meat' because of their protein profile, occupy a unique place in Indian agriculture (Roy *et al.*, 2017). Pulse crops play an important role due to its ability to fix atmospheric nitrogen, improve soil health, check soil erosion, weed suppression, nutrient economy in cropping system and other multiple uses. In the other hand, it is a preferred alternative for the farmers to diversify the cereal based cropping systems through intercropping and crop intensification (Rajpoot and Rana, 2016). The importance of protein in human diet is known to us since time immemorial. Pulses are the rich source of protein, particularly for the majority of vegetarian population. Pulse crops fixes about 30-147 kg nitrogen/ha by biological nitrogen fixation (Paroda, 2000; Ganeshamurthy *et al.*, 2006) (Table 1). Pulses or grain legumes are a group of more than a dozen crops including chickpea, pigeonpea, urdbean, mungbean, lentils, lathyrus (*khesari*), rajmash, fieldpea, cowpea, horsegram, mothbean, *etc.* They are high in protein, fibre, and various vitamins, and provide amino acid (Amarender Reddy, 2015). Pulses are not only good for people, but are good for soils as they have unique inbuilt mechanism to fix atmospheric nitrogen into the soil (Ganai *et al.*, 2016). Pulses remain an integral component of subsistence cropping since time immemorial on account of their values as nutritious food, feed and forage. They are grown as a sole crop, intercrop, catch crop, relay crop, cover crop and green manure crop *etc.*, under sequential/mono cropping in different agro-ecological regions. With the increase in irrigated area, pulse crops suffered the most.

Table 1. Biological nitrogen fixation by different pulse crops

Pulse crop	Biological N- fixation (kg/ha)
Chickpea	41-134
Pigeonpea	31-97
Urdbean	30-74
Mungbean	30-74
Lentil	60-147
Fieldpea	30-125
Cowpea	47-188
Fababean	64-92

Source: Paroda (2000), Subba Rao (1988), Yadav and Singh (1986)

2. INTERCROPPING

Growing two or more crops simultaneously on the same field for the purpose of crop intensification (both temporal and spatial dimension) with intercrop competition during all or in a part of crop growth is known as intercropping (Kumar *et al.*, 2008). It is commonly practiced for growing more than one crop for achieving enhanced land use efficiency and minimizing the risk of complete crop failure against droughts, attack of insects, pests and diseases. The system also leads to improve water and nutrient use efficiency. Generally, the legume crop constitutes a part of this system, as these crops provide better cover to the land and hence good protection of soil from beating action of the rain, protection from soil erosion and assurance of one or more crops to the farmers. Further, the roots of various crops species in the intercropping make use of soil moisture and nutrients from different soil depth (Bhatt and Singh, 2016).

2.1 Prospects and opportunities

There is very slow growth of sugarcane in the initial months of planting, as it takes approximately 30-35 days to germinate in spring (February-March) and even more time during October planted autumn season. The crop takes further 100 days to develop full canopy to cover entire inter-row spaces. Thus, it offers a good opportunity for the cultivation of the short duration crops as intercrops in this space without affecting the growth of sugarcane (Ali *et al.*, 2012). Intercropping allows more intensive cropping in sugarcane which has been traditionally cultivated in 'Monocropping System'. As sugarcane plants have large lateral spread when fully grown, their optimum row spacing is usually 90 cm or 75 cm. The vacant space in between the rows can quickly be covered by weeds, which when allowed to grow might eventually offer severe competition to the main crop. Instead of such a waste of limited available spaces, intercropping provides ample opportunity for profitable utilization of such space while reducing the production cost of sugarcane by cutting down the expenditure incurred on the management of weeds and other inputs. Several researchers have observed that weed growth is suppressed due to the complete cover of soil surface and higher crop-weed competition under intercropping of pulses in sugarcane. Thus, it is helpful in reducing the human labour requirement and cost involved in weeding. Further, being fast growing and short duration crops, pulses are the ideal crops for intercropping with sugarcane in space left in between two rows of sugarcane. Thus, there is no competition between sugarcane and pulse crops during the entire period for which pulse crops are there in the field as intercrop.

2.2 Pre-requisites of intercropping

Pulse crops also stand good on the suitability criterion of intercrops especially in sugarcane which can be assessed by certain characteristics as described by Kumar (1981):

- The duration of intercrop should be short (not more than 3-4 months).
- The growth habit of the intercrop should be short and erect statured to avoid shading effect of cane on intercrop or *vice-versa.*
- There should not be any competition between component crops for natural and applied resources any point of time.
- The intercrops should have compatibility with respect to plant protection measures.
- Cultural practices required by intercrop should not affect the main sugarcane crop.
- There should be similarity in the irrigation and fertilizer requirement in the main crop as well as intercrops.

Sugarcane characteristically widely spaced, initially slow growing, long duration and one time income generating crop, provides ample opportunities for intercropping with short duration, high value and mid-season income generating crops for food, nutritional and livelihood security especially of small and marginal cane growers.

2.3 Benefits of intercropping of pulses in sugarcane

Intercropping is a form of polyculture wherein two or more crops are occupying same space at the same time and it is also associated with sustainable agriculture. Intercropping enhances the total productivity and profitability of the system and is commonly being used in many parts of the country. Intercropping is basic characteristics of subsistance farming which improves per unit area productivity and offers diversified production, insurance against vagaries of nature, creates new opportnities of employment and enhances the farmers income. Sugarcane being a widely spaced crop with late sprouting and initial slow growth offers good prospects for intercropping short duration crops. Pulses are the most suitable crops for intercropping with sugarcane as they improve soil environment including physical, chemical and biological properties of soil, economize use of inorganic nitrogen fertilizer, protect the surface soil from erosion by air and water, and suppressing weed flora due to dense population. Pulse crops are a friendly intercrop, and are being used in many sugarcane based cropping systems.

Pulses are known to adapt to wide range of edaphic and climatic conditions. They are important component in climate change mitigation through nitrogen fixation, role in crop rotation, mixed and intercropping, maintaining soil fertility and thus contribute significantly to sustainability of the farming systems and have great potential to protect the environment (Rajanna *et al.*, 2017). Residues are the plant based organic material produced from the preceding crops. Large portion of unused crop residues are spread by pulses on succeeding crop for better resource conservation and higher productivity. Soil incorporated pulse crop residue has been found beneficial to soil health, crop productivity, nutrient water use efficiency and water retention in the soil (Rajanna *et al*., 2017). Pulses improve the soil physical (soil aggregates, pore space, bulk density), chemical (organic carbon, soil pH) and biological properties (biota population, efficiency and synergy, microbial biomass) of soil. Pulses also release organic acids in soil, thereby mobilizing unavailable soil nutrients. They also add to the organic matter by leaf fall, root biomass and other crop residues. Therefore, the importance of pulses in soil health has made it an integral part of Indian agriculture since time immemorial. They play an important role in sustainable agriculture by improving soil health (addition of organic matter through root biomass and leaf fall, soil pulverization, breaking sub surface hard pan/ soil layer, biological nitrogen fixation, release of organic acids which facilitate mobilization of nutrients, enhancing soil microbial activity, *etc*.), conserving soil and water (reduction in run-off, improving infiltration rate, protecting soil surface against beating action of rain drops, serve as vegetative barrier against soil erosion), crop diversification and intensification (short duration, low input requirements, amenable to intercropping), ecological sustainability (carbon sequestration, low water and nutrient requirement, ability to thrive under harsh climate and marginal soils) (Shukla, 2004; Shahi *et al*., 2003; Singh, 2015; Amarender Reddy, 2015). Pulses can also fix hefty quantities of nitrogen in the soil, boosting fertility and reducing- by millions of tonnes globally-the need to apply the key nutrients in food crops as these crops are a natural nitrogen manufacturing factory in the field. Growing these crops play a vital role in increasing nitrogen production in addition to qualifying for the demands of dietary protein and energy. Incorporation of legumes help in restoring soil organic matter and reducing pest and diseases problems, and improves sustainability (Kumar *et al*., 2016).

2.4 Essential component of intercropping

2.4.1 Crop compatibility

It is an essential ingredient of sound intercropping system. With other crops like potato, mustard, wheat, berseem, sugarbeet, coriander, garlic, tobacco and winter vegetables, *rajmash*, lentil, chickpea and fieldpeas have been found compatible for growing with autumn sugarcane. Urdbean, mungbean and cowpea are most compatible intercrops with spring planted cane and ratoon (Singh *et al*., 2000).

2.4.2 Compatible varieties

Compatible varieties of component crops boost the complementarities to a great extent. Short and erect stature varieties of crops are more suitable for intercropping with sugarcane. Urdbean and mungbean have been quite compatible in spring planted sugarcane. At Bhubaneswar, Dixit and Mishra (1999) observed that intercropping legumes in spring planted sugarcane improved cane yield. Among various pulses, mungbean was found most profitable. At Lucknow, Yadav *et al*. (1993) found that rajmash was more profitable than chickpea and fieldpea. Among these 3 pulses, the least adverse effect on cane yield was observed under fieldpea intercropping. In autumn planted sugarcane at Sehore (Madhya Pradesh), among three varieties of fieldpea, Rachna was more compatible than Pusa 10 and HFP 4 (Aparna). Similarly, in rajmash, VL 63 had an edge over Uday (PDR 14), and JG 74 was superior to JG 315 in chickpea (Sharma *et al*., 1992).

2.4.3 Planting geometry

Mostly additive type of intercropping is followed in sugarcane in which full population of sugarcane crops (base crop) and additional population (in additive series) of intercrop is introduced with different row ratios. Row ratio of 1:1, 1:2 and 1:3 have been recommended for various sugarcane based intercropping systems (Yadav *et al*., 1987; Panwar *et al*., 1990).

2.4.4 Application of fertilizers in intercropping system

Time of fertilizer application of sugarcane plays an important role in deciding the use efficiency of applied fertilizer and yield of sugarcane. Application of nitrogen to sugarcane as basal dose results in foliage growth of intercrops because of luxury consumption of nitrogen and as a consequence growth and yield of sugarcane is adversely affected. Thus, nitrogen application to sugarcane should be made after the harvesting of intercrops. The time of fertilizer application of intercrop may be similar to the sole cropping (Singh *et al*., 2000).

Thus, new look of intercropping for production factor (Singh, 1994) may be expressed as:

$$\text{Production fator} = \frac{\text{Sugarcane yield per unit area} + \text{Intercrop value per unit area}}{\text{Sugarcane value per unit area or sole crop value per unit area}}$$

The production factor may vary depending upon the market rate of sugarcane and intercrops in the specific year and location. To achieve high production factor, while selecting intercrop, the factors like high value crop, erect stature and short duration crop, preserving land productivity and environmental quality, achieving economic and sustained production to meet multiple needs of farm households, maintaining desirable level of biological diversity and ecological stability and ensuring optimum utilization and conservation of available resources by effective recycling of farm residues within the system may be followed.

Thus, in short, intercropping of pulse crops with sugarcane has been found beneficial for following reasons:

- Intercropping of pulse crops in sugarcane ensures efficient utilization of inter-row spaces and vertical increase in land productivity.
- Sugarcane as well as pulse crops meet the multiple needs of the farmers through mixed farming enterprises.
- Pulse crops generate mid-season income from intercrops for better management of sugarcane, *per se*.
- Intercropping of pulses in sugarcane ensures regular on-farm employment and income generating opportunities especially for women and children.
- This system also ensures savings in market purchased inputs through integrated nutrient management.
- This system also ensures proofing against risk due to aberrant weather conditions, disease and insect pests.
- This system has also been found helpful in controlling weeds through sufficient canopy developed by intercrops during germination phase or later.

- Intercropping of pulses in sugarcane provides high yielding environment to pulses which otherwise are grown under sub-marginal conditions.
- Growing legumes in intercrop and incorporation of legume residues after picking of pods also significantly improve the yield of main crop, sugarcane. Incorporation of spring mungbean residues after picking pods economized 60 kg nitrogen/ha. The association of pulse roots with VAM fungi helps to increase the availability of water and nutrients to plants (Kumar *et al.*, 2016).
- Pulse crops also contribute significantly in reducing the Greenhouse Gases (GHGs) emission.
- Intercropping of pulses in the prevailing cropping systems is must for sustaining and improving the productivity, soil health, environment and quality of produce. In this context, pulses with sugarcane intercropping uses and availability to short duration/ short stature photo-insensitive crop with resistance to biotic and abiotic stresses has very high potential for diversification of cropping systems and enhancing the productivity and profitability (Kumar *et al.*, 2016).

Thus, there is immense scope of increasing area under pulse crops through intercropping in sugarcane under Indian sub-tropics (Table 2).

Table 2: Potential area for pulses production through intercropping in sugarcane

Crop	Common name	Scientific name	Potential area (m ha)
Chickpea	Chana	*Cicer arietinum*	0.5
Pigeonpea (Early)	Arhar, Tur	*Cajanus cajan*	1.0
Pigeonpea (*Rabi*)	Arhar, Tur	*Cajanus cajan*	0.3
Mungbean (Spring/summer)	Mung	*Vigna radiata*	1.0
Urdbean (Spring/summer)	Urd	*Vigna mungo*	1.0
Lentil	Masoor	*Lens culinaris*	0.5
Lathyrus	Khesari	*Lathyrus sativus*	0.2
Rajmash	Rajma	*Phaseolus vulgaris*	0.5
Total			5.0

3. TECHNOLOGYPACKAGEFORINTERCROPPINGOFPULSECROPS

Lentil, frenchbean and peas are the suitable pulse intercrops in autumn planted sugarcane, while in spring planted sugarcane, mungbea, blackgram and cowpea (*Vigna unguiculata*) are suitable intercrops (Chakar *et al.*, 1997; Panwar *et al.*, 1990; Yadav *et al.*, 1987; Lal and Singh, 2004). As major emphasis is being placed on both production and processing diversification options in 'Produce to Product Chain' to benefit the cane growers and mill owners alike, the outcome of the research experiments conducted at ICAR-Indian Institute of Sugarcane Research, Lucknow have been developed as a technology package for intercropping of pulse crops.

For achieving higher productivity and harnessing positive associative complementarities of intercrops and making plant-ratoon system economically more viable, the following sugarcane based intercropping systems have been identified (Table 3).

Table 3. Yield and benefit cost ratio of sugarcane based intercropping system

Intercropping system	Yield (t/ha)			Benefit: cost ratio
	Sugarcane	Pulse crop	Sugarcane equivalent	
Autumn planted sugarcane				
Sugarcane sole	85.2	—	85.2	1.63
Sugarcane + *rajmash*	86.8	1.75	132.8	2.54
Sugarcane + lentil	76.5	1.16	99.0	1.73
Spring planted sugarcane				
Sugarcane sole	77.3	—	77.3	1.38
Sugarcane + cowpea (green pods)	75.2	2.90	90.4	1.48
Sugarcane + mungbean	76.6	0.57	91.6	1.54

Source: Lal *et al.,* (2004)

Sugarcane in autumn is planted at wider spacing of 90 cm or more. The bud sprouting is late and initial growth rate of crop is slow. Autumn planted sugarcane provides 15-20% higher cane yield and 0.5 units more sugar recovery than spring planted cane but the area remains limited. However, companion cropping of winter pulses like rajmash and lentil may promote autumn planting of sugarcane on account of higher returns and better resource use efficiency.

Spring planted sugarcane intercropped with mungbean produced significantly taller cane than intercropping with cowpea or urdbean while weight/cane (0.91 kg), net millable canes (96.1 thousand/ha), cane yield (73.6 t/ha), cane equivalent yield (87.4 t/ha) and commercial cane sugar (8.33 t/ha) were at par with sugarcane intercropped with cowpea. The net return as well as B: C ratios were the highest with sugarcane + mungbean closely followed by sugarcane + cowpea intercropping system (Lal *et al*., 2002).

3.1 System based management

Additive series of intercropping system is practiced in sugarcane. Slight modification in plant geometry to compensate the adverse effect on shoot mortality of cane even sometimes accommodates higher plant population of sugarcane. Therefore, the management issues become more crucial than intercrop *per se* in sugarcane based additive series intercropping systems. Development of appropriate nutrient, water and weed management strategies must be given emphasised in this context (Shukla, 2004; Ali, 2004; Shahi *et al*., 2003).

3.2 Plant nutrient management

Autumn planted sugarcane intercropped with *rajmash* receiving 100% NPK was similar in number of millable canes, cane yield and commercial cane sugar. Sugarcane + rajmash system was at par with sugarcane + potato but sugarcane + rajmash system recorded significantly higher number of millable canes, cane yield and commercial cane sugar over sugarcane + mustard or wheat due to additive nutrient synergies.

In-situ incorporation of intercropped dual purpose cowpea (cv. Pusa Komal) after picking the green pods for vegetable added 70.61 kg N/ha followed by *dhaincha (Sesbania esculanta)* green manuring (45.90 kg N/ha). The highest microbial activity biomass nitrogen (97.93 mg/kg/10 day) was recorded when cowpea residue was incorporated in soil between inter row spaces, clearly revealing that incorporation of stubbles of cowpea crop adds to the pool of microbial nitrogen which in turn serves the source of nitrogen nutrition to sugarcane. The values of organic carbon content under these residue management systems were also higher with favourable physical rhizosphere environment (lower bulk density and higher infiltration rate) (Srivastava and Kumari, 2013).

3.3 Water management

Irrigation scheduling at 1.2 IW/CPE ratio produced the highest number of millable canes (97.1 thousand/ha), cane yield (88.9 t/ha) and commercial cane sugar (8.51 t/ha) which were statistically at par with 1.0 IW/CPE ratio (Ali, 2004; Ali and Singh, 1997).

3.4 Weed management

Pendimethalin @ 1.5 kg a.i./ha was found the best chemical herbicide for pre-emergence application in sugarcane based intercropping systems involving pulse crops (Varshney *et al.*, 2007). Sugarcane + mungbean with pendimethalin @ 1.5 kg a.i./ha as pre-emergence application fetched the highest B:C ratio of 1.53 which were very close to the values obtained from sugarcane + mungbean under weed free condition (Benefit : Cost ratio of 1.57).

Intercropping systems and weed management practices in plant crop exhibited positive effects on ratoon cane with the result that significantly higher number of millable canes and cane yield were obtained from ratoon of sugarcane + cowpea system over sugarcane + urdbean, while it remained at par with ratoon of sugarcane sole and sugarcane + mungbean. All the weed management practices in plant crop produced significantly higher number of millable canes and cane yield of ratoon over that from weedy check (Ali, 2004).

4. MANAGEMENT PRACTICES FOR PROFITABLE SUGARCANE BASED INTERCROPPING SYSTEM

Management practices for profitable sugarcane based intercropping system have been summarized below (Table 4).

Table 4. Management practices for profitable sugarcane based intercropping system

Intercropping system	Intercrop genotypes	Planting geometry / row ratio	Fertilizer (NPK kg/ ha) schedule for component crops	Area of adoption
Autumn planted sugarcane		90 cm	150:60:60	
Sugarcane + Rajmash	Uday (PDR 14)	1:2	100:60:40	Uttar Pradesh and Uttarakhand
Sugarcane + Lentil	DPL 62	1:2	20:40:30	Uttar Pradesh and Uttarakhand
Spring planted sugarcane		75 cm	150:60:60	
Sugarcane + Cowpea (Green pods)	Pusa Komal	1:2	20:40:20	Uttar Pradesh and Uttarakhand
Sugarcane + Mungbean	PDM 11 and PDM 84-139	1:2	20:40:20	Uttar Pradesh, Uttarakhand and Maharashtra

Source: Lal *et al.*, (1999); Lal *et al.*, (2000); Lal *et al.*, (2004)

4.1 Package of practices for intercropping in spring planted sugarcane

4.1.1 Sugarcane + mungbean

	 Sugarcane + mungbean
Land preparation:	Field to be prepared with soil turning plough followed by 2-3 harrowing. Field may be ploughed after pre-sowing irrigation and kept free from stubble of previous crop
Seed treatment:	Seed should be treated with thiram or bavistin or any other recommended fungicide @ 4-5 g/kg seed. Seed of mungbean should be inoculated with the particular *Rhizobium* culture, specific to the mungbean crop
Planting period:	*Sugarcane* : Mid February *Mungbean* : Early March
Seed rate:	*Sugarcane* : 70 q/ha *Mungbean* : 20 kg/ha
Sowing method with crop geometry:	1: 2 row ratio, sugarcane planted at 75 cm and two rows of mungbean accommodated at 25 cm spacing
System based fertilizer management (NPK kg/ha):	*Sugarcane* : 50:60:60 (NPK kg/ha) 1/3 N and full P and K at planting 1/3 N after harvesting of mungbean 1/3 N at late tillering stage (first week of June) *Mungbean* : 18: 46 (N & P kg/ha) at the time of sowing
Irrigation schedule:	Irrigation should be given at an interval of 10-15 days for the irrigation.
Weed control:	Pendimethalin @ 2 kg a.i./ha as pre-emergence Two hoeing at 30 and 60 days after harvest of mungbean

Plant Protection:	*Sugarcane* : At the time of planting, application of chlorpyriphos 20 EC @ 1 kg a.i./ha (5 litre formulation) in 1000 litre of water on setts in furrows with the help of rose cane. Application of Carbofuran (Furadon) 3 G @ 33 kg/ha during last week of June or first week of July in the vicinity of root zone when sufficient soil moisture is available. *Mungbean* : Confidor 200 SL @ 100 g a.i./ha or spray with Oxydemeton Methyl 0.05% at 3 weeks interval
Harvesting schedule:	*Mungbean* : Mid May *Sugarcane* : January/February
Production potential:	*Mungbean* : 5.7 q/ha *Sugarcane* : 76.6 t/ha
Sustainability of the system:	Increased infiltration rate and reduced bulk density Accumulation of Soil Microbial Biomass Carbon Maintenance of soil health in plant-ratoon system

4.1.2 Sugarcane + cowpea

	 Sugarcane + cowpea
Land preparation:	Field to be prepared with soil turning plough followed by 2-3 harrowings. Field may be ploughed after pre-sowing irrigation and keeping it free from debris of previous crop
Seed treatment:	Seed should be treated with thiram or bavistin or any other recommended fungicide @ 4-5 g/kg seed. Seed of cowpea should be inoculated with the particular *Rhizobium* culture, specific to the cowpea crop

Planting period:	*Sugarcane* : Mid February *Cowpea* : Early March
Seed rate:	*Sugarcane* : 70 q/ha *Cowpea* : 20 kg/ha
Sowing method with crop geometry:	1:2 row ratio, sugarcane planted at 75 cm and two rows of cowpea accommodated at 25 cm spacing
System based fertilizer management (NPK kg/ha):	*Sugarcane* : 150:60:60 (N, P, K, kg/ha) 1/3 N and full P and K at planting 1/3 N after harvesting of cowpea 1/3 N at late tillering stage (first week of June) *Cowpea* : 18:46:0 (N, P, K kg/ha) at the time of sowing
Irrigation schedule:	Irrigation should be given at an interval of 10-15 days for the irrigation
Weed control:	• Pendimethalin @ 2 kg a.i./ha as pre-emergence • Two hoeings at 30 and 60 days after harvest of cowpea
Plant Protection:	*Sugarcane*: • Application of chlorpyriphos 20 EC @ 1 kg a.i. / ha (5 litre formulation) in 1000 litre of water on setts in furrows with the help of rose cane at the time of planting • Application of carbofuran (Furadon) 3 G @ 33 kg/ ha during last week of June or first week of July in the vicinity of root zone when sufficient soil moisture is available *Cowpea*: • Confidor 200 SL @ 100 g a.i./ha or spray with Oxydemeton Methyl 0.05% at 3 week's interval
Harvesting schedule:	*Cowpea* (Green pods) : Mid April *Sugarcane* : January/February
Production potential:	*Cowpea* (Green pods) : 29 q/ha *Sugarcane* : 75.2 t/ha
Sustainability of the system:	Addition of green biomass to the soil after picking the green pods of cowpea significantly adds to Soil Microbial Nitrogen Pool

4.1.3 Sugarcane + urdbean

	 Sugarcane + urdbean
Land preparation:	Field to be prepared with soil turning plough followed by 2-3 harrowing. Field may be ploughed after pre-sowing irrigation and keeping it free from debris of previous crop
Seed treatment:	Seed should be treated with thiram or bavistin or any other recommended fungicide @ 4-5 g/kg seed. Seed of urdbean should be inoculated with the Rhizobium culture specific to the cowpea crop.
Planting period:	*Sugarcane* : Mid February *Urdbean* : Early March
Seed rate:	*Sugarcane* : 70 q/ha *Urdbean* : 20 kg/ha
Sowing method with crop geometry:	1:2 row ratio, sugarcane planted at 75 cm and two rows of urdbean accommodated at 25 cm spacing
System based fertilizer management (NPK kg/ha):	*Sugarcane* : 150:60:60 (N, P, K, kg/ha) 1/3 N and full P and K at planting 1/3 N after harvesting of cowpea 1/3 N at late tillering stage (first week of June) *Urdbean* : 18:46:0 (N, P, K kg/ha) at the time of sowing
Irrigation schedule:	Irrigation should be given at an an interval of 10-15 days for the irrigation
Weed control:	• Pendimethalin @ 2 kg a.i./ha as pre-emergence • Two hoeing at 30 and 60 days after harvest of urdbean

Plant Protection:	*Sugarcane*: • Application of chlorpyriphos 20 EC @ 1 kg a.i. / ha (5 litre formulation) in 1000 litre of water on setts in furrows with the help of rose cane at the time of planting • Application of Carbofuran (Furadon) 3 G @ 33 kg/ha during last week of June or first week of July in the vicinity of root zone when sufficient soil moisture is available *Urdbean*: • Confidor 200 SL @ 100 g a.i./ha or spray with Oxydemeton Methyl 0.05% at 3 week's interval
Harvesting schedule:	*Urdbean* : Mid May *Sugarcane* : January/February
Production potential:	*Urdbean* : 4.2 q/ha *Sugarcane* : 71.4 t/ha
Sustainability of the system:	Improvement in the total productivity of plant-ratoon system

4.2 Package of practices for intercropping in autumn planted sugarcane

4.2.1 Sugarcane + lentil

	 Sugarcane + lentil
Land preparation:	Field to be prepared with soil turning plough followed by 2-3 harrowing. Field may be ploughed after pre-sowing irrigation and keeping it free from debris of previous crop
Seed treatment:	Seed should be treated with thiram or bavistin or any other recommended @ 4-5 g/kg seed. Seed of lentil should be inoculated with the *Rhizobium* culture, specific to the lentil crop.

Planting period:	Second fortnight of October
Seed rate:	*Sugarcane* : 60 q/ha *Lentil* : 20 kg/ha
Sowing method with crop geometry:	1:2 row ratio, sugarcane planted at 90 cm and two rows of lentil intercropped at 30 cm spacing.
System based fertilizer management (NPK kg/ha):	*Sugarcane* : 150:60:60 (N, P, K, kg/ha) 1/3 N and full P and K at planting. 1/3 N after harvesting of lentil 1/3 N at late tillering stage (first week of June) *Lentil* : 20:40:0 (N, P, K kg/ha) as basal application
Irrigation schedule:	One irrigation should be given at pre-flowering stage of lentil
Weed control:	• Pendimethalin @ 2 kg a.i./ha as pre-emergence. • Two hoeing at 30 and 60 days after harvest of lentil
Plant Protection:	*Sugarcane*: • Application of chlorpyriphos 20 EC @ 1 kg a.i. / ha (5 litre formulation) in 1000 litre of water on setts in furrows with the help of rose cane at the time of planting • Application of Carbofuran (Furadon) 3 G @ 33 kg/ha during last week of June or first week of July in the vicinity of root zone when sufficient soil moisture is available *Lentil*: • Application of Dimecron 25 EC @ 1 litre/ha or Monocrotophos 36 SL @ 0.75 litrres/a against aphids
Harvesting schedule:	*Lentil* : Mid -March *Sugarcane* : November
Production potential:	*Lentil* : 11.6 q/ha *Sugarcane* : 76.5 t/ha
Sustainability of the system:	Improves physical properties of sol by reducing bulk density and increasing infiltration rate. Favourable carryover effects on sugarcane ratoon crop

4.2.2 Sugarcane + rajmash

	 Sugarcane + rajmash
Land preparation:	Field to be prepared with soil turning plough followed by 2-3 harrowing. Field may be ploughed after pre-sowing irrigation and keeping it free from debris of previous crop
Seed treatment:	Seed should be treated with thiram or bavistin or any other recommended fungicide @ 5-6 g/kg seed
Planting period:	Second fortnight of October
Seed rate:	*Sugarcane* : 60 q/ha *Rajmash* : 80 kg/ha
Sowing method with crop geometry:	1:2 row ratio, sugarcane planted at 90 cm accommodating two rows of rajmash intercropped at 30 cm spacing
System based fertilizer management (NPK kg/ha):	*Sugarcane* : 150:60:60 (N, P, K, kg/ha) 1/3 N and full P and K at planting. 1/3 N after harvesting of rajmash 1/3 N at late tillering stage (first week of June) *Rajmash* : 80:40:30 (NPK kg/ha) as basal application 1/2 N and full P and K with sowing, remaining ½ N after first irrigation
Irrigation schedule:	Two-three irrigations at one month interval.
Weed control:	Pendimethalin as pre-emergence @ 2 kg a.i./ha followed by 2 to 3 hoeing after harvest of rajmash.

Plant Protection:	*Sugarcane*: • Application of chlorpyriphos 20 EC @ 1 kg a.i. / ha (5 litre formulation) in 1000 litre of water on setts in furrows with the help of rose cane at the time of planting. • Application of Carbofuran (Furadon) 3 G @ 33 kg/ha during last week of June or first week of July in the vicinity of root zone when sufficient soil moisture is available. Rajmash: • Confidor 200 SL @ 100 g a.i./ha or spray with Oxydemeton Methyl 0.05% at 3 week's interval.
Harvesting schedule:	*Rajmash* : Mid March *Sugarcane* : November
Production potential:	*Rajmash grain* : 17.5 q/ha *Sugarcane* : 86.8 t/ha
Sustainability of the system :	Rajmash offers greater positive associative effect on number of millable cane, length, girth and weight/ cane due to addition of leaf litter and root biomass as well as nutrient synergies

5. CONCLUSION

In nutshell, the comparative research programme on intercropping conducted at ICAR-IISR, Lucknow has led to the development of a number of technologies based on system productivity, soil sustainability, and economic profitability. Autumn sugarcane + rajmash/ lentil has also been reckoned profitable as well as sustainable one due to additive nutrient synergies and positive associative effects of rajmash/lentil on sugarcane yield attributes and yield. Moreover, intercropped rajmash/lentil in autumn sugarcane improved soil fertility through entire leaf fall at pod maturity besides root biomass addition. Further, rajmash being short duration and heavily manured leaves significant amount of unutilized plant nutrients for sugarcane. All these exhibited positive association effects on sugarcane through development of synchronized tillers, taller, thicker and heavier millable canes.

The possibility and success of intercropping system in spring planted cane primarily depend upon the crop geometry and consequently plant population. Further, the level of nitrogen nutrition to sugarcane after the harvesting of intercrop component becomes crucial. Results revealed that increasing the plant density up to 125% caused significant increase in the yield of sugarcane over normal plant density. Moreover, intercropping in spring sugarcane improved soil fertility through incorporation of above ground biomass of urdbean, mungbean and cowpea along with root mass addition. These showed favourable effect on sugarcane plant-ratoon system.

6. USEFUL TIPS FOR MAKING INTERCROPPING IN SUGARCANE SUCCESSFUL

- For intercropping in sugarcane, those crops may be selected which have short duration, short stature, high value, mid-season income generating and eco-friendly.
- Select the recommended varieties of sugarcane and pulse intercrop for the region.
- To ensure germination of pulse crops, sufficient moisture should be there in upper layer of the soil at the time of sowing. Light irrigation can be applied before sowing of intercrops, if required.
- The crops in the intercropping system should be irrigated as per the irrigation requirement of intercrops.
- For getting remunerative price of the crop, the selected intercrop has a demand in the local market.
- Planting of sugarcane and sowing of intercrops should preferably be done simultaneously through especially designed IISR Planter-cum-Seeder.

REFERENCES

Ali, M. (2004). Management of intercrops in sugarcane based production system with pulse. In: Sugarcane Production: Strategies and Technologies, IISR Technical Bulletin No. 40, Edited by H.N. Shahi, Menhi Lal, O.K. Sinha and T.K. Srivastava, Indian Institute of Sugarcane Research, Lucknow. Pp. 76-78.

Ali, M. and Singh, K.K. (1997). Management of pulse crops under intercropping systems. In : Recent Advancess in Pulses Research (Eds. A.N. Asthana and M. Ali), Indian Society of Pulses Research and Development, Kanpur. Pp. 489-508.

Ali, M., Kumar, N. and Ghosh, P.K. (2012). Milestones on agronomic research in pulses in India. *Indian Journal of Agronomy* 57(3rd IAC Special Issue), 52-57.

Amarender Reddy, A. (2015). Pulses production trends and strategies to become self sufficient. *Indian Farming* 65(6), 2-10.

Bhatt, R. and Kukal, S.S. (2016). Soil and water conservation in sub-montaneous tract of Punjab. *Indian Farming* 66(6), 23-25.

Chakar, I.S., Manuja, S. and Vivek. (1997). Studies on pulse intercropping in spring planted sugarcane. *Cooperative Sugar* 29(2), 95-96.

DES (Directorate of Economics and Statistics). (2019). Agricultural Statistics At A Glance 2019. Department of Agriculture, Cooperation and Farmers Welfare; Ministry of Agriculture and Farmers Welfare, Government of India.

Dixit, L. and Mishra, A. (1999). Intercropping in sugarcane. *Indian Journal of Agronomy* 36(2), 261-263.

Ganai, N.A., Shah, T.A. and Hakeem, S.A. (2016). Organic farming, feeding the soil to feed the plant. *Indian Farming* 66(1), 25-27.

Ganeshamurthy, A.N., Ali, M. and Srinivasarao, Ch. (2006). Role of pulses in sustaining soil health and crop production. *Indian Journal of Fertilizers* 1(12), 29-40.

Kumar, N., Prakash, V., Meena, B.L., Gopinath, K.A. and Srivastva, A.K. (2008). Evaluation of *toria* (*Brassica compestris*) and lentil (*Lens culinaris*) varieties in intercropping system with wheat (*Triticum aestivum*) under rainfed conditions. *Indian Journal Agronomy* 53(1), 47-50.

Kumar, N., Hazra, K.K., Singh, S. and Nadarajan, N. (2016). Constraints and prospects of growing pulses in rice fallows of India. *Indian Farming* 66(6), 13-16.

Lal, M. and Singh, A.K. (2004). Technology package of sugarcane-based Intercropping Systems. Indian Institute of Sugarcane Research, Lucknow. 38 p.

Lal, M., Prasad, S.R. and Solomon, S. (2002). Sugarcane production and processing systems diversification options. *Indian Farming* 51 (11), 8-10.

Lal, M., Singh, A.K. and Awasthi, S.K. (2004). Research on sugarcane under NATP at IISR. Indian Institute of Sugarcane Research, Lucknow. 87 p.

Lal, M., Singh, A.K. and Singh, M. (2000). Nitrogen management in autumn sugarcane through lentil intercropping and biofertilizers. Paper personated at International Conference on Managing Natural Resources of Sustainable Agriculture Production in the 21st Century held at New Delhi on February 14-18,2000. pp.927-928.

Lal, M., Singh, A.K., Ali, M and Kumar, R. (1999). Agronomic evaluation of intercropped mungbean/urdbean genotypes in spring planted sugarcane. Annual Report. IIPR, Kanpur.

Panwar, B.S., Singh, B.V. and Sharma, J.C. (1990). Feasibility of intercropping in autumn planted sugarcane. *Indian Sugar* 39, 755-756.

Paroda, R.S. (2000). Expert Committee Report on Pulses. Technology Mission on Oilseeds and Pulses, Department of Agricutlure and Cooperation, Ministry of Agriculture, New Delhi.

Prakash, O., Prakash, B., Sah, A.K., Pathak, A.D. and Yadav, P. (2020). Intercropping of short duration pulses in sugarcane for increasing pulses production and farmers' income. *In Proceedings:* IC Pulse 2020 International Conference on Pulses as the Climate Smart Crops: Challenges and Opportunities held at Bhopal organized by ICAR- Indian Institute of Pulses Research, Kanpur on February 10-12, 2020. In: Abstracts : p. 261.

Rajanna, G.A., Das, A. and Shekhawat, K. (2017). Efficient water management for improving productivity and water-use efficiency of pulse crops. *Indian Farming* 67(6), 39-44.

Rajpoot, S.K. and Rana, D.S. (2016). Crop diversification with vegetable cowpea for improving productivity, resource-use efficiency, soil and human health. *Indian Farming* 66(1), 5-9.

Roy, D., Joshi, P.K and Chandra, R. (2017). Pulses for nutrition in India- Changing patterns from farm to fork. International Food Policy Research Institute, Washington D.C. 256 p.

Shahi, H.N., Lal, M, Shukla, S.K. and Singh, A.K. (2003). Diversification of sugarcane based production system. Extension Brochure No. 2, Indian Institute of Sugarcane Research, Lucknow. 6 p.

Sharma, R.K., Bangar, K.S. Sharma, S.R., Gwal, H.B. and Rathore, O.P. (1992). Comparative performance of intercropping pulses in sugarcane under South Western M.P. Indian *Journal of Agronomy* 37, 420-423.

Shukla, S.K. (2004). Management of oilseed intercrop in sugarcane based production system. In : Sugarcane Production: Strategies and Technologies, IISR Technical Bulletin No. 40, Edited by H.N. Shahi, Menhi Lal, O.K. Sinha and T.K. Srivastava, Indian Institute of Sugarcane Research, Lucknow. Pp. 79-81.

Singh, A. (1972). Conceptual and experimental basis of cropping patterns. In: Proceedings of "Symposium on cropping patterns in India" held at New Delhi, January 27-31, 1968, ICAR, New Delhi. Pp. 271-274.

Singh, A.K. (2015). Crop diversification in sugarcane based production systems. In: Sugarcane Crop Managedmernt for Higher Cane and Sugar Productivity (Edited by A.K. Sah and O.K. Sinha), ICAR-Indian Institute of Sugarcane Research, Lucknow. Pp.40-44.

Singh, A.K., Srivastava, T.K. and Lal, M. (2000). Agro-economic viability of grain legumes as intercrops in sugarcane under Indian sub-tropics. Paper presented at International Conference on Managing Natural Resources of Sustainable Agriculture Production in the 21st Century held at New Delhi on February 14-18, 2000. pp.926-927.

Singh, B.L. (2004). Management of intercrops in sugarcane based production system with cereals/other crops. In: Sugarcane Production: Strategies and Technologies, IISR Technical Bulletin No. 40 , Edited by H.N. Shahi, Menhi Lal, O.K. Sinha and T.K. Srivastava, Indian Institute of Sugarcane Research, Lucknow. Pp. 73-75.

Singh, K.K., Ali, M and Venkatesh, M.S. (2009). Pulses in Cropping Systems. Technical Bulletin, ICAR-Indian Institute of Pulses Research, Kanpur. 39 p.

Srivastava, T.K. and Kumari, V. (2013). Six decades of crop production research at IISR: An Overview. In : 6 Decades of Research at IISR. Editors, T.K. Srivastava, Sanjeev Kumar, Swapna M., P.K. Singh and Brahm Prakash. ICAR-Indian Institute of Sugarcane Research, Lucknow. Pp. 17-22.

Subbarao, N.S. (1988). Biological nitrogen fixation: Recent developments. Oxford and IBH, Pp. 1-9.

Varshney, J.G., Yadav, I.P.S. and Singh, N.B. (2000-2001). Annual Report, Indian Institute of Pulses Research, Kanpur.

Yadav, P., Prakash, O., Prakash, B., Singh, P.K., Chanda, S.S., Singh, S.K., Sah, A.K. and Singh, K. (2019). Intercropping in sugarcane: A major tool for enhancing farmers' income. Paper presented in the National Workshop on Sugarcane : Challenges & Future Strategies for Doubling Farmers' Income held at ICAR-Indian Institute of Sugarcane Research, Lucknow on November 14, 2019. In Souvenir. p. 200.

Yadav, D.S. and Singh, S.N. (1986). Studies on nitrogen economy in legume based cropping system. *Indian Journal of Agronomy* 31(4), 380-383.

Yadav, R.L. (1996). Cropping Systems. In: 50 Years of Crop Science Research in India (Eds. R.S. Paroda and K.L. Chaddha, ICAR, New Delhi, Pp. 117-128.

Yadav, R.L. and Prasad, K. (1997). Identification of prominent cropping systems in different districts of India. Annual Report, Project Directorate of Cropping Systems Research, Modipuram, Meerut, Pp. 30-49.

Yadav, R.L., Prasad, S.R. and Singh, K. (1987). Fertilizer requirement and row arrangements of pulses in sugarcane based intercropping systems. *Indian Journal of Agronomy* 32, 80-84.

CHAPTER 4

Potential of pigeonpea intercropping systems in NEH region

Lowrence Kithan

Nagaland University, Medziphema Campus 797106, Nagaland

*Corresponding author email: lowrencekithan@gmail.com

Abstract

It is well known that the crop production is unstable and many times uneconomic due to vagaries of monsoon in many parts of the country. Suitable intercropping systems besides meeting the varied requirements of farmers provide stability in rainfed agriculture and improve the total productivity through better utilization of natural resource. Cereal-legume intercropping has been recognized as one of the sustainable intensification pathways because intercropping provides greater stability than sole cropping (monocultures) in terms of soil fertility improvement, yields enhancement, and economic returns. Cereal-legume intercropping also ensures diversification of diets and risk reduction in the case of failure of one of the crop. Pigeonpea being a predominantly rainfed crop is one of the most important and potential component of intercropping in NEH. Due to its complementarities with cereals and its ability to fix nitrogen (N) biologically from the atmosphere, the benefits of cereal-pigeonpea intercropping in long-term soil fertility improvement have been well documented. Pigeonpea based intercropping is a potential system for economizing the use of nitrogenous fertilizers and increasing the productivity and profitability in resource poor areas of NEH.

Keywords: Cereals, Intercropping, Legumes, Pigeonpea, Productivity, Profitability

1. INTRODUCTION

The greatest challenge of the 21st century in many developing countries are to produce more and more basic necessities namely food, fodder, fuel and fibre for ever increasing human and animal population from the limited available land. The availability of land for agriculture is shrinking every day as it is increasingly utilized for non-agricultural purposes. Under this situation, one of the important strategies to increase agricultural productivity and intensive land use is development of high intensity cropping systems including intercropping. Mono-cropping production system has significant problems and non-sustainable issues, and that there exists a sufficient justification for following of intercropping. Consequently, researchers have proposed general categories of benefits and utilities of intercropping. Benefits of intercropping are enhanced crop yield, productivity of various plant constituents, economic return, yield stability, social benefits, pest control, and fertilizer use efficiency. The most important advantage of intercropping systems includes both tall and short plant components for their potential complementarity in sunlight utilization for crop production. Because of these advantages intercropping is practiced in many parts of the world.

Intercropping is a multiple cropping practices involving growing two or more crops in proximity. In other words, intercropping is the cultivation of two or more crops simultaneously on the same field. The most common goal of intercropping is to produce a greater yield on a given piece of land by making use of resources or ecological processes that would otherwise not be utilized by a single crop (Gomez and Gomez, 1983; Kumar *et al.*, 2008). It is an intensive land use system with an objective to utilize the space between the rows of main or base crop and to produce more per unit area. By growing more than one crop at a time on the same field, farmers maximize resource use efficiency, maintain soil fertility, and minimize soil erosion, which are the serious drawbacks of mono-cropping (Hoshikawa, 1991). Numerous researchers cover the theory and mechanisms of yield stability in intercropping. Willey (1979) clearly and evidently proposed that intercropping gives higher yields in a given season and greater stability of yields in different seasons compared with sole cropping. Moreover, Mead and Willey (1980) stated in detail that in intercropping systems, yields are more stable. Its relation to yield stability is the notion of risk, in terms of either productivity or income or both.

Pigeonpea is one of the major grain legume crops of tropical and subtropical regions and it is grown successfully under rain fed NEH regions. India accounts for 90% of world's pigeonpea growing area and 85% of world's production of pigeonpea. The area and production of pigeonpea for the year 2017-18 in NEH states was 17.15 thousand ha with total production of 14.76 thousand tonnes and productivity of 967 kg/ha (Table 1). The maximum area of pigeonpea in NEH is in Assam (5.16 thousand ha) followed by Tripura (5.59 thousand ha). Production also followed similar trend with highest value in Assam (4.67 thousand tonnes). However, pigeonpea yield was maximum in Meghalaya (1295 kg/ha) which is higher than the country average yield of pigeonpea. Majority of pigeonpea area in NEH are under rainfed and thus, great potential exist for following of intercropping with pigeonpea to realizing the potential benefit.

Table 1. Area, production and productivity of pigeonpea in NEH states of India

NEH state	Area ('000 ha)					Production ('000 tonnes)					Yield (kg/ha)				
	2013-14	2014-15	2015-16	2016-17	2017-18	2013-14	2014-15	2015-16	2016-17	2017-18	2013-14	2014-15	2015-16	2016-17	2017-18
Arunachal Pradesh	0.45	0.55	0.61	0.79	0.81	0.50	0.60	0.55	0.64	0.66	1111	1091	905	814	825
Assam	6.05	6.10	6.37	5.72	5.61	5.64	5.74	5.60	4.91	4.67	932	941	880	858	833
Meghalaya	1.05	1.15	1.15	1.17	1.18	1.43	1.47	1.49	1.52	1.53	1362	1278	1295	1299	1295
Manipur	0.00	0.53	0.53	0.55	0.53	0.00	0.52	0.58	0.61	0.60	0	989	1094	1109	1132
Mizoram	0.00	0.00	0.00	0.32	0.24	0.00	0.00	0.00	0.31	0.25	0	0	0	965	1031
Nagaland	2.97	3.01	3.05	3.20	3.20	2.66	2.71	2.75	2.89	2.92	896	900	902	903	913
Tripura	3.85	2.52	4.20	5.35	5.59	2.76	1.82	2.89	3.77	4.13	717	722	687	705	738
NEH total	14.37	13.86	15.91	17.10	17.15	12.99	12.86	13.86	14.65	14.76	717	846	823	951	967
All India	3904.4	3853.5	3963.3	5337.9	4438.3	3174.4	2807.3	2561.0	4873.2	4289.8	813	729	646	913	967

2. FEATURES OF PIGEONPEA BASED INTERCROPPING

Pigeonpea, a deep rooted crop with slow rate of initial growth upto 70-90 days after sowing is well suited for intercropping (Ramamoorthy *et al.*, 2004). As a soil ameliorant, pigeonpea is known to provide several benefits to the soil in which it is cultivated. Due to the initial slow growth and deep root system of pigeonpea, fast growing early maturing and shallow rooted cropscan be profitably intercropped (Willey *et al.*, 1980). For successful and profitable intercropping system, there must be proper row ratio or planting geometry of component crop in order to avoid limitation of reduced plant population of base crop as under traditional inter-cropping system (Pandey *et al.*, 1999). By modifying of planting geometry into paired rows, pigeonpea plant population can be maintained to its sole cropping and bonus yield of intercrops like cowpea, mungbean, urdbean, maize, millets, groundnuts, etc. can be obtained which increase the total returns from the system.

2.1 Resource use efficiency

During growth and development, crop plants must intercept and absorb growth factors such as soil moisture, light energy and nutrients and use them in processes that produce biomass. Increased crop production (over-yielding) often observed in intercrops compared to sole crops has been attributed to enhanced resource use (Szumigalski and Van-Acker, 2008). Francis (1986) and Sivakumar (1993) also reported that efficient and complete use of growth resources such as solar energy, soil nutrients and water is one of the advantages of intercropping system over sole crops. Light interception and light use efficiency are powerful concepts for characterizing the resource capture and use efficiency of cropping systems, including intercrops. Improved productivity can result from either greater interception of solar radiation, higher light use efficiency, or a combination of the two (Willey, 1990). Light interception as a result of mixing two species and growing them together instead of alone is sometimes increased, either as a result of a lengthening of the period of soil coverage (temporal advantage), or as a result of a more complete soil cover (spatial advantage) (Keating and Carberry, 1993). Carandang (1980) thought that intercrops allow maximum utilization of sunlight by increasing light interception by 30-40%.

Intercrops are most productive when their component crops differ greatly in growth duration so that their maximum requirement for growth resources occur at different times (Fukai and Trenbath, 1993). Baker (1975) and Anitha *et al* (2001) reported that to have yield advantages in intercropping system, there should be minimum of 25 per cent difference in duration of crops. For higher intercrop productivity, plants of the early maturing component should grow with little interference from the late maturing crop. The later may be affected by the associated crop, but a long time period for further growth after the harvest of the first crop should ensure good recovery and full use of available resources (Fukai and Trenbath, 1993). Intercropping allows effective utilization of growth resources through crop intensification both in space and time dimensions. The conventional ways of intensifying crop production are vertical and horizontal expansions. Intercropping offers two additional dimensions, time and space (Francis, 1986). The intensification of land and resource use in space dimension is an important aspect of intercropping. For example, enhanced and efficient use of light is possible with two or more species that occupy the same land during a significant part of the growing season and have different pattern of foliage display. Different rooting patterns can explore a greater total soil volume because of the roots being at different depths (Francis, 1986). These differences in foliage display and rooting patterns create the space dimension of intercropping.

Advantages from intercropping of short and long duration species is due to enhanced radiation capture over time. Improved utilization of radiation energy resulted in more efficient production of biomass or increased proportion of biomass partitioned to yield. Adoption of suitable intercropping systems might increase the total production through efficient utilization of production factors like space, water, nutrients etc., and stability of crop yield in rainfed situation can be achieved with crop substitution and intercropping (Singh and Rana, 2006). When the crops of different growth habits are grown together in an intercropping system, it provides greater opportunity to secure higher yield from the same piece of land. Paired-row technique is a simple way of exploiting land resources to harness the maximum yield advantage in intercropping system.

2.3 Interactions in intercropping

Competition and complementarities are the two most important interactions in intercropping. Willey (1979) suggested three broad categories of competitive relationships in intercropping: 1) when the actual yield of each species is less than expected, termed mutual inhibition, 2) where the yield of each species is greater than expected (mutualism); and 3) the most common situation, where one species yields less than expected and the other more; termed compensation. Complementarity is a key feature of intercrops and natural vegetation. According to Willey (1979), yield advantage in multiple cropping occurs when component crops differ in their use of growth resources in such a way that when they are grown in combination they are better able to complement each other and so make better overall use of resources than when grown separately in terms of competition. The component crops are not competing for exactly the same resources (in space or time) and intercrop competition is less than intracrop competition.

Temporal and spatial complementarities can be differentiated from one another (Willey 1979). In temporal complementarities, growth patterns differ in time (typically at least 30-40 days maturity difference), crops use water at different times, particularly where the system is moisture limited. It involves a time displacement that results in the capture of more resources by the intercrop rather than a change in the efficiency of utilization. Spatial complementarity is the combined leaf canopy or root system of an intercrop that makes better use of available resources when grown together, such as total light interception, water and nutrient uptake because component crops exploit different soil layers or canopy heights in intercropping. Component crops differ in their nutrient requirements, the form of nutrients which they can readily exploit and their ability to extract them from the soil. One crop exploits a greater volume of soil. Where the total quantities of resource captured is relatively similar, the efficiency of utilization of the resources captured is increased in intercrops compared to the sole crops.

2.3 Plant population in intercropping

Plant population defines the number of plants per unit area which determines the size of area available to the individual plant. However, for the crops regularly arranged in rows, the spatial arrangement can be concisely defined by the rectangularity which is the ratio of inter-row spacing to intra-row spacing (Holliday, 1963). In intercropping systems, plant population and spatial arrangement play a pivotal role affecting the total yield of intercrop combinations over the sole crops. Research on this aspect has been spurred recently to understand the biological validity of the system by way of possible increase in yield, efficient use of solar energy and better land use resulting in higher returns. De and Singh (1979) observed that by keeping the plant population constant and altering row orientation for paired or trebled row planting offers more space for accommodating the companion crop. De *et al* (1978) reported that keeping the plant population per unit area of the base crop constant, no deviation in its yield has been noted by altering the orientation of the rows.

Many vegetation and yield variables are potentially influenced by the competition of the plant with a second crop in an intercrop system and by competition with other plants of the same species in monocrop systems, and this influence may be affected by changes in plant population density (Fortin *et al.*, 1994). The structure of plant vegetation and its geometric elements combined with the total amount of leaf area determine the distribution of light within the canopy (Geno and Geno, 2001). Thus, it would be useful to know optimum or critical population densities to avoid population as limiting factor for crop yield (Balasubramaniyan and Palaniappan, 2001). Further, plant population depends on type and growth habit of crops, soil fertility, rainfall and other growth requirements. The higher plant population/density has negative effect on crop yield.

In terms of total population pressure, two broad classes of intercropping systems can be distinguished (Geno and Geno, 2001). One is substitutive or replacement series of intercropping in which proportional populations are related to sole crop of the series and whatever the population is added the two proportions must always add up to 100%. The second is additive or superimposed intercropping in which one component crop is added to the other so that the final plant population is generally more than either crops sown sole. Substitutive intercropping generally consists of crops from the same phenological group and the yield gain in such mixture is from a simple response to reduced population because of complementary in space and to some extent to time or both. The challenge comes in knowing how much to be substituted to optimize the yield (Sullivan, 2003). Additive refers to a situation where the component crops are plastic enough to take advantage of their lower plant population in intercrop and when specific objectives of the farmers is a particular proportion of the product which consists of crops from different phenological groups (Cannell, 1983). Singh *et al* (2015) from a study on maize (*Zea mays* L.) + legume based additive series paired-row intercropping, concluded that inclusion of legumes in intercropping improved both production and rain water use efficiencies with definite yield and economic advantage.

Pigeonpea and maize as sole crop failed to respond to plant densities beyond 60×10^3 plants per hectare, but the yield advantage in their intercropping continued to increase with increase in their plant density upto 90×10^3 plants per hectare (Willey and Rao, 1977). Balyan (1997) found that maize yield was increased by all intercropping systems compared to maize grown alone. For higher production a higher density of maize than suggested by the intercrop row proportion is required as the mixture requires higher plant population pressure to produce their maximum yield (Willey and Osilu, 1972).

2.4 Weed smothering effect

Liebman and Dyck (1993) indicated that weed population density and biomass production may be markedly reduced using intercropping (spatial diversification). Intercrops may demonstrate weed control advantages over sole crops in two ways. First, greater crop yield and less weed growth may be achieved if intercrops are more effective than sole crops in usurping resources from weeds or by suppressing weed growth through alleopathy. Alternatively, intercrops may provide yield advantages without suppressing weed growth if intercrops use resources that are not exploitable by weeds or convert resources to harvestable material more efficiently than sole crops (Geno and Geno, 2001). Short duration legumes, *viz.* urdbean, mungbean, soybean and cowpea when grown with pigeonpea under intercropping system suppressed the weed flora considerably. Highest suppression ability was recorded with cowpea (45.8%) followed by urdbean (41.5%) and mungbean (38.2%). Talnikar *et al* (2008) reported 79.93% reduction in pigeonpea grain yield if weeds were allowed to grow till harvest, however, grain yield losses were only 38.19% in pigeonpea +soybean intercropping system. Ali (1988) reported that in pigeonpea-based intercropping, legumes (cowpea, urdbean and mungbean) suppress weed flora by 30 to 40% compared with 22% by sorghum, whereas Shetty and Rao (1977) observed weed suppression up to 75%.

2.5 Social benefit

Besides the benefit of yield and income, intercropping can be seen to produce social benefits to both the land-holder and the surrounding community (Geno and Geno, 2001). Bradfield (1986) noted that updating traditional intercropping practices (as opposed to promoting monocultures) offers the potential of scale specific technologies that favor the small farmer. Addressing the question of equity, Willey (1981) found that the advantages of multiple cropping, that the benefits are achieved not by means of costly inputs but by the simple suitability of growing crops together. Thus, intercropping offers a very genuine way in which the poorer or smaller farmer can benefit at least as much as the better return can. Similarly, Jodha (1981) noted its potential for greater employment. Because intercropping is often a system used on small farms, any breakthrough in intercropping technology will help poor farmers more than the rich, thus better serving the goals of equity.

3. PIGEONPEA BASED INTERCROPPING FOR NEH

Considerable growth rate in area, production and productivity of pigeonpea was observed in NEH region during last four decades. The increased profitability from this crop has endorsed the future promotion of pigeonpea cultivation in this region (Hazari *et al.*, 2016). Review of literatures suggests that the groundnut yield was maximum in sole groundnut, but there was significant increase in groundnut equivalent yield recorded in pigeonpea + groundnut intercropping system (Reddy and Reddy, 1980). Singh and Rahman (1999) and Singh and Rahman (1999) reported the highest pigeonpea equivalent yield from pigeonpea + groundnut intercropping planted in 1: 2 row ratio, whereas Shindhe *et al* (1990) recorded highest system yield under 1: 3 row ratio. Intercropping systems of pigeonpea + pearlmillet and pigeonpea + groundnut gave average system yield increase of 24 and 46%, respectively, compared with both component crops grown separately (Reddy and

Willey, 1981). Chaniyara *et al* (1999) observed that intercrops such as castor, sunflower, greengram and pigeonpea reduced the yield of groundnut in comparison to sole crop, but the reduction was less when groundnut was intercropped with pigeonpea.

In a study conducted by Ray *et al* (2016) in Tripura revealed that pigeonpea grain yield remain unaffected under all intercropping systems except pigeonpea + groundnut (Table 2). The maximum pigeonpea yield and system productivity was recorded in pigeonpea + blackgram/greengram in 1:1 row ratio. The economics i.e., net return, B:C ratio and return per day were also higher under these intercropping systems. Land equivalent ratio (LER) was higher than 1.0 in all intercropping systems that showed the advantage of intercropping over sole cropping of component crops. However, maximum value of LER was recorded in pigeonpea + blackgram (1:1) followed by pigeonpea+greengram (1:1) and least under pigeonpea+groundnut (1:1).

Table 2. Effect of intercropping on component crop yield, system productivity, LER and economics in NEH (pooled data of 2 years)

Inter-cropping system	Main crop yield (kg/ha)	Intercrop yield (kg/ha)	PEY (kg/ha)	Net return (Rs/ha)	B:C ratio	LER	Per day return (Rs/ha/day)
Pigeonpea sole	1684		1684	48527	1.96	1.00	300
Pigeonpea + cowpea (1:2)	1672	475	2108	66455	2.63	1.56	428
Pigeonpea + sesame (1:1)	1506	405	1935	58149	2.24	1.59	384
Pigeonpea + sesame (1:2)	1832	428	2285	74628	3.02	1.82	490
Pigeonpea + blackgram (1:1)	2090	414	2504	84115	3.39	1.79	528
Pigeonpea + blackgram (1:2)	1558	451	2009	62130	2.46	1.53	387
Pigeonpea + greengram (1:1)	2032	437	2494	82554	3.18	1.85	535
Pigeonpea + greengram (1:2)	1557	473	2057	64712	2.61	1.63	423
Pigeonpea + groundnut (1:1)	1281	254	1748	49845	1.90	1.17	327
CD (p=0.05)	286	13		11937			

*PEY: Pigeonpea equivalent yield, LER: Land equivalent ratio; Source: Ray *et al.* (2016)

The results of field experiment at Medziphema, Nagaland showed that row ratio is also important harnessing the maximum benefit while planning to take pigeonpea based intercropping system (Table 3). Among different row ratio, paired row planting (2:2) was found better in terms of system productivity, LER and net income in pigeonpea + soybean intercropping than other combinations.

Table 3. Yield, LER and economics of pigeonpea+ soybean intercropping system

Treatments	**Grain yield (kg/ha)**		**System productivity (PEY, kg/ha)**	**LER**	**Net return (INR/ha)**	**B:C ratio**
	Pigeonpea	**Soybean**				
Pigeonpea + soybean (1:1)	1319	1005	931.4	1.59	75160	1.68
Pigeonpea + soybean (1:2)	1481	1130	1045.8	1.79	91007	1.94
Pigeonpea + soybean (2:1)	1343	988	947.7	1.58	79572	1.87
Pigeonpea + soybean (2:2)	1553	1169	1096.4	1.86	100558	2.19
Sole pigeonpea	1690	--		1.00	66756	3.41
Sole soybean	--	1245		1.00	54389	2.31
CD (p=0.05)	245	282				

*PEY: Pigeonpea equivalent yield, LER: Land equivalent ratio

In NEH region, *Jhum* cultivation practiced in many areas by clearing the forest. In *Jhum* areas, cultivation of pigeonpea is practiced along with other cereal crops like rice and maize, and horticultural crops like colocasia, turmeric, ginger, etc. The farmers also practice pigeonpea based intercropping with soybean. With the popularity of plantation crops such as beetle nut, rubber and coffee, it has been encouraged by many farmers to take up intercropping with this plantation crops in their initial stages (upto 3 years) of establishment.

Pigeonpea intercropping with plantation crop

4. CONCLUSION

In general, through intercropping farmers can achieve the full production of the main crop and also an additional yield (bonus) associated with an increased plant population of the second component. Though all intercrops produced higher productivity, the farmers could better use the appropriate population of component crops in intercropping systems in order to maximize yield of both crops as well as total productivity. It is, therefore, important to support intercropping systems with appropriate agronomic practices such as timely irrigation, pest protection and the likes to sustain the cropping system in particular and in the countries where labor is not problem for proper management in general even though sometimes sole cropping may became more productive. Hence, pigeonpea based intercropping systems need to be promoted for increasing incomes and nutritional security of resource poor farmers in NEH.

REFERENCES

Anitha, S., Geethakumari, V.L. and Filial, G.R. (2001) Effect of intercrops on nutrient uptake and productivity of chilli-based cropping system. *Journal of Tropical Agriculture* 39, 60-61.

Baker, E.F.I. (1975) Research on mixed cropping with cereals in Nigeria farming systems: A system for improvement. Proceedings of International Workshop on Farming System. ICRISAT, Hyderabad. pp. 287-300.

Balasubramaniyan, P. and Palaniappan, S.P. (2001) Principles and Practices of Agronomy. Agrobios, Jodhpur, India. pp. 486-499.

Balyan, J.S. (1997) Performance of maize (*Zea mays*) based intercropping systems and their after effect on wheat (*Triticum aestivum*). *Indian Journal of Agronomy* 42(1), 26-28.

Bradfield, S. (1986) Sociocultural factors in multiple cropping. In: C.A. Francis (eds.) Multiple Cropping Systems. Macmillan, New York. pp. 267-283.

Cannell, M.G.R. (1983) Plant management in agroforestry: Manipulation of trees, population densities and mixtures of trees and herbaceous crops. In: P.A. Huxley (eds.) Plant Research and Agroforestry. Nairobi, Kenya. pp. 456-487.

Carandang, D.A. (1980) Resource utilization in integrated farming system with crops as the major enterprise. In: M.H. Telangco (eds.) Integrated Crop-Livestock-Fish Farming. Laguna, Philippines. pp. 8-21.

Chaniyara, N.J., Solanki, R.M. and Bhalu, V.B. (1999). Comparative performance of groundnut based intercropping system. *Gujarat Agricultural University Research Journal* 25(1), 1-4.

De, R. and Singh, S.P. (1979) Management practices for intercropping systems. In: Proceeding of International Workshop on Intercropping. ICRISAT, Hyderabad, India. pp. 17-21.

De, R., Gupta, S., Singh, S.P., Sharma, R.N.and Kaushik, S.K. (1978) Interplanting maize, sorghum and pearl millet with short duration grain legumes. *Indian Journal of Agricultural Sciences* 48(3), 132-137.

Fortin, M.C., Culley, J. and Edwards, M. (1994) Soil water, plant growth, and yield of strip-intercropping corn. *Journal of Agricultural production* 7, 63-69.

Francis, C.A. (1986) Future perspectives of multiple cropping. In: C.A. Francis (eds.) Multiple Cropping Systems. Macmillan, New York. pp. 351-370.

Fukai, S. and Trenbath, B.R. (1993) Processes determining intercrop productivity and yields of component crops. *Field Crops Research* 34, 247–271.

Geno, L. and Geno, B. (2001) Polyculture Production: Principle, benefits and risk of multiple cropping. A report for the Rural Industry Research and Development Corporation (RIRDC), Publication, No. 01134.

Gomez, A. A. and K. A. Gomez, 1983. Multiple Cropping in the Humid Tropics of Asia. Ottawa. 32p. (3): 354-359.

Hazari, S., Ray, S., Das, P., De, B. and Sen, D. (2016) Momentum of pigeonpea cultivation in Tripura- an economics analysis. *Indian Journal of Hill Farming* 29(2), 120-123.

Holliday R. (1963)The effect of row width on the yield of cereals. *Field Crop Abstracts* 16, 71-81.

Hoshikawa, K. (1991) Significance of legumes crops in intercropping, the productivity and stability of cropping system. In: C. Johanson, K.K. Lee and K.L. Saharawat (eds.) Phosphorus Nutrition of Grain Legume in the Semi Arid Tropics. ICRISAT. pp. 173-176.

Jodha, N.S. (1981) Intercropping in traditional farming systems. In: R. Willey (eds.) Proceedings of the International Workshop on Intercropping. ICRISAT, Patanancheru, India. pp. 282-291.

Keating, B.A. and Carberry, P.S. (1993) Resource capture and use in intercropping: Solar radiation. *Field Crops Research* 34, 273-301.

Kumar, N., Prakash, V., Meena, B.L., Gopinath, K.A. and Srivastva, A.K. (2008) Evaluation of*toria* (*Brassica compestris*) and lentil (*Lens culinaris*) varieties in intercropping system with wheat (*Triticum aestivum*) under rainfed conditions. *Indian Journal Agronomy* 53(1), 47-50.

Liebman, M. and Dyck, E. (1993) Crop rotation and intercropping strategies for weed management. *Ecological Applications* 3(1), 92-122.

Mead, R. and Willey, R.W. (1980) The concept of a land equivalent ratio and advantages in yields from intercropping. *Experimental Agriculture* 16, 217-228.

Pandey, A.K., Prakash, V., Singh, R.D. and Mani, V.P. (1999) Effect of intercropping pattern of maize and soybean on yield and economic under mid hills of N-W Himalayas. *Annals of Agricultural Research* 20(3), 354–359.

Ramamoorthy, K., Christopher, A.L., Alagudurai, S., Kandasamy, O.S. and Murugappan, V. (2004) Intercropping pigeonpea (*Cajanus cajan*) in finger millet (*Eleusine coracana*) on productivity and soil fertility under rainfed condition. *Indian Journal of Agronomy* 49, 28-30.

Ray, S., De, B. and Hazari, S. (2016) Enhancing productivity potential of pigeonpea (*Cajanus cajan* L.) based intercropping system on a Lateritic Red soil of Tripura. *Journal of Food Legumes* 29(1), 33-36.

Reddy, A.R. and Reddy, M.R. (1980) Relative efficiency of a multi-intercrop system in pigeon pea under rainfed condition. *Indian Journal of Agronomy* 25(3), 508-510.

Reddy, M.S. and Willey, R.W. (1981) Growth and resources use studies in an intercrop of pearl millet/groundnut. *Field crop Research* 4(1), 13-24.

Shetty, S.V.R. and Rao, M.R. (1977) *Weed management studies in pigeonpea (Cajanus cajan L.) based intercropping.* In: Proceedings of the Sixth Asian-Pacific Weed Science Society Conference, 11-17 July 1977, Jakarta, Indonesia.

Shinde, S.H., Dandwate, V.G., Magdum, G.D., Pol, P.S. and Umrani, N.K. (1990) Studies on planting pattern of pigeon pea and groundnut intercropping system during summer. *Indian Journal of Agronomy* 35(1 and 2), 67-72.

Singh, S., Bawa, S.S., Singh, S. and Sharma, S.C. 2015. Evaluation of maize (*Zea mays* L.) based intercropping for productivity, resource-use efficiency and competition indices in the rainfed foothills of northwest Himalayas. *Indian Journal of Agricultural Sciences* 85(5), 614-21.

Singh, T. and Rana, K.S. (2006) Effect of moisture conservation and fertility on Indian mustard (*Brassica juncea*) and lentil (*Lens culinaris*) intercropping system under rainfed conditions. *Indian Journal of Agronomy* 51(4), 267-270.

Singh, R.S. and Rahman, A. (1999) Economic feasibility of pigeon pea (*Cajanus cajan* L.) based intercropping systems in Chotanagpur plateau. *Journal of Research Birsa Agrilcultural University* 11(1), 27-30.

Sivakumar, M.V.K. (1993) Growth and yield of millet and cowpea in rely and intercrop systems in the Sahelian Zones in years when the onset of the rainy season is early. *Experimental Agriculture* 29(4), 417-427.

Sullivan, P. (2003) Intercropping principles and production practice. Agronomy Systems Guide. Appropriate Technology Transfer for Rural Areas (ATTRA). 1-12p. Available on: www.attra.necta.org

Szumigalski, A.R. and Van-Acker, R.C. (2008) Intercropping: Land equivalent ratios, light interception, and water use in annual intercrops in the presence or absence of in-crop herbicides. *American Agronomy Journal* 100, 1145-1154.

Talnikar, A.S., Kadam, G.L., Karande, D.R. and Jogdand, P.B. (2008) Integrated weed management in pigeonpea [*Cajanus cajan* (L.) Millsp.] International Journal of Agricultural Sciences 4(1): 363-370 Willey, R.W., Rao, M.R. and Natarajn. M. (1980) Traditional cropping systems with pigeonpea and their improvement. Proceedings of International Workshop on Pigeonpea. 15 December, ICRISAT, Patancheru (India). pp. 11-25.

Willey, R.W. (1981) A scientific approach to intercropping research. In: Proceedings of the International Workshop on Intercropping, International Crops Research Institute for the Semi-Arid Tropics. Andhra Pradesh, India.

Willey, R.W. (1979) Intercropping - its importance and research needs part 1. Competition and yield advantage. *Field Crop Abstracts* 32(1), 1-10.

Willey, R.W. and Osilu, D.S.O. (1972) Studies on mixtures of maize and beans with particular reference to plant population. *Journal of Agriculture Science Cambridge* 79, 517-529.

Willey, R.W. and Rao, M.R. (1997) Pearl millet intercropping. Paper presented at the International Workshop 1977. ICRISAT, Hyderabad.Andhra Pradesh, India.

Willey, R.W. (1990) Resource use in intercropping systems. *Agriculture and Water Management* 17, 215-231.

CHAPTER 5

Sustainable intensification of cereal based cropping systems with summer mungbean in Indo-Gangetic Plains

C.P. Nath*, Narendra Kumar[1], Debarati Datta[2], T.K. Das[3], Asik Dutta[1], K.K. Hazra[1] and C.S. Praharaj[1]

1. *ICAR–Indian Institute of Pulses Research, Kanpur 208 024*

2. *ICAR–Central Research Institute for Jute and Allied Fibers, Barrackpore 700 120*

3. *ICAR–Indian Agricultural Research Institute, New Delhi 110 012*

*Corresponding author email: cpnath4@gmail.com

Abstract

Rice-wheat and maize-wheat systems contributing the major share in food grain production are now facing the problem of decline in factor productivity with reduction in farm income. Increasing the land productivity with highly intensive cropping system is the need of the day to meet the growing demand of food grain. Introducing summer mungbean after harvesting of wheat is a potential option for increasing system productivity and long-term sustainability in these cereal based production system. Summer mungbean in rice-wheat and maize-wheat systems is also viable option for increased system productivity as well as the yield of component cereal crops. The result of long-term cropping system research showed that inclusion of summer mungbean in rice/maize-wheat system improved soil health and increased farm income. Hence, introducing summer mungbean for high intensive systems is needed for maximizing land productivity, long-term sustainability and farm profitability.

Keywords: Climate resilience, Conservation agriculture, Indo-Gangetic plains, Resource use efficiency, Soil health, Water productivity

1. INTRODUCTION

Long-term cultivation of cereal-cereal cropping systems is now resulting in declining total factor productivity and sustainability. In the coming years with increasing pressure of population, the problem will be much more serious. Therefore, we have to move towards a more productive as well as sustainable production system. In India, cereal based cropping systems are dominating both in area as well as production. Rice (*Oryza sativa* L.)-wheat (*Triticum aestivum* L.) and maize (*Zea mays* L.)-wheat are the two leading cropping systems in India contributing major share of the total foodgrains production. Summer mungbean

(*Vigna radiata* L.) being a short duration crop (60-65 days) can be easily accommodated in irrigated rice-wheat and maize-wheat production system. Apart from the yield advantage of mungbean crop, the crop being a legume, provides the additional benefits of system diversification, maintenance of soil health and often used as a source of organic as a green manure crop. In this chapter, potential benefits of introducing summer mungbean in rice-wheat and maize-wheat production system and its long-term effect on soil health and sustainability are discussed. The introduction of zero tillage (ZT) in wheat in the Indo-Gangetic plains (IGP) of south Asia created a window of opportunity for crop intensification. For example, it facilitated inclusion of summer mungbean in rice–wheat rotation which resulted in higher cropping intensity and system productivity (Gathala *et al.*, 2013; Das *et al.*, 2020). The diversified rotations with legumes promote biological N fixation, nutrient cycling and disruption of weed, insects and disease cycle (Kumar *et al.*, 2019). Thus, cropping intensification of cereal–cereal system with legumes under conservation agriculture (CA) platform is recommended as future drivers of agricultural sustainability in the south Asian countries. Concerning the evident challenges in continuous cereal–cereal rotations, crop diversification with the inclusion of legumes may be a promising approach to sustain the crop productivity and mitigating the soil and environmental issues. Short–duration mungbean and other grain legumes like chickpea (*Cicer arietinum* L.), pigeonpea (*Cajanus cajan* L.) having wider adaptability in different agro–ecologies, and could be accommodated in cereal–based cropping systems (Nath *et al.*, 2019a).

2. POTENTIAL AREA FOR CROPPING INTENSIFICATION WITH SUMMER MUNGBEAN

The IGP is the most important food producing domain of India, occupying an area of 44 M ha. The IGP is dominated by the rice–wheat rotation (9.64 M ha) in lowland and maize–wheat rotation (1.83 M ha) in upland (Nath et al., 2015). A plateauing in the productivity is now appearing in continuous cereal-cereal rotations of the IGP, because of fatigue natural resource base, soil structure disintegration, and soil organic carbon (SOC) depletion. In fact, soil physical and chemical health are integral to the ecosystem functioning as it governs many processes such including nutrient cycling, water transport, SOC protection, and greenhouse gases emissions (Nath *et al.*, 2019). Inappropriate cropping practices such as continuous cereal-cereal rotations and chemical fertilization can induce dramatic SOC losses and significant soil quality degradation. On the contrary, rational cropping practices such as legume inclusion, crop residue recycling, and manure application can significantly increase the SOC storage and soil quality. Hence, diversification with legumes and manure application has been widely recommended since 1990 in the IGP (Baghel *et al.*, 2020).

The spread of CA is concentrated in the rice–wheat system in the Indian IGP. Indian IGP comprises of Trans (GP), upper (GP), middle (GP) and the lower (GP). The TGP is the food hub of South Asia's 'Green Revolution'. No doubt, it heralded the introduction, opportunities and challenges of CA (Erenstein and laxmi, 2008). The IGP of South Asia includes India, Nepal, Bangladesh and Pakistan. Resource conservation technologies (RCTs) are one of the major drivers of sustainable agricultural intensification in the IGP vis-à-vis the increasing soil carbon depletion, declining groundwater table, increasing air pollution and the stagnating or low yields of the rice–wheat system. Fundamentally, diversification of maize-wheat (MW) rotation with legumes can be attempted in several ways. In practice, after wheat harvest in April, land remains vacant upto June in the IGP region. Hence, diversification can be achieved with inclusion of short duration mungbean in the MW rotation. Also, wheat crop in winter season can be replaced by legume crop like chickpea (*Cicer arietinum* L.) for eliminating monotony of the MW rotation for higher system productivity and resource-use efficiency. During the past decades, many efforts have been paid on the impact of crop rotations on crop yield, but little is known about its impact on soil aggregation and SOC sequestration (Das *et al.*, 2014; Nath *et al.*, 2019b).

3. BENEFICIAL ASPECTS OF SUMMER MUNGBEAN

3.1 Base crop productivity

Summer mungbean inclusion in rice-wheat cropping system increased rice and wheat yield by 12.3 and 6.7%, respectively. A good harvest of summer mungbean (1.2-1.4 t/ha) was also realized under lowland rice-wheat-mungbean rotation. Similarly, under upland maize based system with inclusion of summer mungbean, maize yield was increased by 17.2% while the corresponding increase for *rabi* season wheat was almost 8% (Fig. 1). An additional average yield of 1.21 t/ha summer mungbean was recorded under upland maize based system. System productivity with reference to mungbean equivalent yield (MBEY) was computed 2.43 and 2.15 t/ha in rice-wheat and maize-wheat system respectively and with introducing mungbean in summer fallow increased the MBEY 3.98 and 3.63 t/ha, respectively. Therefore, in long-term, system diversification through summer mungbean not only increased the system productivity, but was equally effective to increase the yield of the component cereal crops of the system (Ghosh *et al.*, 2020). The residual effect of summer mungbean was found more prominent for the immediate *kharif* season cereals and less residual effect was observed for *rabi* season wheat in both the systems. In a worldwide meta-examination inspecting 5,463 yield observations from 610 studies across crops and 63 nations, ZT resulted in yield decrease (5.7%) contrasted with CT frameworks (Pittelkow et al., 2015). They accentuated that this yield response is variable, especially when ZT is adopted together with the other two CA principles (crop residue retention and crop diversification), produces comparative or more yields than CT.

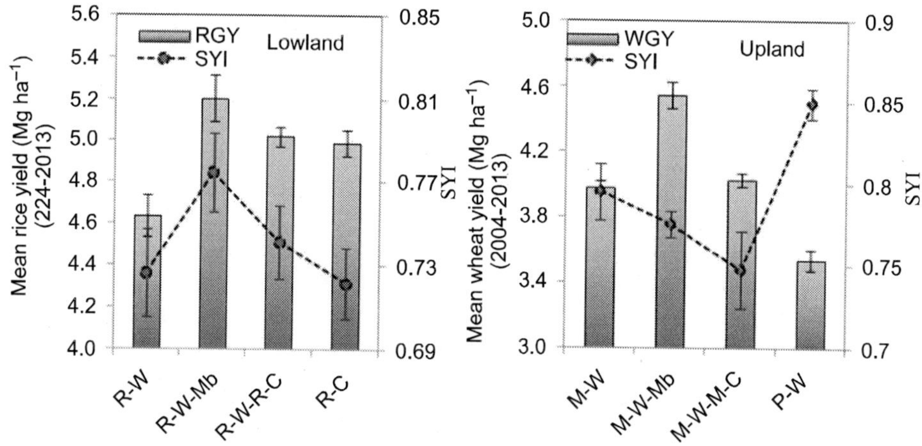

Fig. 1. Impact of munbean in rice-wheat and maize-wheat cropping system on base crop grain yield and sustainable yield index (Ghosh *et al.*, 2020).

Cropping intensification/diversification of R-W rotation with grain legume increased the base-crop (rice) productivity. Inclusion of mungbean in R-W rotation (R-W-Mb) increased the rice (base-crop) grain yield by 15% ($p < 0.05$). Results further demonstrated that the changes in SOC, microbial activity and biochemical properties with different crop rotation treatments influence the base-crop (rice) productivity. Base-crop is the common crop in all the rotations, and thus base crop productivity could be used as indicator of soil productive capacity as influenced by the crop rotation. In lowland, crop diversification with grain legume increased rice crop (base–crop) productivity in long–run. Inclusion of mungbean in R–W rotation increased the rice grain yield by 12% ($p < 0.05$) and 16% ($p < 0.05$) during the ninth and tenth–year of rotation, respectively. Inclusion of mungbean as a summer crop (April–May) in M–W rotation increased average wheat grain yield by 5–11% (2011–2013). Higher productivity of base–crop in grain legume inclusive rotations was attributed to the increased availability of nutrients (N and P in particular) and higher SOC. Mungbean inclusion in summer fallows of R–W and M–W systems was found as a sustainable approach of system intensification with higher economic return.

3.2 Summer mungbean profitability

Introducing summer mungbean in cereal-cereal cropping systems increases profitability. Being a short duration leguminous crop, input requirement and cost of cultivation for mungbean is quite lower than cereals that leads to a higher net return. The benefit cost ratio was increased in both the production system with inclusion of summer mungbean. Cultivation of summer mungbean in the ZTDSR-ZT mustard- ZT summer mungbean with crop residue (+R) treatment incurred a cost of INR 15,500/ha (five-year mean). As a result, the total cost of cultivation in this increased by INR 2,900/ha compared to the conventional TPR–CTM system. Simultaneously, this ZTDSR-ZTM-ZTSMB (+R) system fetched higher net returns of INR 2,500, 18,900, and 53,000 and 21,400/ha from rice, mustard, and the rice-mustard system including and excluding mungbean, respectively over the TPR-CTM system.

Table 1. Cost of cultivation and net returns of rice, mustard, and rice-mustard system under conservation agriculture (mean of 5 years) (Das *et al.*, 2020).

Treatment	Net returns (x 1000 INR/ha)		
	Rice	**Mustard**	**System**
ZTDSR-ZTM	32.1	52.7	84.9
ZTDSR+BM-ZTM	21.4	61.7	83.1
ZTDSR-ZTM (+R)	26.7	66.6	93.3
ZTDSR+BM-ZTM (+R)	25.3	68.7	94.0
ZTDSR-ZTM-ZTSMB	36.8	65.6	129.4 (27.0)[†]
ZTDSR-ZTM-ZTSMB(+R)	42.2	68.9	142.7 (31.6)[†]
TPR-ZTM	39.8	54.7	94.5
TPR-CTM	39.7	50.0	89.7

[†]ZTDSR-ZTM = zero till direct seeded rice (ZTDSR) – zero till mustard (ZTM); ZTDSR+BM-ZTM = ZTDSR with *Sesbania* brown manuring (BM) – ZTM; ZTDSR-ZTM (+R) = mustard residue in ZTDSR – rice residue in ZTM; ZTDSR+BM-ZTM (+R) = mustard

residue in ZTDSR with BM – rice residue in ZTM; ZTDSR-ZTM-ZTSMB = ZTDSR – ZTM- ZT summer mungbean (ZTSMB); ZTDSR-ZTM-ZTSMB (+R) = mungbean residue in ZTDSR - rice residue in ZTM- mustard residue in ZTSMB; TPR-ZTM = transplanted puddled rice (TPR)-ZTM; TPR-CTM = TPR-conventional till mustard (CTM).

3.3 Opportunities in conservation agriculture

Recently, Conservation Agriculture (CA) is being promoted and adopted for sustainable cropping intensification and profitable production (Das *et al.*, 2014). Fundamentally, maximum gain from CA can be realized, if the location-specific appropriate crop rotations are considered and system-based CA practices are developed (Susha *et al.*, 2018). However, developing location-specific appropriate CA practices requires substantial research works both on-stations and on-farms. Some of the CA-based component technologies such ZT, crop residue retention on the soil surface, and crop diversification have been evaluated in the IGP as alternative to conventional tillage practice (Das *et al.*, 2014; Saad *et al.*, 2016; Nandan *et al.*, 2018a). In India, the exact estimation of CA area is not available because of its adoption in a single crop following only one or two principles. It is estimated that ZT wheat is grown after puddled rice on an area of about 2 M ha in the IGP (Kassam *et al.*, 2019; Nandan *et al.*, 2018b). The appraisal of CA revealed that this system is being adopted as ZT wheat in the IGPs across India, Pakistan, Bangladesh and Nepal under rice–wheat cropping system, but there is only marginal adoption of permanent ZT system and full CA (Friedrich *et al.*, 2012; Nandan *et al.*, 2019). The best success story of CA is the cropping system intensification with mungbean and other legumes in the pre-dominating cereal-cereal rotations across the globe. Similar mungbean yield and N_2 fixation was accomplished by ZT while at the same time keeping away from current intensive tillage practice in semi-arid region of Pothwar, Pakistan (Ali *et al.*, 2013). The highest mungbean grain yields (1.2 t ha^{-1}) were acquired in ZT+ wheat straw, which additionally fixed N (82.6 kg ha^{-1}) in the soil. The five-year mean rice-mustard system productivity (rice equivalent yield) in different tillage and residue management practices followed the order: ZTDSR-ZTM-ZTSMB (+R) > ZTDSR-ZTM-ZTSMB > TPR-ZTM = TPR-CTM = ZTDSR+BM-ZTM (+R) > ZTDSR-ZTM (+R) > ZTDSR-ZTM = ZTDSR+BM-ZTM

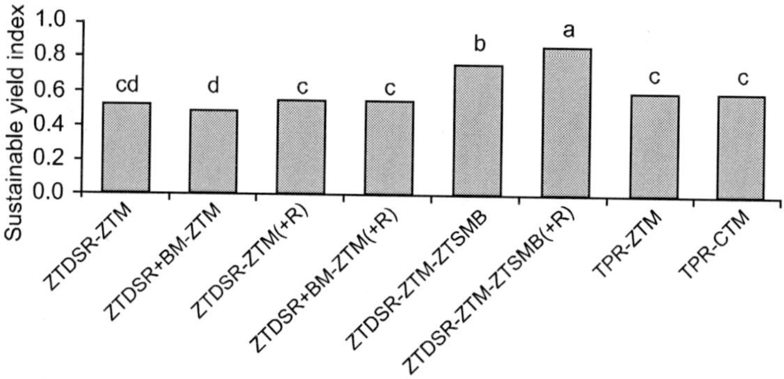

Fig. 2. Sustainable yield index of rice-mustard system under different conservation agriculture practices for five years; Between bars different lowercase letters indicate significant difference between treatments at $P \leq 0.05$ (LSD test). ZTDSR-ZTM = zero till direct seeded rice (ZTDSR) – zero till mustard (ZTM); ZTDSR+BM-ZTM = ZTDSR with *Sesbania* brown

manuring (BM) – ZTM; ZTDSR-ZTM (+R) = mustard residue in ZTDSR – rice residue in ZTM; ZTDSR+BM-ZTM (+R) = mustard residue in ZTDSR with BM – rice residue in ZTM; ZTDSR-ZTM-ZTSMB = ZTDSR –ZTM- ZT summer mungbean (ZTSMB); ZTDSR-ZTM-ZTSMB (+R) = mungbean residue in ZTDSR - rice residue in ZTM- mustard residue in ZTSMB; TPR-ZTM = transplanted puddled rice (TPR)-ZTM; TPR-CTM = TPR-conventional till mustard (CTM).

3.4 Weed management

Crop rotation is an effective practice for weed control rotating crops with different life cycles is a very effective cultural practice of controlling in problematic weed like *Phalaris minor* in wheat. The retention of crop residue in suppressing weeds is well documented. Thus CA can go a long way in reducing weeds and its seedbanks over time. CA systems advocate that at least 30% of the soil covered– this amount of residue may enhance soil quality, but insufficient to significantly reduce weed population. In another study at IARI, New Delhi Das and Yaduraju (2002) had observed that mungbean residue in DSR followed by zero-till wheat with rice residue retention and summer mungbean provided higher system productivity than TPR (transplanted rice)- CTW (conventional till wheat) system. Weed infestation in wheat crop was reduced due to zero tillage adoption in rice–wheat system in the IGPs. The CA is one of the major drivers of sustainable agricultural intensification in the IGP vis-à-vis the increasing soil carbon depletion, declining groundwater table, increasing air pollution and the stagnating or low yields of the rice–wheat system. The ZT wheat after rice is the most widely adopted resource conserving technology in South Asia and in the Indian IGP. Thus it has become the predominant CA based cropping system. Notably, intensive cropping (M–W–Mb) reduce seed density than that of M–W rotation across depth.

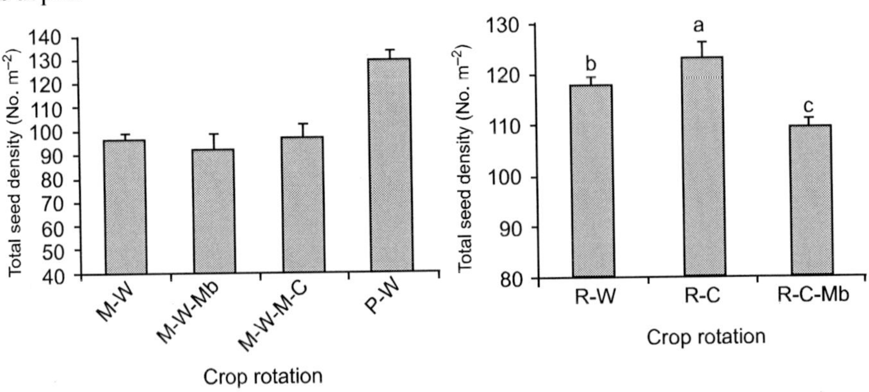

Fig. 3. Total seed density (seedlings/m^2) in four crop rotations Values shown in the figure are square-root [$\sqrt{(x + 0.5)}$]-transformed means. Error bars represent standard error of mean. M-W = maize-wheat; M-W-Mb = maize-wheat–mungbean; M-W-M-C = maize-wheat-maize-chickpea; P-W = pigeonpea-wheat (Not published).

Zero-till wheat is aided by significant costs savings and potential yield increases. In these systems, ZT is only applied to the wheat crop and does not essentially involve the retention of crop residue as mulch or the use of crop rotations. Also, the subsequent rice crop continuously puddled and transplanted. This anomaly in CA practices (in one season and not in the other) present a serious inadequacy from the ecologically-sustainable intensification outlook, as the benefits accumulated in the wheat season is lost in the subsequent puddled and transplanted rice (Nath *et al.*, 2017). Even in zero tillage wheat, farmers usually do not intentionally retain mulch and often burn the preceding rice straw– although the anchoring straw remained in the soil after burning may be enough to satisfy the requirements of residue mulch in CA. This suggests that farmers decides what components of CA practices that satisfies their aspiration and are available or easy to use vis-à-vis the prospects, limitations and trade-offs they face. Moving towards a full conservation agriculture calls for an improved management of crop residue and its retention and the shift towards direct-seed aerobic rice and crop diversification. Regional inequality in terms of agricultural productivity seems to favour the less intensified eastern IGP areas than the highly intensified north-western (NW-IGP), in terms of yield gains and cost savings from ZT practice. Socio-economic and system benefits of ZT in India is not a function of farm size. Smallholders have taken the advantage of ZT-drill in contract services. However, the reduced labour savings may boomerang against employment generation for farm labours who depend on land preparation for their livelihoods. The use of ZT in wheat unwraps the opportunity for the adoption of a full CA cropping system, and to other crops (pulses and vegetables) in the IGP. It also opens the scope for triple cropping in rice–wheat systems thereby increasing cropping intensity and diversity. For the expansion and scaling up of CA, it will have to deal with the impeding trade-offs or short falls associated with this anomaly.

Table 2. Total weed (grassy + broad-leaved + sedge) population (No./m^2) in mustard over the years at 60 DAS (Das *et al.*, 2020).

Treatments	Total weed population (No./m^2)					
	2013-14	2014-15	2015-16	2016-17	2017-18	Mean
ZTDSR-ZTM	79^b	76^b	156^a	208^c	219^a	148^b
ZTDSR+BM-ZTM	72^b	71^{bc}	78^{dc}	88^f	129^c	88^d
ZTDSR-ZTM (+R)	14^e	16^{ef}	63^d	96^{ef}	41^f	46^f
ZTDSR+BM-ZTM (+R)	5^f	8^f	28^e	132^d	23^g	39^{fgh}
ZTDSR-ZTM-ZTSMB	44^d	48^d	79^c	148^d	69^e	78^e
ZTDSR-ZTM-ZTSMB (+R)	21^e	24^e	23^e	126^{de}	21^g	43^{fg}
TPR-ZTM	61^c	65^c	69^{dc}	265^b	89^d	110^c
TPR-CTM	93^a	90^a	128^b	336^a	183^b	166^a

ZTDSR-ZTM = zero till direct seeded rice (ZTDSR) – zero till mustard (ZTM); ZTDSR+BM-ZTM = ZTDSR with *Sesbania* brown manuring (BM) – ZTM; ZTDSR-ZTM (+R) = mustard residue in ZTDSR – rice residue in ZTM; ZTDSR+BM-ZTM (+R) = mustard residue in ZTDSR with BM – rice residue in ZTM; ZTDSR-ZTM-ZTSMB = ZTDSR – ZTM- ZT summer mungbean (ZTSMB); ZTDSR-ZTM-ZTSMB (+R) = mungbean residue in ZTDSR - rice residue in ZTM- mustard residue in ZTSMB; TPR-ZTM = transplanted puddled rice (TPR)-ZTM; TPR-CTM = TPR-conventional till mustard (CTM).

3.5 Soil health

The inclusion of legumes in cereal-based cropping system assumes a great significance to restore soil fertility. Inclusion of greengram in the double cereal-based crop rotation following conservation agricultural practices was also suggested as future drivers of agricultural change in the north-western IGP. At the end of 9th year (2012) soil samples were analysed in both the long-term experiments and the results indicated that continuous growing of summer mungbean after rice -wheat and maize-wheat system improved the soil health. In rice based system, continuous cultivation of summer mungbean followed by rice-wheat significantly improved soil available nitrogen (N), phosphorus (P), and sulphur (S). Among the micronutrients, DTPA extractable Zn was significantly increased with summer mungbean inclusion. Highly intensive rice-wheat-mungbean rotation increased soil organic carbon (SOC) by 12.5% over continuous cultivation of rice-wheat (0.28%). Similarly in upland maize-wheat system, with inclusion of summer mungbean, the greater increase in soil available P, K and S was noticed whereas the improvement of available N was moderate/marginal. Long-term effect of summer mungbean in maize-wheat system improved SOC by 12% at the end of 9 year crop rotation. Including legumes in crop rotations under NT resulted in comparable yield in CT without N addition. If ZT crop rotations and residues addition were practiced at the same time with ZT, the ill effects of NT diminished. In tropical areas, yield reductions without N and with residue addition and crop diversification were significantly lower contrasted with humid climates. Further, crop rotation with legumes can minimize pH with their higher rhizospheric modification, release of root exudates and N fixation. For instance, mungbean inclusion in maize-wheat rotation decreased soil pH in mild alkaline soil of Inceptisol in India (Borase *et al*., 2020; Kumar *et al*., 2019; Nath *et al*., 2019a). Thus, CA can enhance soil fertility and minimize salt accumulation/ stress on surface soil compared with CT. The CA in rice–wheat–mungbean rotation in the IGP increased the macro- and micro-nutrients availability in the 0-5 cm soil depth. The PW and MWMb rotations increased the coarse macroaggregate (>2 mm) fraction by 67.4 and 26.6% ($p < 0.05$) over the MW, respectively. Legume based cropping (PW, MWMb, and MWMC) being at par with each other, recorded significantly higher mesoaggregates (0.25-2 mm) compared with the MW system. While, MW system constituted the lower 'silt+clay' (<0.053 mm) fraction than that of PW, MWMb, and MWMC rotations (Table 3). The INM treatment accounted 96.6 and 58.3% higher ($p < 0.05$) coarse macroaggregate fraction compared with those of CT and NPKSZnB, respectively. Further, INM enhanced the meso- and 'silt+clay'-sized fractions by 78.3 and 28.9% ($p < 0.05$) compared with CT, and by 17.6 and 9.7% ($p < 0.05$) comparison with NPKSZnB.

Table 3. Soil structural indices at 0-0.2 m depth in different crop rotations and nutrient management practices after 13 years (2003-2016).

Crop rotation	Water stable macroaggregate (g aggregate 100/g dry soil)	Water stable microaggregate (g aggregate 100/g dry soil)	Aggregate ratio	Mean weight diameter (mm)
MW	37.5[c*]	62.5[a]	0.81[b]	1.09[c]
MWMb	59.1[b]	40.9[b]	4.71[a]	1.13[b]
MWMC	60.4[ab]	39.6[bc]	2.12[b]	1.08[c]
PW	63.6[a]	36.4[c]	4.57[a]	1.18[a]

Incorporation of mungbean stover in MWMb sequence resulted in lower bulk density and higher hydraulic conductivity. Fundamentally, fungi present in pigeonpea and mugbean rhizosphere produces a glycoprotein called "glomalin". The sticky part of glomalin entraps soil mineral, organic matter, and debris to form a stable soil aggregates. Hence, microbial activity of rhizosphere is directly responsible for the improved soil structure in crop rotation involving legumes. Pulse-inclusive crop rotations (PW, MWMb and MWMC) increased the alkaline phosphatase (Fig. 4) by 80, 44, and 20% over the MW, respectively ($p \leq 0.05$). Higher enzyme activity in intensive cropping compared with the double cropping of maize-wheat from a long-term experiment of Brazil. They attributed higher microbial biomass for the increased enzyme activity as microbial biomass produced a higher amount of substrates for microbial growth and production of enzymes. Rice-wheat-mungbean rotation increased MBC and MBN by 27% and 59%, respectively over R-W rotation Likewise, R-C rotation had higher MBN (16%, $p < 0.05$) over R-W rotation (Fig. 5).

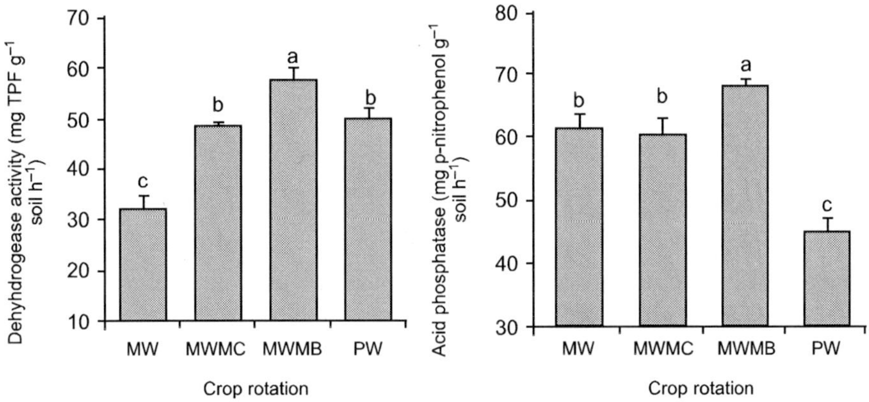

Fig. 4. Soil enzyme activity in four crop rotations; M-W = maize-wheat; M-W-Mb = maize-wheat–mungbean; M-W-M-C = maize-wheat-maize-chickpea; P-W = pigeonpea-wheat (Borase *et al.*, 2020a).

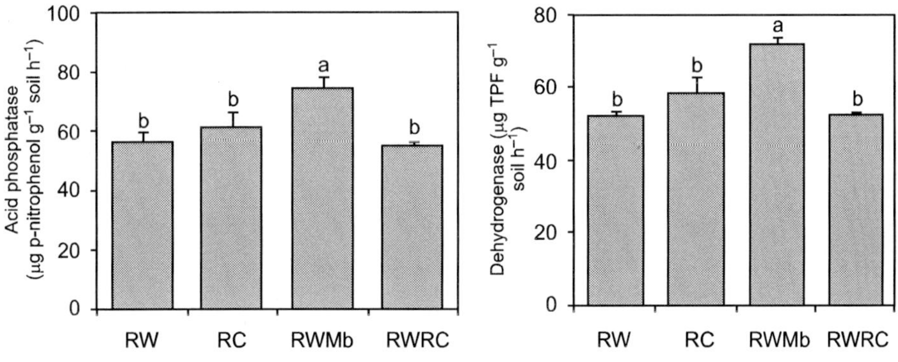

Fig. 5. Soil enzyme activity in four crop rotations; RW = rice-wheat; RWMb = Rice-wheat–mungbean; RWRC = rice-wheat-rice-chickpea; RC = rice-chickpea (Borase *et al.*, 2020b).

Soil respiration rate was recorded highest in R-W-Mb rotation followed by R-W-R-C and was lowest in R-W rotation. Rice-wheat-mungbean rotation resulted in higher MBC/SOC ratio compared to other rotations. Rice-wheat-mungbean rotation increased acid phosphatase (32%), alkaline phosphatase (32%), and arylsulfatase (41%) activities over R-W rotation ($p < 0.05$). Notably, R-W-Mb, R-C and R-W-R-C rotations increased β-glucosidase activity by 16%, 13%, and 16%, respectively over R-W rotation ($p < 0.05$). Soil dehydrogenase activity was highest in the R-W-Mb rotation, which was higher over other crop rotations ($p < 0.05$). Cropping intensification with inclusion of mungbean (R-W-Mb) enhances enzymes activities due to the higher carbon turnover over R-W rotation. Grain legume exudates higher amount of phosphatase enzymes than cereals.

3.6 Resources-use efficiency

Soil deterioration, depletion of water tables, salinization, increased pests and diseases and environmental pollution due to continuous cropping of cereals can be overcome by diversifying crop rotations with greengram. Zero tillage was observed to provide higher yield of 'SML 668' in summer over tillage and tillage plus wheat straw incorporation. Short duration summer greengram variety 'SML 668' sown after wheat gave 2.5% higher yield than CT. The grain yield in CT + wheat straw incorporation was about 4% less than CT and about 7% less than NT. An experiment conducted by Gathala *et al.* (2013) reported that greengram grown in transplanted rice–ZT wheat–ZT greengram rotation yielded about 0.7 t/ha, no grain yield of greengram could be harvested as the crop was killed in DSR/ZT maize –ZT wheat –ZT greengram in order to timely sowing of DSR or ZT maize. However, 0.3 – 0.5 t/ha of greengram grain yield were obtained when it was sown as relay crop prior to the wheat harvest. Comparable greengram grain yield and nitrogen fixation can be achieved by minimum tillage while avoiding current intensive tillage practice in semi-arid of Pothwar, Pakistan (Ali *et al.*, 2013). Maximum greengram grain yields (1.2 t/ha) were obtained in NT+ wheat straw, which also fixed maximum amount of nitrogen (82.6 kg/ha) in the soil. When greengram crop is drill-seeded after the wheat as a residual crop it did not receive any fertilizer or pesticide.

Table 4. Irrigation water and total water (irrigation + rainfall) productivities of rice and mustard under conservation agriculture (mean of 5 years) (Das *et al.*, 2020).

Treatment	Irrigation water productivity (kg grain/m³)		Total water productivity (kg grain/m³)	
	Rice	Mustard	Rice	Mustard
ZTDSR-ZTM	4.21^{c*}	8.03^{e}	2.07^{c}	5.61^{d}
ZTDSR+BM-ZTM	3.73^{d}	9.04^{d}	1.97^{c}	6.23^{c}
ZTDSR-ZTM (+R)	3.93^{cd}	9.70^{bc}	2.02^{c}	6.66^{b}
ZTDSR+BM-ZTM (+R)	3.98^{cd}	10.27^{ab}	2.08^{c}	7.10^{a}
ZTDSR-ZTM-ZTSMB	4.63^{b}	9.42^{cd}	2.48^{b}	6.53^{bc}
ZTDSR-ZTM-ZTSMB (+R)	5.01^{a}	10.51^{a}	2.67^{ab}	7.30^{a}
TPR-ZTM	3.89^{d}	7.90^{e}	2.73^{a}	5.51^{d}
TPR-CTM	3.92^{d}	7.78^{e}	2.74^{a}	5.38^{d}

ZTDSR-ZTM = zero till direct seeded rice (ZTDSR) – zero till mustard (ZTM); ZTDSR+BM-ZTM = ZTDSR with *Sesbania* brown manuring (BM) – ZTM; ZTDSR-ZTM

(+R) = mustard residue in ZTDSR – rice residue in ZTM; ZTDSR+BM-ZTM (+R) = mustard residue in ZTDSR with BM – rice residue in ZTM; ZTDSR-ZTM-ZTSMB = ZTDSR – ZTM- ZT summer mungbean (ZTSMB); ZTDSR-ZTM-ZTSMB (+R) = mungbean residue in ZTDSR - rice residue in ZTM- mustard residue in ZTSMB; TPR-ZTM = transplanted puddled rice (TPR)-ZTM; TPR-CTM = TPR-conventional till mustard (CTM).

3.7 Climate resilience

Crop diversification through rotations, cover- and inter-crops contributes to recycling nutrients, disrupt weed, pest and disease cycles, enhance biological nitrogen fixation (BNF) when legumes are included and ensure diversify food diets. Agroecosystems sustainability can be enhance by changing from monoculture to rotation cropping. Das *et al.* (2014) evaluated the impacts of CA in a cotton–wheat system; diversified with maize, wheat and greengram on total SOC addition in IGP. Results showed CA-based practices had 28 and 26% higher total SOC stock than CT in the 15 cm soil depth increments, but similar SOC stocks at 30 cm layer (Fig. 6). The PW and MWMb rotations had significantly higher values of all carbon fractions (very labile, labile, less labile and non labile) compared with the MW system. Probably, PW and MWMb rotations provided better root biomass that contributed to enhanced soil organic matter. Further, PW and MWMb rotations provided the better habitats for the soil flora and fauna, which enhanced the soil aggregation. Therefore, PW and MWMb rotations owned the higher water stable macroaggregates and lower microaggregates compared with the MW rotation.

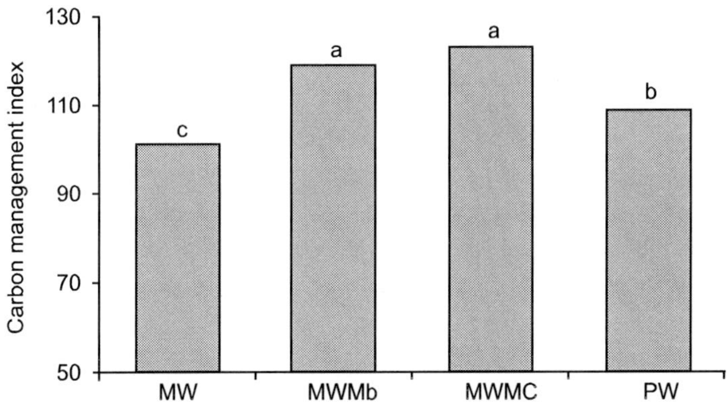

Fig. 6. Carbon management index in four crop rotations; M-W = maize-wheat; M-W-Mb = maize-wheat–mungbean; M-W-M-C = maize-wheat-maize-chickpea; P-W = pigeonpea-wheat (Hazra *et al.*, 2019).

Indeed, with three crops in an annual rotation R-W-Mb added the higher amount of carbon into soil through non-harvested crop remnants and recycling of crop residues (particularly in the INM treatment) as compared to other rotations having two-crop in a year (R-W, R-C, and R-W-R-C). Studies have shown that intensive cropping systems with legume cover crop favour soil aggregation and carbon sequestration (Kumar *et al.* 2019; Ghosh *et al.* 2020). Extensive ground cover (all three seasons i.e. rainy, winter, and summer) in R-W-Mb rotation might be a reason for higher SOC and elevated microbial activity over other rotations with summer fallow (R-W, R-C, and R-W-R-C) (Table 5).

Table 5. Soil C and N status under different crop rotation in long-term mungbean inclusion in cereal-cereal system (Ghosh *et al.*, 2020).

Parameter	Crop rotation	Mean
Very –labile carbon	R–W	2.55
(g/kg)	R–C	2.59
	R–W–Mb	2.90
	R–W–R–C	2.65
Soil organic carbon	R–W	5.95
(g/kg)	R–C	6.25
	R–W–Mb	6.94
	R–W–R–C	6.28
Total organic carbon	R–W	7.86
(g/kg)	R–C	8.41
	R–W–Mb	9.52
	R–W–R–C	8.45
Available nitrogen	R–W	103.4
(mg/kg)	R–C	112.0
	R–W–Mb	117.7
	R–W–R–C	109.6

RW = rice-wheat; RWMb = Rice-wheat–mungbean; RWRC = rice-wheat-rice-chickpea; RC = rice-chickpea

4. CONCLUSION

It can be concluded that cropping intensification of R-W rotation with inclusion of mungbean (R-W-Mb) could increase soil carbon pools, microbial activity and biochemical functions over the time. Likewise, mungbean inclusive diversification of M-W rotation could enhance soil enzymes activities namely phosphatase, β-glucosidase and protease in long-run. The study also suggests that sole reliance on chemical fertilizers for nutrient management is not a sustainable approach and organic matter (crop residue/manure) application at regular interval is crucial to maintain the soil productive capacity in tropical agro-regions. Improved soil carbon pools and microbial activity in legume-inclusive rotations effectively translated in the base-crop productivity.

REFERENCES

Ali, S., Hasan, A., Ijaz, S.S. and Ansar, M. (2013) Munbean yield and Di-nitrogen fixation under minimum tillage at semi-arid Pothwar. *Pakistan Journal of Animal and Plant Sciences* 23, 198 – 200.

Baghel, J.K., Das, T.K., Mukherjee, I., Nath, C.P., Bhattacharyya, R., Ghosh, S. and Raj, R. (2020) Impacts of conservation agriculture and herbicides on weeds, nematodes, herbicide residue and productivity in direct-seeded rice. *Soil and Tillage Research* 201, 104634.

Borase, D.N., Murugeasn, S., Nath, C.P., Hazrab, K.K., Singh, S.S., Kumar, N., Singh, U. and Praharaj, C.S. (2020b) Long-term impact of grain legumes and nutrient management practices on soil microbial activity and biochemical properties. *Archives of Agronomy and Soil Science*, DOI: 10.1080/03650340.2020.1819532.

Borase, D.N., Nath, C.P., Hazra, K.K., Senthilkumar, M., Singh, S.S., Praharaj, C.S., Singh, U., Kumar, N. (2020a) Long-term impact of diversified crop rotations and nutrient management practices on soil microbial functions and soil enzymes activity. *Ecological Indicators* 114, 106322.

Das, T.K., Bhattacharyya, R., Sudhishri, S., Sharma, A.R. Saharawat, Y.S., Bandyopadhyay, K.K. Sepat, S. Bana, R.S., Aggarwal, P., Sharma, R.K., Bhatia A., Singh, G., Datta, S.P., Kar, A., Singh, B., Singh, P., Pathak, H., Vyas, A.K., Jat, M.L. (2014). Conservation agriculture in an irrigated cotton–wheat system of the western Indo-Gangetic Plains: Crop and water productivity and economic profitability. *Field Crops Res*. 158, 24–33.

Das, T.K., Nath, C.P., Das, S., Biswas, S., Bhattacharyya, R., Sudhishri, S., Raj, R., Singh, B., Kakralia, S.K., Rathi, N. and Sharma, A.R. (2020) Conservation Agriculture in rice-mustard cropping system for five years: Impacts on crop productivity, profitability, water-use efficiency, and soil properties. *Field Crops Research* 250, 107781. DOI: 10.1016/j.fcr.2020.107781

Das, T.K. and Yaduraju, N.T. (2002) Optimization of metribuzin use for controlling isoproturon-resistant *Phalaris minor* Retz. in wheat. *Pesticide Research Journal* 14, 47-56.

Erenstein, O. and Laxmi, V. (2008) Zero tillage impacts in India's rice–wheat systems: A review. *Soil and Tillage Research* 100, 1–14.

Gathala, M.K., Kumar, V., Sharma, P.C., Saharawat, Y.S., Jat, H.S., Singh, M., Kumar, A., Jat, M.L., Humphreys, E., Sharma, D.K. and Sharma, S. (2013) Optimizing intensive cereal-based cropping systems addressing current and future drivers of agricultural change in the northwestern Indo-Gangetic Plains of India. *Agriculture, Ecosystems & Environment* 177, 85-97.

Ghosh, P.K., Hazra, K.K., Venkatesh, M.S., Praharaj, C.S., Kumar, N., Nath, C.P., Singh, U. and Singh, S.S. (2020) Grain legume inclusion in cereal–cereal rotation increased base crop productivity in the long run. *Experimental Agriculture* 56(1), 142-158.

Hazra, K.K., Nath, C.P., Singh, U., Praharaj, C.S., Kumar, N., Singh, S.S. and Singh, N.P. (2019) Diversification of maize-wheat cropping system with legumes and integrated nutrient management increases soil aggregation and carbon sequestration. *Geoderma* 353, 308-319.

Kumar, N., Nath, C.P., Hazra, K.K., Das, K., Venkatesh, M.S., Singh, M.K., Singh, S.S., Praharaj, C.S. and Singh, N.P. (2019) Impact of zero-till residue management and crop diversification with legumes on soil aggregation and carbon sequestration. *Soil and Tillage Research* 189, 158–167.

Nandan, R., Singh, S.S., Kumar, V., Singh, V., Hazra, K.K., Nath, C.P., Malik, R.K., Poonia, S.P. and Solanki, C.H. (2018b) Crop establishment with conservation tillage and crop residue retention in rice-based cropping systems of Eastern India: yield advantage and economic benefit. *Paddy Water and Environment* 16, 477-492.

Nandan, R., Singh, V., Singh, S.S., Kumar, V., Hazra, K.K., Nath, C.P., Poonia, S.P. and Malik, R.K. (2018a) Comparative assessment of the relative proportion of weed morphology, diversity, and growth under new generation tillage and crop establishment techniques in rice-based cropping systems. *Crop Protection* 111, 23-32.

Nandan, R., Singh, V., Singh, S.S., Kumar, V., Hazra, K.K., Nath, C.P., Poonia, S.P., Malik, R.K., Bhattacharyya, R. and McDonald, A. (2019) Impact of conservation tillage in rice–based cropping systems on soil aggregation, carbon pools and nutrients. *Geoderma* 340, 104-114.

Nath, C.P., Das, T.K., Bhattacharyya, R., Pathak, H., Paul, S., Chakraborty, D. and Hazra, K.K. (2019b) Nitrogen effects on productivity and soil properties in conventional and zero tilled wheat with different residue management. *Proceedings of the National Academy* of Sciences, *India*, *Section B*: *Biological Sciences* 89, 123-135.

Nath, C.P., Das, T.K., Rana, K.S., Pathak, H., Bhattacharyya, R., Paul, S., Singh, S.B., Meena, M.C., (2015). Weed-management and wheat productivity in a conservation agriculture-based maize (*Zea mays*)-wheat (*Triticum aestivum*)-mungbean (*Vigna radiata*) system in north-western Indo-Gangetic plains of India. *Indian Journal of Agronomy* 60, 554-563.

Nath, C.P., Das, T.K., Rana, K.S., Pathak, H., Bhattacharyya, R., Paul, S. and Meena, M.C. (2017) Greenhouse gases emission, soil organic carbon and wheat yield as affected by tillage systems and nitrogen management practices. *Archives of Agronomy and Soil Science* 63(12), 1644–1660.

Nath, C.P., Hazra, K.K., Kumar, N., Praharaj, C.S., Singh, S.S., Singh, U. and Singh, N.P. (2019a) Including grain legume in rice–wheat cropping system improves soil organic carbon pools over time. *Ecological Engineering* 129, 144-153.

Pittelkow, C.M., Liang, X., Linquist, B.A., Van Groenigen, K.J., Lee, J., Lundy, M.E., VanGestel, N., Six, J., Venterea, R.T. and van Kessel, C. (2015a) Productivity limits and potentials of the principles of conservation agriculture. *Nature* 517, 365–368.

Saad, A.A., Das, T.K., Rana, D.S., Sharma, A.R., Bhattacharyya, R. and Lal, K. (2016) Energy auditing of a maize–wheat–greengram cropping system under conventional and conservation agriculture in irrigated north-western Indo-Gangetic Plains. *Energy* 116, 293-305.

CHAPTER 6

Tillage management in pulse crops under diverse agricultural production systems

Bishal Mukherjee[1*], Purabi Banerjee[1], Rajib Nath[1], V. Visha Kumari[1] and Mousumi Ghose[2]

1. *Department of Agronomy, Bidhan Chandra KrishiViswavidyalaya, Mohanpur, Nadia, West Bengal, India.*

2. *Department of Agriculture, Government of West Bengal*

*Corresponding author email: bishalmukherjee@gmail.com

Abstract

Pulses or grain legumes have been a part of balanced diet in different continents across the globe since early civilization. Pulses play a pivotal role in ensuring nutritional security to a large vegetarian population of the country. To achieve the potential yield, tillage management plays an important role. Tillage is the physical manipulation of soil to result in good tilth for better germination and subsequent growth of crops. Tillage is very much necessary for proper seed germination, seedling establishment as well as improving soil health that ultimately increases yield of pulses. Due to wider adaptability of pulse crops, they can grow well under most of the modern tillage practices such as minimum tillage, zero tillage and conservation tillage despite of following of conventional tillage. Pulses mainly grow with residual soil moisture which is also ensured by proper tillage management. Soil moisture and temperature which are influenced by tillage practices, affect the biological nitrogen fixation in pulse crops. Tillage operations also influence pathogens, insects and weeds infestation in pulse crops. Thus, utilization of newly reformed tillage implements for situation based proper tillage operations in the field can improve the soil health as well as pulses productivity.

Keywords: Conservation tillage, Land management, Minimum tillage, Nodulation, Zero tillage

1. INTRODUCTION

Ensuring food and nutritional security for the huge population is one of the major concerns for the whole world. Agriculture plays a key role in maintaining economic scenario and rural livelihoods of India. Pulses have been a part of balanced diet in different continents across the globe since early civilization. Malnutrition and poverty is one of the major issues of concern in India. In India, people are mostly vegetarian in dietary habits and depend on cereals and pulses as their staple food to fulfill their dietary requirements. Pulses are dietary protein in the daily diet of human beings as well as animal feed also. Looking to the importance of pulses in human diet and agricultural sustainability, Food and Agriculture Organization (FAO) and United Nations have declared 2016 as '*International Year of Pulses*' and seeds as '*Nutritious Seeds for Sustainable Future*'.

Pulses is cheap source of high quality vegetable protein and dietary fiber with high in digestibility, free of gluten, low in fat, low in cholesterol and low in glycemic index. In addition, pulses have health benefitting properties which help in preventing illnesses such as cancer (Vohra *et al.*, 2015), diabetes (Ramdath *et al.*, 2016) and heart disease. The Indian Council of Medical Research has recommended an intake of 80 g/day of pulses in diet for active male adult (ICMR, 2010). Pulses are the richest and cheapest source of protein which can act as lifeline for the people with low income groups living in rural and suburban areas in the country. The total production of pulses in India is about 25.23 Mt from 29.99 M ha area which can't meet the requirement to achieve self-sufficiency in pulses and thus still have to depend on foreign countries to some extent. The projected food legume requirement of the country by the year 2030 is 32 Mt demanding an annual growth rate of 4.2% (IPGA, 2018).

Proper tillage management of the cultivating land is one of the important aspects for ensuring good tilth for germination and subsequent growth of crop, weed control as well as soil and water conservation. Tillage methods affect the sustainable resources through its influence on soil properties and crop growth, however, use of excessive and un-necessary tillage operations is often harmful to soil (Nazeer *et al.*, 2012). Deep tillage is reported to be beneficial than normal ploughing in rice-chickpea system at Kanpur (Arya *et al.*, 2002). But, after sorghum, maize and oilseed, cross harrowing is generally adequate for winter season chickpea. Whereas, under rainfed condition, double cross planking (compact soil) recorded higher seed yield of chickpea than single planking (Kumar *et al.*, 2006). Lower soil nitrate is observed under zero-tillage in comparison to conventional tillage (Doran, 1980). The low level of nitrate under zero-tillage may be associated with higher N-fixation by legumes (Hughes and Herridge, 1989). Zero-tillage, in general, increased the soil water content (Lafond *et al.*, 1992) and this reduced water stress may increase the N-fixation by pulses (Bennet and Albretch, 1984). Therefore, following of proper tillage as per season, cropping systems and agro-ecological is the most important way forward to achieve higher yield in pulses.

2. BRIEFING TILLAGE MANAGEMENT WITH IMPORTANCE IN PULSES

Tillage is the physical manipulation of soil to obtain good tilth for better seed germination and subsequent growth of crops. Size distribution of aggregates depends on soil type, soil moisture content at which ploughing is done and subsequent cultivation. The word tillage is derived from 'Anglo-Saxon' words 'Tilian' and 'Teolian', meaning 'to plough and prepare soil for seed to sow, to cultivate and to raise crops'. *JethroTull*, who is considered as father of tillage suggested that thorough ploughing and land preparation is necessary to make the soil into fine particles. Size distribution of aggregates depends on soil type, soil moisture content at which ploughing is done and subsequent cultivation. Better crop management practices which include proper tillage practices provide greater opportunities to increase in pulse productivity in India by mitigating the abiotic and biotic stresses (Rana *et al.*, 2016). Tillage is necessary for obtaining ideal conditions for seed germination, seedling establishment and growth of crops (Das *et al.*, 2014).

Fig 1. Conventional tillage with spade for lentil cultivation at West Bengal

For dryland pulses, deep ploughing results in better moisture conservation which leads to better root proliferation and higher productivity over shallow cultivation (Rana *et al.*, 2016). Traditionally, pulses are broadcast sown, but with improvement of production technologies for different crops, most of the farmers now a day go for tillage management under different production systems for pulses with tractor/animal drawn or manually operated (Fig 1) tillage implements which help in line sowing of seeds also.

The generalized importance of tillage management in pulses as well as in other crops is as follows:

- Good tilth always ensures proper sized soil aggregates as well as improves soil structure.
- When soil is in good tilth, capillary and non-capillary pores would be roughly equal.
- Organic matter is mainly responsible for dark brown to dark grey colour of soil. Tillage increases oxidation and decomposition of organic matter resulting in fading of colour.
- Air filled spaces between soil particles constitute pore space. With tillage pore space is increased in soil.
- Tillage ensures proper aeration between the soil pores which is very much required for any kind of crop production in fertile land.
- Tillage creates optimum temperature for seed germination and seedling establishment.
- Tillage loosens the soil surface and decreases thermal conductivity and heat capacity.
- Crop residues and farmyard manure decomposition increases when incorporated properly in the soil.
- Degradation of herbicides, pesticides and allelopathic chemicals increases under tillage.

3. TYPES OF TILLAGE OPERATIONS

Different kinds of tillage operations can be possible for many crops which are generally practiced by farming community. The tillage operations may be grouped into 2 types: i. On season tillage and ii. Off-season tillage

3.1 On-season tillage

Tillage operations that are done for raising crops in the same season are known as on-season tillage. They may be further divided into two types: A. preparatory cultivation and B. After cultivation.

3.1.1 Preparatory cultivation

It refers to tillage operations that are done to prepare the field for raising crops. It consists of deep opening and loosening of the soil to bring about a desirable tilth as well as to incorporate or uproot weeds and crop stubble when the soil is in a workable condition. Types of preparatory cultivation are: a. Primary tillage, b. Secondary tillage and c. Layout of seed bed.

3.1.2 Primary tillage

The tillage operation that is done after the harvest of crop to bring the land under cultivation is known as primary tillage or ploughing. Ploughing is the opening of compact soil with the help of different ploughs. Country plough, mould board plough, tractor and power tiller drawn implements are used for primary tillage. It has favourable effect on pulse crops.

3.1.3 Secondary tillage

The tillage operations that are performed on the soil after primary tillage are known as secondary tillage. Secondary tillage consists of lighter or finer operation which is done to clean the soil, break the clods and incorporate the manure and fertilizers. Harrowing and planking is done to serve those purposes. Planking is done to crush the hard clods, level the soil surface and to compact the soil lightly. Harrows, Guntakas, cultivators and spade are used for secondary tillage.

3.1.4 Layout of seed bed

This is also one of the components of preparatory tillage. Leveling board, buck scrapers etc. are used for leveling and markers are used for layout of seedbed.

3.2 After cultivation

The tillage operations that are carried out in the standing crop after the sowing or planting and prior to the harvesting of the crop plants are called after tillage. This is also called as inter cultivation or post planting cultivation. After cultivation includes side dressing of fertilizers, earthing up and intercultivation. Spade, hoe, weeders etc. are used for inter cultivation. In wider rows planted pulse crops like pigeonpea, mechanical weeder can be used to control weeds.

3.3 Off-season tillage

Tillage operations done for conditioning the soil suitably for the forthcoming main season crop are called off-season tillage. Off-season tillage may be, post-harvest tillage, summer tillage, winter tillage, fallow tillage, etc. Deep summer tillage found beneficial in controlling weeds, insect-pests and pathogens. It also increases the rain water infiltration as well as retention in soil. Deep ploughing play an important role in stabilizing the productivity of rainfed pulses through *in-situ* soil moisture conservation. Summer tillage is recommended to make the land ready for planting of rainy season crops with the onset of monsoon. This practice helps in greater retention of rainwater (36% higher than conventional method) and enhances the yield of pigeonpea by 86% compared to farmers' practice (Venkateswarlu *et al.,* 2009). In another experiment at Arjia (Bhilwara district, Rajasthan), *in-situ* moisture conservation system involving summer deep ploughing with raised bed of 40 cm width gave highest blackgram yield (1243 kg/ha), rainwater use efficiency and lowest runoff and soil loss compared to farmers' practice of flat bed (AICRPDA, 2011).

3.4 Special purpose tillage

Tillage operations done to serve various special purposes are said to be special purpose tillage. They are:

3.4.1 Sub-soiling

To break the hard pan beneath the plough layer, special tillage operation (chiseling) is performed to reduce compaction. Sub-soiling is essential and once in four to five years where heavy machineries are used for field operations, seeding, harvesting and transporting. Advantages of sub-soiling are greater volume of soil may be obtained for cultivation of crops, reduce runoff and soil erosion, excess water may percolate downward to recharge the permanent water table and roots of crop plants can penetrate deeper to extract moisture from the larger soil profile. As pulses are deep rooted crops, it helps in proper development of roots and nodules, and also nutrients utilization from deeper zones (Ghosh *et al.*, 2006)

3.4.2 Clean tillage

It refers to working of the soil of the entire field in such a way no living plant is left undisturbed. It is practiced to control weeds, soil borne pathogen and pests. This also reduced the crop-weed competition during initial slow growth phase of pulse crops.

3.4.3 Blind tillage

It refers to tillage done after seeding or planting the crop (in a sterile soil) either at the pre-emergence stage of the crop plants or while they are in the early stages of growth so that crop plants (sugarcane, potato, etc.) do not get damaged, but, extra plants and broad leaved weeds are uprooted. This is in practice by farmers in alluvial soil of low lying area in lower IGP where field is flooded with water during rainy season and only *rabi* crops like lentil and chickpea are grown on residual soil moisture.

3.4.4 Dry tillage

Dry tillage is practiced for crops that are sown or planted in dry land condition having sufficient moisture for germination of seeds. This is suitable for crops like broadcasted rice, jute, wheat, oilseed crops, pulses, potato and vegetable crops. Dry tillage is done in a soil having sufficient moisture (21-25%). The soil becomes more porous and soft due to dry tillage. Besides, the water holding capacity of the soil and aeration are increased which are favourable for soil micro-organisms and root development of pulse crops.This also helps in timely sowing of crops under rainfed area during rainy season.

3.4.5 Wet tillage or puddling

The tillage operation that is done in a land with standing water is called wet tillage or puddling. Puddling operation consists of ploughing repeatedly in standing water until the soil becomes soft and muddy. Puddling creates an impervious layer below the surface to reduce deep percolation losses of water and to provide soft seed bed for planting rice. Puddling disrupts the soil structure which is a limiting factor for growing pulses under rainfed rice fallow (Kumar *et al.*, 2016).

4. MODERN TILLAGE CONCEPTS IN PULSE CROPS

Conventional tillage involves primary tillage to open and turn the soil which is usually followed by secondary tillage to obtain fine seed bed for sowing or planting of *kharif* as well as *rabi* pulses. With the introduction of herbicides in intensive farming systems, the concept of tillage has been changed. *Rabi* pulses are characterized to grow on residual soil moisture after harvesting *kharif* cereals. But continuous use of heavy mould board ploughs or animal drawn cultivators create hard pan in the subsoil, results in poor infiltration. It is more susceptible to erosion and run-off. It is capital intensive and increase soil degradation. To avoid these kinds of ill effects, modern developed concepts on tillage is in rule.

4.1 Minimum tillage

Concept of minimum tillage was first introduced in USA. Reason for introducing minimum tillage was high cost of tillage due to steep rise in oil prices in 1974. It aims at reducing tillage operations to the minimum necessity for ensuring a good seed bed. Minimum tillage practices under the concept of conservation agriculture (CA) can reverse loss of carbon and reduced nutrient sequestration in heavily tilled soils (Lupwayi *et al.*, 1999).

The advantages of minimum tillage over conventional tillage in pulses are:

- The cost and time for field preparation for pulse cultivation is reduced by reducing the number of field operations.
- Water loss through evaporation is minimum due to less disturbance of soil.
- Soil compaction is comparatively less that means fine seedbed can be ensured for pulses cultivation.
- Soil structure is not destroyed which support root growth and nodulation (Bandyopadhyay *et al.*, 2016).
- Water storage in the plough layer is increased and will be available for longer period (Saxena *et al.*, 1997).

4.2 Zero tillage (No tillage)

Zero tillage is an extreme form of minimum tillage. It is also known as no-till farming. In this, crop is planted in the residues of the previous crop without any prior soil tillage or seed bed preparation (Fig 2&3). No till farming or concept of zero tillage is one of the age old practices followed by the pulse growing farmers. No-till farming practices have been in use for thousands of years, with primitive farmers using a stick to make a hole in the ground, putting seeds in the soil, and then covering the seeds. Zero-tillage practices can have beneficial impacts on productivity (Fig 4) as well as minimizing environmental degradation, such as soil erosion in legume and cereal crop-growing areas (Das *et al.*, 2014; Kumar *et al.*, 2019).

Fig 2. Zero tillage with hand tyne in rice fallow areas for chickpea cultivation in West Bengal

Fig 3. Sowing of pulses with zero-till drill machine

Fig 4. Performance of zero tilled chickpea at B.C.K.V., West Bengal

The advantages of zero tillage in pulses cultivation are as follows:

- Zero tilled soils are more or less homogenous in structure with more microbiology that ensures good yield of pulse crops.
- No-till farming can lead to improvement in soil health by improving soil physical

structure, and enhancing soil biological activities, nutrient cycling, soil water holding capacity and input use efficiency (Kumar *et al*., 2019).

- Ogle *et al* (2005) analyzed data from 126 studies worldwide and estimated that soil carbon stocks in surface soil layers increased by an average of 10 to 20 per cent over a 20 years' time period under no-till practices compared with intensive tillage practices. The relative increases in carbon stocks were higher under humid than dry climate and higher under tropical than temperate regimes.
- With the adoption of zero-tillage practice, weeds are more during initial years. Weed seeds which remain on soil surface can be damaged by heat during summer season or eaten by birds, ants, etc and subsequently the remaining weeds can be controlled by effective herbicides, which resulted in decline in weed population in subsequent years (Kumar *et al*., 2014).
- In a long-term experiment at Alabama, USA revealed no-till treatment had significantly higher soil organic carbon and microbial biomass carbon contents in the surface layer than the conventional till treatment (Feng *et al*., 2002).

4.3 Conservation tillage

The key principles defined by FAO (2011) to characterize conservation agriculture are: minimum soil disturbance, permanent organic soil cover and crop rotation. The conservation tillage system is one such tillage option designed to conserve soil moisture in moisture-deficit areas (Rana *et al*., 2016). This could overcome both abiotic and biotic stresses in pulse crops. The major objective of this tillage is to conserve soil and soil moisture. Zero tillage is also a conservation approach of tillage. It is a system of tillage in which organic residues are not inverted into the soil such that they remain on surface as protective cover against evaporation losses of soil moisture and erosion of soil. If stubble forms the protective cover on the surface, it is usually referred to as stubble mulch tillage. The residues left on soil surface interfere with seed bed preparation and sowing operations. It is a year round system of managing plant residue with implements that undercut residues, losses the soil and kills the weeds.In a study conducted at IIPR, Kanpur in Chickpea expresses yield advantage of conservation tillage in rice-chickpea system over conventional tillage (Table 1). The higher yield of chickpea was recorded in zero till drill and ZT dibbling sown chickpea crop when crop residue was retained as mulch after rice harvest under rainfed condition. The increase in chickpea productivity was upto 28.2% in comparison to conventional tillage.

Table 1. Effect of conservation tillage on chickpea productivity in rice-chickpea system

Treatment	Chickpea yield (kg/ha)	Increase over conventional tillage (%)
ZT dibbling+ mulching	1660	28.2
No till drill+ mulching	1589	22.7
Deep tillage	1314	1.5
Deep tillage+ mulching	1482	14.4
Conventional tillage	1295	—
CD (P= 0.05)	115	—

Source: Kumar *et al.,* (2012)

Moreover conservation tillage (CT) practices in pulses also ensure:

- Residue retention increases water storage capacity through *in-situ* soil moisture conservation.
- Short winter window as well as lack of irrigation facilities under rice fallow ecology in lower gangetic plains makes the cool season food legumes (CSFL) vulnerable to terminal stress. In this context, growing of CSFL (e.g. lentil, chickpea etc.) by following of CT practices offer better utilization of residual soil moisture left after rice harvest.

5. TILLAGE EFFECT ON PULSES PRODUCTION

5.1 Growth and yield

Tillage has significant influence on growth parameters and yield of pulse crops. Gill (2013) reported that conventional tillage has increased dry matter production (6.70% and 13.63%), plant height (1.55% and 4.79%), branches/plant (3.77% and 6.54%) and yield (8.09% and 30.65%) over minimum tillage and no tillage in lentil. The highest yield of lentil was recorded with the treatment that received conventional tillage. Banjara *et al* (2017) has conducted a field experiment to see tillage effect rice harvest on chickpea at IGKV, Raipur, Chhattisgarh with 4 tillage treatments. The tillage treatment consists of T_1- Zero tillage direct drilling of seeds and fertilizers at 2nd days after harvesting of rice, T_2 -Minimum tillage and line sowing of seeds at 3rd days after harvesting of rice, T_3-Minimum tillage at 6th days after harvesting of rice, T_4-Farmer practice broadcasting seeds and fertilizer at 12th days after harvesting of rice. The results showed significant difference in yield attributes and yield of chickpea under different tillage management. The significantly higher number of pods/plant and seeds/pod were recorded in minimum tillage and line sowing of seeds at 3rd days after harvesting of rice (Table 2).

Table 2. Yield attributes and yields of chickpea as influenced by tillage practices

Treatment	No. of pods/ plant	No. of seeds/ pod	Seed index (g)	Seed yield (kg/ha)	Stover yield (kg/ha)	Harvest Index (%)
T_1	23.5	1.27	22.43	1109	1553	39.7
T_2	28.3	1.27	22.47	1135	1828	38.3
T_3	22.6	1.20	22.47	930	1446	39.1
T_4	18.3	1.20	22.32	715	1137	38.7

Source: Banjara *et al.* (2017)

In another study on *rabi* crops *viz.,* lentil, field pea, fababean, lathyrus and chickpea sown under zero as well as conventional tillage after rice harvest revealed that all pulses performed equally well under both tillage practices. Similarly in another set of study, performance of chickpea sown after rice in zero tillage (ZT) was at par with conventional tillage, however, retention of rice residue on surface had advantage over no-residue in zero tillage (Table 3).

Table 3. Chickpea productivity after rice under different tillage practices

Crop rotation	Residue management	Tillage practice	
		Zero tillage	Conventional tillage
Rice-chickpea	Residue	2020	2033
	No-residue	1972	1910
Rice-chickpea-mungbean	Residue	2486	2498
	No-residue	2177	2288
Mean		2164	2182

Source: Kumar *et al* (2012)

5.2 Soil moisture conservation

The repeated tillage operations followed under conventional tillage loosen the soil particles which may prone to soil erosion. The use of heavy machineries for tillage operations leads to soil compaction and develop hard pan below plough layer. Tillage operations cause the change in soil bulk density in turn modifies pore size distribution. Thus, tillage directly or indirectly influences the soil hydraulic properties such as water infiltration, hydraulic conductivity, and water retention which determine the ability of the soil to capture and store water through precipitation or irrigation. Therefore, tillage systems conserving *in-situ* water in soil are important for plant growth under rainfed pulses production systems. Conservation tillage systems increase the soil water by reducing evaporation, increasing water infiltration because of crop residues remained on soil surface (Kumar *et al.*, 2012). Dangolani and Narob (2013) reported highest moisture in the no-tillage treatment and the lowest moisture level in the moldboard/disk treatment throughout crop season. Fig 5 indicates the root zone soil moisture storage and soil drying pattern during critical lentil crop growth periods (sowing to harvesting) under different contrasting tillage practices. It also depicts that conventional tillage (CT) faced soil drying earlier than minimum tillage (MT) and no-tillage (NT), especially from flowering period onwards. Treatments NT and MT had significantly ($P<0.05$) higher water use efficiency producing 35.3 kg/ha more seed yield per cm of water as compared with CT. The increase in yield under NT and MT was primarily ascribed to the favourable soil moisture content, which increased the plant growth rate (96% as compared with CT), thereby helping the crop to overcome the terminal drought during the later stages of the growth of lentil (Bandyopadhyay *et al.,* 2018).

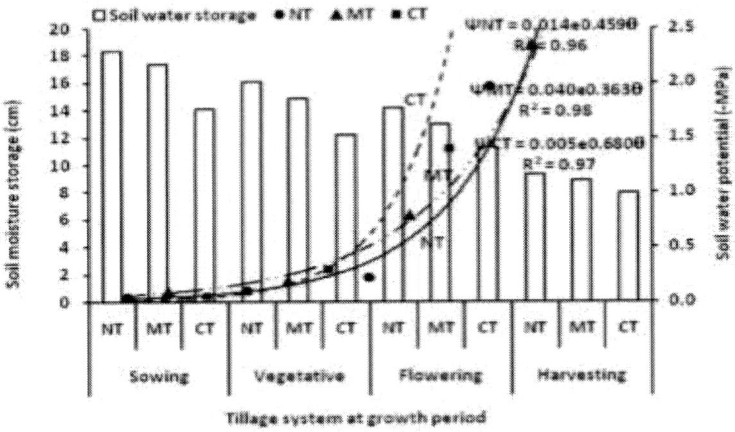

Fig 5. Root-zone (0–60 cm) soil moisture storage and soil drying out pattern during lentil crop growth period under no tillage (NT), minimum tillage (MT) and conventional tillage (CT) practices; Source: Bandyopadhyay *et al.* (2018)

5.3 Root nodulation

Depon the biological nitrogen fixation (BNF) of grain legumes is a strategy to ease the burden that commercial fertilizers exert on poor farmers. The different sized nodules which are present in the root of pulses are mainly responsible for BNF. The amount of nitrogen fixed by grain legumes is affected by the degree of colonization by soil *Rhizobia*, by their interaction with other biological, physical and chemical properties of the soil (Giller *et al.*, 1995). Tillage is among the major practices that influence physical, biological and chemical properties of the soil environment and subsequently affects nitrogen fixation (Kihara *et al.*, 2012). Soil moisture and temperature, which are influenced by tillage, affect nodulation and thus BNF of pulse crops. Studies have indicated that legumes can fix up to 450 kg N/ha/year under optimal field conditions (Giller, 2001). Nitrogen fixation by lentil grown using zero tillage management was 10% higher than when grown using conventional tillage, whereas N-fixation by pea was 31% higher using zero tillage (Matus *et al.*, 1997). Hughes and Herridge (1989) concluded that reduced soil nitrate in zero tillage soils increased N-fixation in soybean, whereas increased levels of soil nitrate under conventional tillage decreased N-fixation (Cowie *et al.,* 1990). Quddus *et al.* (2020) has reported higher nodulation in chickpea under zero-tillage. Kombiok *et al.,* (2013) reported higher nodulation in soybean under deep tillage in comparison to shallow tillage.

5.4 Weed management

Tillage effect on weeds is well established. It is one of the most important factors determining the prevalence of weeds in an agricultural production system. Weed response to tillage system vary with the location and the weed species (Derksen *et al.*, 1996). Tillage affects weeds by uprooting, dismembering and burying them deep in soil to prevent emergence (Clements *et al.*, 1996; Swanton *et al.*, 2000; Kumar *et al.*, 2013). Dixit *et al.* (2015) reported higher weed density under reduced tillage than conventional tillage.

One of the main objectives of summer ploughing is to kill the weeds as well as weed seeds under hot and dry weather. Summer ploughing significantly reduced the density and biomass of purple nutsedge (*Chenopodium album*). In zero tillage, the population of purple nutsedge increased significantly over normal tillage in rice-lentil system. Gopinath *et al.* (2009) reported the benefit of following of state seed bed technique in controlling weeds in pulse crop under organic production systems. Types of soil tillage management also affect the vertical distribution of weed seeds in the soil (Colbach *et al.*, 2014). With the adoption of conservation agricultural practices, weeds are more during initial years. Weed seeds are also confined to surface layer in the soil (Fig 6). Therefore, a well planned strategy should be adopted to control weeds during initial adoption period of conservation tillage.

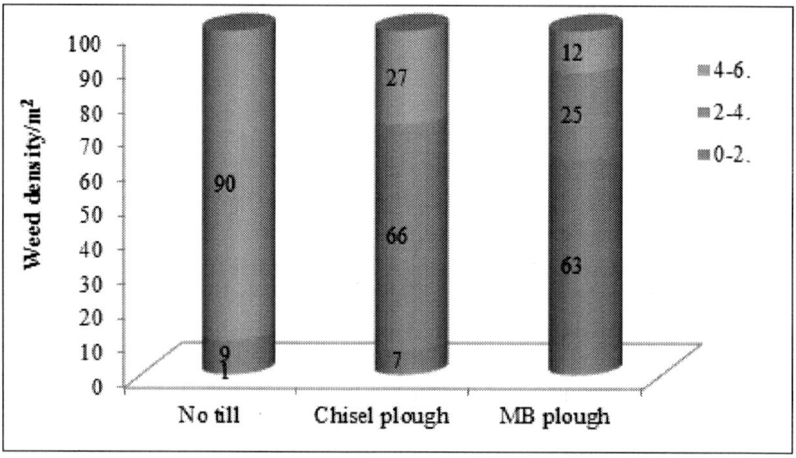

Fig 6. Weed seed population in different soil depth (inches)

(Source: Clements *et al.* 1996)

5.5 Insect-pest and disease management

Tillage and other crop management practices also influence pathogens, insects and the incidence of different diseases in pulses (Bailey *et al.*, 2001). The presence of crop residue on the soil surface in conservation tillage changes the microclimate in the soil and provides substrate for the growth and survival of microbial communities (Bailey and Duczek, 1996). Therefore, the severities of residue-borne pathogens as well as many insects are generally expected to increase as tillage is reduced in pulses and other crop plants. Rootworm (*Diabrotica* sp.) damage was less in no-tillage than in plowed systems in corn. With respect to soil macro-arthropods, herbivore numbers were highest in plowed systems and lowest in no-tillage systems. Spider and cryptostigmata mite density were highest in the no-tillage systems, whereas, in contrast, non-cryptostigmata mite density was highest in fallow—plowed systems (Stenner *et al.*, 1986). The reduced incidence of gram pod borer (*Helicoverpa armigera),* tobacco caterpillar (*Spodoptera litura)* and hairy caterpillar *(Spilosoma obliqua)* in pulse crops were recorded with following of summer tillage (Prasad, 2014). The diseases of pulses like wilt, collar rot, yellow mosaic disease and powdery mildew can also be prevented by continuous practice of summer/deep ploughing with different implements or following reduced tillage.

6. CONCLUSION

Pulses being an important part of food nutrition, there is an urgent need to match improved pulse production to the increasing population through intensification of sustainable land management strategies. The conventional approaches of soil perturbation have been reported largely as unsustainable and non-ecofriendly. Tillage management through improved techniques can be a viable option in mitigating several issues regarding soil management. Different international and national institutions are in favor of less disturbing the soil especially in the fine textured and poorly drained soil to improve its properties. Tillage practices like minimum tillage, zero tillage and conservation tillage seems to be beneficial in terms of soil physico-chemical health and well as soil microbial activities. Apart from the soil health these improved tillage practices are known for their reduced soil and water runoff. Though there are contradictory reports, the reduced or conservation tillage practices are reported to be sustainable in long run. The highly concerned issue to global climate change and greenhouse gas emission is also well addressed by conservation tillage practices. Hence, it can be concluded that utilization of newly reformed tillage practices in the field can revamp the soil health in marginal and poor soil. The improvement in soil health could improve the pulses production and the living standard of the farmers in a longer run.

REFERENCES

AICRPDA (2011) Annual Report, All India Coordinated Research Project for Dryland Agriculture, CRIDA, and Hyderabad. pp. 420.

Arya, R.L., Singh, K.K. and Kumar, L. (2002) Indian Institute of Pulses Research, Kanpur, India.

Bailey, K.L. and Duczek, L.J. (1996) Managing cereal diseases under reduced tillage. *Canadian Journal of Plant Pathology*18, 159–167.

Bailey, K.L., Gossen, B.D., Lafond, G.P., Watson, P.R. and Derksen, D.A. (2001) Effect of tillage and crop rotation on root and foliar diseases of wheat and pea in Saskatchewan from 1991 to 1998: Univariate and multivariate analyses. *Canadian Journal of Plant Science* 81, 789–803.

Bandyopadhyay, P.K., Halder, S., Mondal, K., Singh, K.C., Nandi, R. and Ghosh, P.K. (2018) Response of Lentil (*Lens culinaries*) to Post-rice Residual Soil Moisture under Contrasting Tillage Practices. *Agricultural Research.* DOI 10.1007/s40003-018-0337-3.

Bandyopadhyay, P.K., Singh, K.C., Mondal, K., Nath, R., Ghosh, P.K., Kumar, N., Basu, P.S. and Singh, S.S. (2016) Effects of stubble length of rice in mitigating soil moisture stress and on yield of lentil (*Lens culinaris* Medik) in rice-lentil relay crop. *Agricultural Water Management* 173, 91-102.

Banjara, T.R., Pali, G.P., Tigga, B.K., Kumar, S. and Shori, A. (2017) Effect of Different Tillage Practices on Growth, Yield and Economics of Chickpea (*Cicer arietinum* L.) under Rainfed Condition of Chhattisgarh. *International Journal of Current Microbiology and Applied Sciences* 6(2), 1464-1470.

Barzegar, A.R., Asoodar, M.A., Khadish, A., Hashemi, A.M. and Herbert, S.J. (2002) Soil physical characteristics and chickpea yield responses to tillage treatments. *Soil and Tillage Research* 71, 49-57.

Bennett, J.M. and Albrecht, S.L. (1984) Drought and flooding effects on N fixation, water relations, and diffusive resistance of soybean. *Agronomy Journal* 76, 735–740.

Clements, D.R., Benoit, D.L., Murphy, S.D. and Swanton, C.J. (1996) Tillage effect on weed seed return and seed bank composition. *Weed Science* 44, 314-322.

Colbach, N., Busset, H., Roger-Estrade, J. and Caneill, J. (2014) Predictive modelling of weed seed movement in response to superficial tillage tools. *Soil and Tillage Research* 138, 1-8.

Dangolani, S.K. and Narob, M.C. (2013) The effect of four types of tillage operations on soil moisture and morphology and performance of three varieties of cotton. *European Journal of Experimental Biology* 3(1), 694-698.

Das, T.K., Choudhary, A.K., Sepat, S., Vyas, A.K., Das, A., Bana, R.S. and Pooniya, V. (2014) Conservation agriculture: A sustainable alternative to enhance agricultural productivity and resources-use efficiency. Technical Extension Folder, Indian Agricultural Research Institute, New Delhi, India.

Derksen, D.A., Blackshaw, R.E. and Boyetchko, S.M. (1996) Sustainability, conservation tillage and weeds in Canada. *Canadian Journal of Plant Science* 76, 651-659.

Dixit, A.K., Kumar, S., Rai, A.K. and Kumar, T.K. (2015) System productivity, profitability, nutrient uptake and soil health under tillage, nutrient and weed management in rainfed chickpea (*Cicer arietinum*)–fodder sorghum (S*orghum bicolour*) cropping system. *Indian Journal of Agronomy* 60(2), 205-211.

Doran, J.W. (1980) Soil microbial and biochemical changes associated with reduced tillage. *Soil Science Society of America Journal* 44, 765–771.

Feng, Y., Motta, A.C., Burmester, C.H., Reeves, D.W., Santen, E. and Osborne, J.A. (2002) Effect of Tillage Systems on Soil Microbial Community Structure Under A Continuous Cotton Cropping System. Proceedings of 25th Annual Southern Conservation Tillage Conference for Sustainable Agriculture. pp. 222-226.

Ghosh, P.K., Mohanty, M., Bandyopadhyay, K.K., Painuli, D.K. and Misra, A.K. (2006) Growth, competition, yield advantage and economics in soybean/pigeonpea intercropping system in semi-arid tropics of India: I. Effect of subsoiling. *Field Crops Research* 96(1), 80-89.

Gill J.S. (2013) Yield, protein and nutrient uptake in grain as influenced by sowing dates and tillage systems in lentil (*Lens culinaris* Medik.). *Crop Research* 46(1to3), 99-101.

Giller, K.E. (2001) Nitrogen Fixation in Tropical Cropping Systems, 2nd edn. CAB International, Wallingford.

Giller, K.E., Cadisch, G. (1995) Future benefits from biological nitrogen fixation: An ecological approach to agriculture. *Plant Soil* 174, 255-277.

Gopinath, K.A., Kumar, N., Mina, B.L., Srivastva, A.K. and Gupta, H.S. (2009) Evaluation of mulching, stale seedbed, hand weeding and hoeing for weed control in organic garden pea (*Pisum sativum* Sub Sp. Hortens L.). *Archives of Agronomy and Soil Science* 55(1), 115-123.

Haque, M.E., Esdaile, R.J., Kabir, E., Vance, W., Bell, R.W., Musa, A.M., Shahidullah, A.K.M., Mia, M.N.N., Maruffuzaman, M. and Johansen, C. (2010) Minimum-tillage, mechanized sowing of pulses with two-wheel tractors. In 'Proceedings of the 19th World Congress of Soil Science, Soil Solutions for a Changing World', 1-6 August, 2010. Brisbane, Australia. pp. 156-159.

Hughes, R.M. and Herridge, D.F. (1989) Effect of tillage on yield, nodulation and nitrogen fixation of soybean in far north-coastal New South Wales. *Australian Journal of Experimental Agriculture* 29(5), 671-677.

ICMR. (2010) Nutrient Requirement and Recommended Dietary Allowances for Indians-A Report of the Expert Group of the Indian council of Medical Research. National Institute of Nutrition, Hyderabad.

IPGA. (2018) Pulse sector in India. *http://ipga.co.in/pulse-growth-in-indian-region/ Accessed 10 May 2018.*

Kar, G. and Kumar, A. (2009) Evaluation of post-rainy season crops with residual soil moisture and different tillage methods in rice fallow of eastern India. *Agricultural Water Management* 96(6), 931-938.

Kar, G. and Kumar, A. (2009) Evaluation of post-rainy season crops with residual soil moisture and different tillage methods in rice fallow of eastern India. *Agricultural Water Management* 96, 931-938.

Khan, S.A. and Chatterjee, B.N. (1987) Multiple cropping in rainfed upland entisol under different soil management conditions in the sub-humid tropics. *Soil and Tillage Research* 9(2), 135-150.

Kihara, J., Bationo, A., Waswa, B., Kimetu, J.M., Vanlauwe, B., Okeyo, J., Mukalama, J. andMartius, C. (2012) Effect of reduced tillage and mineral fertilizer application on maize and soybean productivity. *Experimental Agriculture* 48(2), 159-175.

Kombiok, J.M. and Buah, S.S.J. (2013) Tillage depth effects on nodulation, nitrogen fixation and yield of three soybean varieties in the Northern Savanna zone of Ghana. *African Journal of Agricultural Research* 8(20), 2340-2345.

Kumar, M., Naik, B.M., Karthika, M., Kumar, N. and Kumar, A. (2019) Effect of Tillage and Nutrient Management Practices on Yield and Economics of Rice (*Oryza sativa*)-Maize (*Zea mays*) Cropping System in North Bihar. *International Journal of Current Microbiology and Applied Sciences* 8(3), 1365-1370.

Kumar, N., Hazra, K.K. and Yadav, S.K. (2014) Issues related to weed management in RCT. In- Ghosh PK, Narendra Kumar, Venkatesh MS, Hazra KK and Nadarajan N (Ed.) Resource Conservation Technology in Pulses. Scientific Publisher, Jodhpur. pp. 567-575.

Kumar, N., Hazra, K.K., Singh, M.K., Venkatesh, M.S., Kumar, L.,Singh, J. and Nadarajan, N. (2013) Weed management Techniques in Pulse Crops. *Technical Bulletin 10/2013.* Indian Institute of Pulses Research, Kanpur. 47 pages.

Kumar, N., Hazra, K.K., Singh, S. and Nadarajan, N. (2016) Constraints and prospects of growing pulses in rice fallows of India. *Indian Farming* 66(6), 13-16.

Kumar, N., Singh, M.K., Ghosh, P.K., Hazra, K.K., Venkatesh, M.S. and Nadarajan, N.(2012) Resource Conservation Technology in Pulse based Cropping Systems. (*Technical Bulletin 1/2012*), Indian Institute of Pulses Research, Kanpur. 35 pages.

Kumar, R., Arya, R.L. and Mishra, J.P. (2006) Effect of seed priming and tillage management on productivity of chickpea (*Cicer arietinum)* genotypes under rainfed conditions. *Indian Journal of Agronomy* 51(1), 54-56.

Lafond, C. P., Loeppfy, H. and Derksen, D.A. (1992) The effects of tillage system and crop rotations on soil water conservation, seedling establishment and crop yield. *Canadian Journal of Plant Science* 72, 103-lI5.

Lopez-Bellido, L., Lopez-Bellido, R.J., Castillo, J.E. and Lopez-Bellido, F.J. (2004) Chickpea response to tillage and soil residual nitrogen in a continuous rotation with wheat: I. Biomass and seed yield. *Field Crops Research* 88(2-3), 191-200.

Lupwayi, N.Z., Rice, W.A. and Clayton, G.W. (1999) Soil microbial biomass and carbon dioxide flux under wheat as influenced by tillage and crop rotation. *Canadian Journal of Soil Science* 79, 273–280.

Matus, A., Derksen, D.A., Walley, F.L., Loeppky, H.A. and van Kessel, C. (1997) The influence of tillage and crop rotation on nitrogen fixation in lentil and pea. *Canadian Journal of Plant Science* 77(2), 197-200.

Ministry of Women and Child Development (MoWCD) (2011). Report on the Working Group on Nutrition for The 12th Five year plan (2012- 2017). Government of India. Retrieved from *http://planningcommission.gov.in /aboutus/committee/wrkgrp12/ wcd/ wgrep_nutition.pdf.*

Nazeer, S., Malik, A.U., Nazir, G. and Ahmad, J. (2012) Effectiveness of tillage systems and farm manure levels on rice productivity. *The Journal of Animal & Plant Sciences* 22(2), 334-338.

Ogle, S., Breidt, M.F.J. and Paustian, K. (2005) Agricultural management impacts on soil organic carbon storage in temperate and tropical systems. *Biochemistry* 72, 87-12.

Pooniya, V., Choudhary, A.K., Dass, A., Bana, R.S., Rana, K.S., Rana, D.S., Tyagi, V.K. and Puniya, M.M. (2015) Improved crop management practices for sustainable pulse production: An Indian perspective. *Indian Journal of Agricultural Sciences* 85(6), 747–758.

Prasad, T.V. (2014) Handbook of Entomology. New Vishal Publications, New Delhi. pp. 340- 343.

Quddus, M.A., Naser, H.M., Siddiky, M.A., Ali, M.R., Mondol, A.T.M.A.I and Islam, M.A. (2020) Impact of Zero Tillage and Tillage Practice in Chickpea Production. *Journal of Agricultural Science* 12(4), 106-118.

Ramdath, D., Renwick, S. and Duncan, A.M. (2016) The Role of Pulses in the Dietary Management of Diabetes. *Canadian Journal of Diabetes* 40(4) 355–363.

Rana, D.S., Dass, A., Rajanna, G.A. and Kaur, R. (2016) Biotic and Abiotic stress management in pulses. *Indian Journal of Agronomy* 61(4th IAC Special issue), S238-S248.

Reddy, K.N., Zablotowicz, R.M., Locke, M.A. and Koger, C.H. (2003) Cover crop, tillage and herbicide effects on weeds, soil properties, microbial populations and soybean yield. *Weed Science* 51, 987-994.

Saxena, A., Singh, D.V. and Joshi, N.L. (1997) Effects of Tillage and Cropping Systems on Soil Moisture Balance and Pearl Millet Yield. *Journal of Agronomy and Crop Science* 178(4), 251-257.

Sharma, P.K., De Datta, S.K. and Redulla, C.A. (1988) Response of maize and mungbean to tillage in relation to water table depth in tropical low land rice soils. *Soil and Tillage Research* 12, 65-79.

Stenner, B.R., Krueger H.R. and McCartney, D.A. (1986) Insecticide and tillage effects on pest and non-pest arthropods in corn agroecosystems. *Agriculture, Ecosystems & Environment* 15(1), 11-21.

Swanton, C.J., Shrestha, A., Knezevic, S.Z., Roy, R.C. and Ball-Coelho, B.R. (2000) Influence of tillage types on vertical weed seedbank distribution in a sandy soil. *Canadian Journal of Plant Science* 80, 455-457.

Thompson, H.J., Heimendinger, J., Haegele, A., Sedlacek, S.M., Gillette, C., O'Neill, C., Wolfe, P. and Conry, C. (1999) Effect of increased vegetable and fruit consumption on markers of oxidative cellular damage. *Carcinogenesis* 20, 2261-2266.

Uysal, O. and Subaþý, O.S. (2014) A study on determination of strategy for pulse industry through SWOT and SOR analyses in Mersin Province. *Turkish Journal of Agriculture- Food Science and Technology* 2(6), 256-259.

Vadi, H.D., Kachot, N.A., Polara, J.V., Sekh, M.A. and Kikani, V.L. (2006) Effect of tillage and mulching on yield and yield attributing chatacters of pigeon pea. *Advances in Plant Sciences* 19(2), 497–499.

Venkateswarlu, B., Mishra, P.K., Ravindra Chary, G., MaruthiSankar, G.R. and Subba Reddy, G. (2009) Rainfed farming – A compendium of improved technologies. All India Coordinated Research Project for Dryland Agriculture, CRIDA, Hyderabad. pp. 132.

Vohra, K., Dureja, H., and Garg, V. (2015) An Insight of Pulses: From Food to Cancer Treatment. *Journal of Pharmacognosy and Natural Products* 1,108.

CHAPTER 7

Management strategies for enhancing phosphorus use efficiency in pulse crops

Asik Dutta, Narendra Kumar, C.P. Nath, K.K. Hazra and C.S. Praharaj

ICAR- Indian Institute of Pulses Research, Kanpur-208024

*Corresponding author email: asikdutta975@gmail.com

Abstract

Phosphorus (P), being an essential nutrient for plant growth and productivity but, due to its complex reaction with different soil constituents its availability to the crops is highly limited. Global P-reserves are highly finite and depleting at an alarmingly faster rate. In India high quality rock phosphate (32% P_2O_5) is concentrated only in a few states and almost entirely dependent on foreign imports. Studies reported 58% (20 out of 34 states) of the Indian states are low in soil available P due to intensive agriculture, mono-cropping, faulty agricultural practices, residue removal and unavailability of crop varieties with higher phosphorus use efficiency (PUE). India due to its agro-climatic conditions provides cultivating ground for all kinds of pulses. Pulses are excellent user of native and applied P due to its root mediated characteristics like secretion of different enzymes and exudates. So, to reduce the dependency on foreign imports inclusion of pulses in the cropping system with use of modern agronomic and microbial interventions such as, resource conservation technologies, reclaiming the problem soils, use of microbial inoculants are need of the hour. Modern technologies like breeding of pulses for higher PUE vis-à-vis intervening molecular techniques are surely edge over the conventional methods and improve PUE.

Keywords: Apatite, Conservation agriculture, Micro-organisms, P-pools, P-use efficiency, Rhizospere, Rock phosphate

1. INTRODUCTION

Phosphorus (P) is the second most important nutrient after nitrogen (N), but shares only 0.13% (11th most abundant element) in the earth's crust. Phosphorus is the known as fulcrum of Indian agriculture, curbing the crop production by 40% (Dey *et al*., 2017). Soil-P concentration hardly exceeds 10^{-6} M in the soil solution due to P adsorption with different soil components (oxides and hydroxides) depending on the pH (Batjes *et al*., 1997). Plants mostly take primary ortho-phosphate ($H_2PO_4^-$) but, with increasing pH it is evident that some plants also use the secondary orthophosphate (HPO_4^{2-}) ion too. The major source of P in the universe is phosphate rock (PR) or apatite which is mainly of sedimentary origin. Depending on the co-precipitated molecule apatite has been classified mainly of four types namely- 1. Fluoroapatite [$Ca_5(PO_4)_3F$], 2. Chloroapatite [$Ca_5(PO_4)_3Cl$]

3. Hydroxyapatite [$Ca_5(PO_4)_3OH$] and 4. Francolite or most commonly carbonate apatite [$Ca_5(PO_4)_3CO_3$]. Countries with major deposits of PR reserve are China, Morocco, Russia, Peru, USA, Jordan, Egypt although, India holds a very few amount of PR reserve, fulfilling the domestic needs from foreign imports. In India PR found in patches like Purulia (West Bengal), Parts of Madhya Pradesh and Chhattisgarh and Rajasthan, whereas, only high grade PR (P_2O_5 content is > 30%) is found only in the later.

Phosphorus in the soil present in the organic and inorganic forms although former is most dominant than the latter. The proportion of organic and inorganic P in the soil is about 20-80% and 54-84% of the total P, respectively (Sanyal *et al.*, 2015). The range of total P in Indian soil is between 120- 2166 mg kg^{-1} and it depends on the soil minerology, cropping practise, organic matter content etc. (Sanyal *et al.*, 2015). Mostly soils derived from granite gneiss than other metamorphosed rock like limestone, shales generally rich in total P but, it is very ambiguous to say that high available P is linked with high total P content in the soil. In order to classify the soil P status of Indian soils, Ministry of statistics and Programme Implementation, GOI characterised the Indian soils based on nutrient index approach (Parker *et al.*, 1951, Ministry of Statistics and Programme Implementation (http://mospi.gov.in/), 2019). Details of the state and union territories with soil P level are given in Table 1. From this table it can be inferred that only 20 out of 34 (58%) states and districts reported low P content and only 2 states (Andhra Pradesh and West Bengal) showed adequate P content in the soil pointing out the importance of P-management for sustainable crop production. It is important to develop important work plan for harnessing adequate productivity given utmost care to our soils. Also, wider range of regional variation exists while summarising nation level reports but, many times it's getting masked. So, there is need of more exhaustive district or block level datasets with minimal error for implementing successful farmer policies.

Table 1. Soil P status of all the states and union territories of India (MOSPI, GOI, 2019).

States	Cycle-I (2015-17)			Cycle-II (2017-19)		
	Low	Medium	High	Low	Medium	High
A & N Islands	*			*		
Andhra Pradesh			*			*
Arunachal Pradesh	*			*		
Assam	*			*		
Bihar		*			*	
Chhattisgarh		*			*	
D & N Nagar Haveli	*			*		
Daman And Diu	—	—	—	*		
Delhi	*			*		
Goa	*			*		
Gujarat		*			*	
Haryana	*			*		
Himachal Pradesh		*			*	
Jammu & Kashmir	*			*		

Jharkhand	*			*		
Karnataka		*			*	
Kerala		*			*	
Madhya Pradesh	*			*		
Maharashtra		*			*	
Manipur	*			*		
Mizoram	*			*		
Meghalaya	*			*		
Nagaland	*			*		
Odisha	*			*		
Puducherry	*			*		
Punjab	*			*		
Rajasthan		*		*		
Sikkim		*		*		
Tamil Nadu		*		*		
Telangana	*			*		
Tripura	*			*		
Uttar Pradesh	*			*		
Uttarakhand		*		*		
West Bengal			*			*

2. PRODUCTION AND CONSUMPTION OF P FERTILIZER IN INDIA

As a nation of 1.3 billion people, there is a huge burden on Indian agriculture to feed its people through sustainable intensification and to do so there must be unhindered supply of plant nutrients especially P. There are mainly two kind of raw materials used for P fertilizer production- 1. Apatite and 2. Rock phosphate. In India, apatite mining is restricted in two states namely Andhra Pradesh and West Bengal whereas, all together other 4 mines, three in Madhya Pradesh (one in each Chhatarpur, Sagar and Jhabua districts) and one in Rajasthan (Udaipur) are responsible for rock phosphate mining. As of now India depends entirely (~90%) on foreign countries for either ores or finished products like di- or mono- ammonium phosphate (Indian Minerals Yearbook, 2016). If we look into the statistics from 2010 onwards (Fig. 1) there is a huge gap between production and consumption of P fertilisers and at the same time apatite production declined drastically by almost cent percent from 2000-01 to 2015-16 (Fig. 2). So to cope up the challenge of 'peak phosphorus' Government of India, apart from importing either raw or finished products, adopted some crucial steps like collaborative work with nation's rich rock phosphate reserve and strengthen *in-situ* production with imported inputs (Saeid *et al.*, 2014, Indian Minerals Yearbook, 2016).

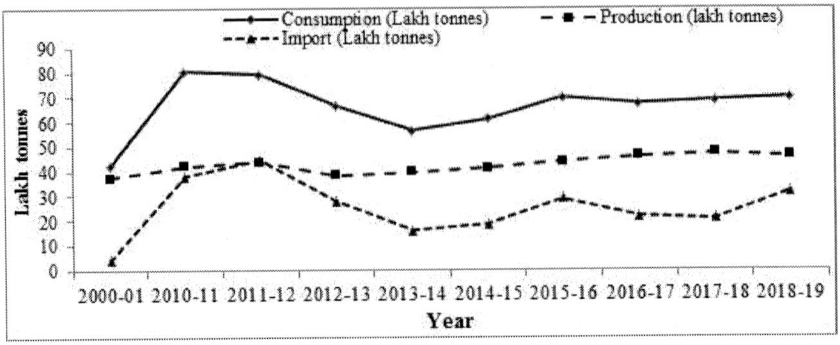

Fig. 1. Production, consumption and import of phosphate fertilisers in India

(*Source: DES, Ministry of Agriculture and Farmers Welfare, GOI*)

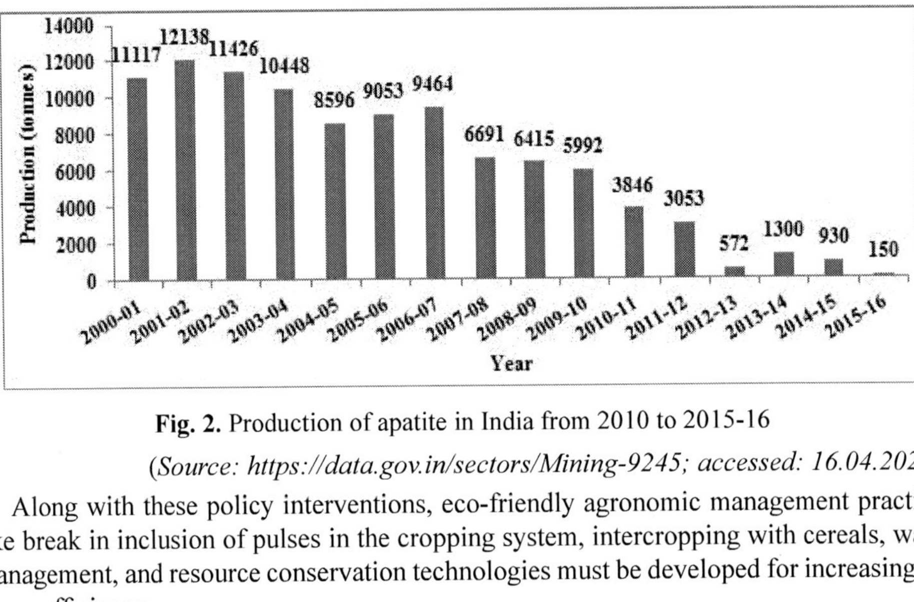

Fig. 2. Production of apatite in India from 2010 to 2015-16

(*Source: https://data.gov.in/sectors/Mining-9245; accessed: 16.04.2020*)

Along with these policy interventions, eco-friendly agronomic management practices like break in inclusion of pulses in the cropping system, intercropping with cereals, waste management, and resource conservation technologies must be developed for increasing the P-use efficiency.

3. IMPORTANCE OF P IN PULSES

Phosphorus regulates a whole set of physiological activities for example root growth, indispensable structural component of bio-chemical compounds like, nucleic acids (DNA and RNA), phospholipids, phosphoproteins etc., storing the light energy in the form of chemical energy adenosine diphosphate (ADP), adenosine tri phosphate (ATP) during photosynthesis, carry forward the genetic material from one generation to another and transferring the nutrients (Jin *et al.*, 2015). The normal P concentration in the plant varies from 0.1-0.5%. Hence, P deficiency in the soil hampers the normal crop growth and metabolism (Zhang *et al.*, 2014). Phosphorus deficiency symptoms are stunted growth and reduced tillers in cereals. Often, but not in all cultivars, older leaves becomes narrow, short, very erect and development of dark green of purplish pigmentation on the leaves due to anthocyanin pigmentation (Tisdale *et al.*, 1993). Pulses fundamentally legumes are important part of sustainable integrated farming system as they are highly resource efficient (Suzaki *et al.*, 2015). But, many biotic and abiotic facets muddle the unique symbiotic relationship with the nature like drought, salinity, pH, extreme temperature and nutrient deficiency. Among the nutrients P comes first as it is important part of biological nitrogen fixation (BNF). Apart from BNF other important role of P in pulses are-(i) Boost vegetative growth and leaf area development (Sulieman *et al.*, 2013), (ii) Better carbon absorption and distribution in above and below ground plant part (Zhang *et al.*, 2014), (iii) Convey the metabolic energy to nodules during BNF (Suzaki *et al.*, 2015, Cabeza *et al.*, 2014),(iv) Commercial seed production (Akram *et al.*, 2017), 5. Elevating the root growth (Niu *et al.*, 2012), (vi) Resistance to the soil borne root disease (Laliberte *et al.*, 2015) and (vii) Increasing stalk and stem robustness (Khan *et al.*, 2008).

P-deficiency symptoms of Chickpea

P-deficiency symptoms of fieldpea

(*Image courtesy: Google*)

Deficiency symptoms of P in the pulses are:

- Obstruct in the normal BNF cycling pathways due to poor N transformation and enzymatic activities (Zhang *et al.*, 2014).
- Reduction in the rate of plant metabolism, nutrient translocation in the above ground parts of plant hampering the source-sink pathways (Chaudhary *et al.*, 2008).
- Plant respiratory activities and glycolysis pathway affected severely under P deficiency (Chaudhary *et al.*, 2008).
- Curtailing in photosynthetic rate and nucleic acids (DNA and RNA) synthesis pathways (Yadav *et al.*, 2017).
- One of the major drawbacks of poor P supplementation is that nodule degeneration. Phosphorus is important in energy transfer and transforming ammonium ($-NH4^{+}$) in to aminoacids and ureids during the BNF so, as a result P deficiency cutback the nodular activity in legumes so forth the plant growth and metabolism (Sulieman *et al.*, 2014).

4. PHOSPHORUS USE EFFICIENCY

Phosphorus use efficiency (PUE) is one of the heavily discussed but, still a debateable issue as there is still a lot of confusion regarding its nomenclature. Basically, on one side absence of proper definition and on another side multiple definitions exists which makes it more ambiguous in addition, multiple term and acronyms makes the situation more worst such as, PUE can be used as P-uptake efficiency (Jones *et al.*, 1992) or as P-use efficiency (Parentoni and Junior, 2008). Apart from this, these acronyms used by different authors to justify different points for example P-efficiency ratio (PER) used for expressing multiple points (Table 2). So, we need some robust terminologies for a clear understanding and at the same time about contradictions.

Table 2. Different definitions with their units and criteria used for assessing P-use efficiency

Definition and units	Terminology	Reference
Grain yield per unit of P accumulated in shoots at maturity (kg grain g^{-1}P)	P-efficiency ratio (PER)	Jones *et al.* (1992)
	P- internal utilization efficiency (PUTIL)	Parentoni and Junior (2008)
	P utilization efficiency quotient (PEQ)	Romer and Schenk (1998)
	P utilization efficiency (PUE)	Yaseen and Malhi (2009a)
	P physiological efficiency index (PPEI)	Ahmad *et al.* (2001)
	Physiological P use efficiency (PPUE)	Manske *et al.* (2001, 2002)
	Phosphorus utilization efficiency (PUTE)	Yaseen and Malhi (2009b)
	P-efficiency ratio (PER)	
Shoot dry matter per unit P accumulated (g DM mg^{-1}P)	Internal phosphorus utilization efficiency (PUE)	Rose *et al.* (2011)
	Phosphorus utilization efficiency (PUE)	Oracka and Lapinski (2006)
Shoot DM/shoot P concentration (g^{2}DM mg^{-1}P)	Phosphorus utilization efficiency (PUTE)	Sepehr *et al.* (2009)
	Phosphorus utilization index (PUI)	Yaseen and Malhi (2009b)
	Phosphorus utilization efficiency (PUE)	Gorny (1999); Gourlay *et al.* (1994)
Tissue P concentration required for 90% maximum yield	Physiological phosphorus use efficiency (PPUE)	Hammond *et al.* (2009); Chen *et al.* (2009)

5. PHOSPHORUS POOLS IN PULSES

Phosphorus (P) in the plant is mainly present in two forms namely inorganic (Pi) and organic (Po) forms. Inorganic orthophosphate ions (Pi) mostly present in tissues in two distinct compartments such as (i) Cytoplasmic Pi which is metabolically active and mostly controls the tissue Pi level (0.1-0.8 mg P g^{-1} of dry weight) and (ii) Vacuole Pi which act as a buffer for the tissue or cellular Pi (Veneklaas *et al.*, 2012). A study by Lauer *et al.* (1989) in soybean showed that in absence of external P supply in the full bloom stage vacuolar Pi concentration reduced by almost cent percent although, tissue Pi concentration dropped but not markedly from 8.3mM to 0.23 mM. Coming to organic P pools its predominant pools are nucleic acids, phospholipids, phosphoesters, and phosphorylated proteins although, a school of scientist thought that because of regulatory mechanism of phosphorylated proteins it no longer part of organic P pools (Veneklaas *et al.*, 2012). Highlighting the organic P pools, nucleic acids (mostly ribosomal RNA and a small extent of tRNA and mRNA) make up the organic P pools in plants. The share of nucleic acid in plants is about

40-60% of the total P i.e. 0.3-2 mg P g^{-1} of dry weight depending on crop type, agronomic management and plant P supply (Tachibana, 1987). One of the major opportunities for increasing PUE is to optimize protein synthesis. Other than this, membrane phospholipids constitute a portion of organic P in plants.

6. MANAGEMENT STRATEGIES FOR INCREASING PUE

6.1 Agronomic interventions

Reactions products derived from applied fertilizes with different soil constituents make a dynamic relation with soil P pools and govern P availability. The two most important points of utilising this stored pools are: (i) agronomic interventions and (ii) crops ability to forage the P-bank. Pulses are the excellent utilisers of this native pools because they are well responsive to the interventions and root system with some unique traits. So, here under some of the well proven agronomic interventions for PUE are discussed from pulse cultivation points of view.

6.1.1 4Rs of nutrient management

4R of nutrient management is the key to success for increasing nutrient use efficiency of any nutrient. The 4R is an acronym for four basic principles for increasing nutrient use efficiency, i.e. right time, the right method, right source, and right rate. P-application as a basal during sowing is most widely practicable. There are some experiments tried for split or delayed application of P but, results were not fruitful and highly inconsistent. The reasons for these shortfalls are the initial amount of available P in the soils, fluctuation in soil temperature regimes and disease and pest infestation. The major form of P loss in the soil is a fixation with carbonates and oxides and hydroxides of iron and aluminium. So, to minimize the loss it is recommended to apply soluble P fertilizers through drilling or band placements over broadcasting although, the success of achieving higher use efficiency is highly dependent on soil attributes (Sanchez *et al.*, 1991; Valizadeh *et al.*, 2003). Unlike N, phosphorus in the soil moves via diffusion, but the diffusion coefficient of phosphate (P_2O_5) is 1000 times lower in the later than the former (Marschner, 2011) as a result of this P-fertilisers should be placed as much as close to the roots. Banding is specifically effective in dry soils where precipitation is a major issue (McLaughlin *et al.*, 2011). For harnessing the maximum use efficiency it is necessary to have adequate moisture in the soil so that the nutrient can diffuse easily and the roots can forage it easily. Therefore, placement and efficacy of P are highly correlated with moisture, in succession result of texture, structure, tillage management, cropping history, and pattern (Ma *et al.*, 2009). Newer, application methods like foliar fertigation are in the trail but, more field trials with robust outcomes should be needed for its large scale application particularly for pulses (Noack *et al.*, 2011). Given the level of competition between plant and soil for P, applying the nutrient to the leaves of a crop represents an easy and recommendable practice but, it should be properly validated before application. The right rate or dose of P fertilizer can be achieved through scientific soil testing procedures. For, P depending on the soil reaction (pH) Olsen-P (Olsen *et al.*, 1954) for neutral to the alkaline range and for acidic soil Bray P1 (Bray and Kurtz, 1945) is mostly adapted. Other important P-testing procedures are Colwell P (Colwell, 1963), Mehlich-3 P (Mehlich, 1984), Mehlich No.1 (Mehlich, 1953),

Morgan reagent (Wolf, 1982), AB-DTPA (Soltanpour and Schwab, 1977), etc. Apart from soil test values plant requirement, soil type, cropping system, weather condition of the experiment site should be considered while calculating the dose. The phosphate (P_2O_5) requirement of different pulse crops is given in Table 3. It is always a great challenge to choose the right source of nutrients for a specific group of crops that is always challenging. The most commonly used P-fertiliser for pulses is diammonium phosphate (DAP) because of its easy availability throughout India. Unlike N, the losses due to leaching of P is very low still to minimize the losses relatively less soluble materials like phosphate rock can be used to trimming down the chances of eutrophication (Hart *et al.*, 2004). Besides, this rock phosphate is highly effective for acidic soils where P-fixation is a huge issue specifically in the tropics (Chein *et al.*, 2009). From, Indian perspective as our rock phosphate reserves are not of high grade, it can be utilized for dual purpose of reclamation as well as source of P alone or in combination with a water-soluble source. Transforming rock phosphate by partial acidulation, mixture with elemental sulfur (S), co-application with some phosphorus solubilizing bacteria (PSB), can be tried for making it more applicable in the fields (Prochnow *et al.*, 2008; Evans and Condon, 2009). In the case of pulses, root mediated acidification could solubilize the phosphate and increase uptake. Pulses secret a sizeable amount of organic acids and phosphates enzymes (acid and alkaline phosphatase) which in turn promote P-uptake and increase PUE (Veneklaas *et al.*, 2003).

The advanced fertilizer technology or improved agronomic practices like soil application of P-fertilisers with organic acids (humic and fulvic acids) is now practiced so that the organic moiety of the acids acts as a chelating agent for the metal cations that would act as a binding site for P (Gordon and Tindall, 2006; Cornish, 2009). Karamanos and Puurveen (2011) reported like neem coated urea, coating the P-fertilisers with polymers significantly increases the yield of cereals. But the efficacy of the coated materials in the field condition should be thoroughly checked in case of pulses. Recently, fluid P (phosphoric acid or ammonium polyphosphate) has gained momentum as an alternate P source and may be better over the granular depending on the soil condition (Hettiarachchi *et al.*, 2006). McLaughlin *et al* (2011) found a significantly higher performance of liquid MAP over its granular form. The reason they stated, that due to a higher concentration of P_2O_5 and slower reactivity, its chelation with different metal cations is lower over its counterpart making it highly useful for the tropical and sub-tropical soils.

Table 3. Phosphate dose of important pulse crops in India

Crops	**Phosphate dose (kg P_2O_5/ha)**
Blackgram (*Vigna mungo* L.)	25 (rainfed) 50 (irrigated)
Greengram (*Vigna radiata* L.)	25 (rainfed) 50 (irrigated)
Chickea (*Cicer arietinum* L.)	25 (rainfed) 50 (irrigated)
Redgram (*Cajanus cajan* (L.) Millsp.)	25 (rainfed) 50 (irrigated)
Field pea (*Pisum sativum* var. arvense L.)	50
Soybean (*Glycine max* (L.) Merr.)	80
Lentil (*Lens culinaris* L.)	60-70
Cowpea (*Vigna unguiculata* (L.) Walp. aggreg.)	25 (rainfed) 50 (irrigated)

6.1.2 Organic and inorganic amendments

Incorporation of organic and inorganic amendments like crop residue, green manuring, farm wastes are highly relevant for improving physicochemical and biological properties of the soil hence plant growth by improving soil organic matter, microbial activity and nutritional status. Research by Pooniya and Shivay (2013) showed that periodic incorporation of *dhaincha* (*Sesbania aculeata* L.), cowpea and mungbean green manuring improved soil macro- and micro- nutrient content also typically helpful for sustaining crop growth in long run system. Intercropping of sesbania with cowpea enhances main crop yield and crop growth (Bana *et al.*, 2012). Manures apart from directly supplying nutrients to the soil helps to build a soil organic carbon content (SOC) and Chan *et al.* (2010) found that there is a strong positive relationship between SOC and fertiliser P-use efficiency. Manures generally contain more than 2/3rd (50-90%) of total P in the labile inorganic form and typically holds a sufficient amount of organic P too which on due course of time transforms into Pi through microbial solubilisation (Turner, 2004; Shen *et al.*, 2011). As previously discussed the negatively charged organic moiety (e.g., carboxyl and hydroxyl groups) of the manure protects inorganic P-ions from chelation (Shen *et al.*, 2011). Manure lowers down the pH of the soils and typically important for the alkaline soils with pH > 8.5. In general, pulses favour pH range between 6-6.5 and manures helps in doing so. Coming to inorganic amendments, the efficacy of rock phosphate can be increased in alkaline soil while co-applied with cattle dung. Now days, phospho-compost is gaining importance as it contains higher P (6-8% P_2O_5 compared to 0.2% in normal compost). Use of farm yard manure also increased the use efficiency of phosphate fertilisers and applied rock phosphate as it improves soil organic matter, normalises soil pH, accelerate microbial enzymatic activity and lastly higher p uptake.

6.1.3 Water management

Water management is needed for not only getting higher efficiency of the native or applied fertiliser but, also for uniform crop growth. Pulses respond positively with irrigation particularly in the critical growth stages like pod formation in the dry spells of rainy (*kharif*) and spring season (Prasad, 2012). Soils with field capacity dissolve almost 50-80% of the applied P fertiliser whereas, it is only 20-50% when the soil contains only2-4% moisture within 24 h (Siddique *et al.*, 2012). For fertilisers, where portion of P (nitro-phosphate) may or may not be water soluble, surface broadcast followed by mixing is more advisable than band placement. The movement of P requires water, which acts as a medium for the fertiliser to move and solubilise. However, powdered materials are better to apply in the drier condition for better PUE. Flooding of the soil increases P availability because Fe^{3+}-P transforms into Fe^{2+}-P, release of P from the occluded pools, Ca-phosphate dissolution in the higher partial pressure of $CO_2(P_{CO2})$ but, the results are hysteretic because upon drying the Fe and Al oxides will react with Pi and making it unavailable. The chemistry of P upon flooding or prolong rainfall is one of the interested and heavily researched topic (Sanyal *et al.*, 2015). From agronomic point of view, furrow irrigation with raised bed system solve the dual issue regarding water use efficiency and PUE although crop type, drainage, water requirement should always be taken into consideration.

6.1.4 Reducing losses

Phosphorus loss in the soil is mainly due to erosion (both water and wind), runoff, crop uptake and leaching. Due to faulty practices we are not only losing our precious resources (land, water and fossilised ores) but also contaminate our ecosystem with residual reactive nitrogenous and phosphate elements and thus losing our biodiversity (Correll, 1998). Loss of P from the agriculture field can be checked by curtailing inorganic P dose, use of resource conservation technologies, and most importantly preventing soil erosion. Generally, P is lost via finer soil fractions (clay and silt) as compared to sand (Quinton *et al.*, 2003). These eroded soil particles along with adsorbed P comes down to the natural water bodies and increased the level of bio-available P which leads to eutrophication. Research by Farias and co-workers (2018), found that 81% of the São Domingos Stream Watershed (northwestern São Paulo State, Brazil) contains >0.02 ppm reactive P (critical content of P for eutrophication). Leaching is considered less important for P loss. The protective mechanisms for reducing the erosion and trimming the P load to the reservoirs are zero-tillage practice and choosing pulse cultivars with higher canopy development, conservation practices like terracing and intercropping with crops having good root growth, contouring, cover crop practice and applying fertiliser only when it is optimum and placing close to the roots (Schroder *et al.*, 2011).

6.1.5 Management of problem soils

In India around 1/3rd of the total cultivated area comes under acidic soils. Acid soils hampers plant growth by preventing plants from foraging roots, nutrient imbalance like toxic concentration of metal cations and deficiency of P, toxicity of specific cations like Al^{3+}, Fe^{3+}, poor microbial diversity resulted below par crop growth and yield. But, with suitable management practices acidic soils can be properly used. Pulses are generally hardy crop with amazing ability to cope up the constraints. Under such kind of soils Al^{3+} reacts with phosphate ions (P_2O_5) can forms insoluble aluminium phosphate ions. On strongly acidic soils (pH<4) variscite ($AlPO_4.2H_2O$) and strengite ($FePO_4.2H_2O$) are the end products. As the reaction products vary in their solubility and solid-phases are linked with each other depending on the soil reaction only a minute amount of P is available to the crops. In the neutral and alkaline soils calcium carbonates ($CaCO_3$) comes into picture and reacts with the mono-calcium phosphate and forms in soluble apatite. The reactions are presented here under.

In neutral and alkaline soils:

$$Ca(H_2PO_4)_2 + 2CaCO_3 \Leftrightarrow Ca_3\,(PO_4)_2 \text{ (Tricalcium phosphate-insoluble)} + 2CO_2 + 2H_2O$$

In the acidic soils:

$$Al^{3+} + H_2PO_4^- \Leftrightarrow Al\,(OH)_2H_2PO_4 \text{ (Aluminium hydroxyl phosphate-insoluble)}$$

Liming up to a certain pH is the best way to reclaim an acid soil whereas; use of manures or any acidifying agent can be used as amendment in alkaline soils. Pulses secrets different organic acids in the rhizosphere making congenial condition for the roots to grow and increase use efficiency of P. Now-a-days, introduction of crop cultivars suitable for problem soils and introducing of Al-resistance genes have come out with an important tool for increase P use efficiency. Delhaize *et al.* (2009) reported barley (*Hordeum vulgare* L.) cultivars with higher PUE and capable to grow under acidic soil conditions but, this kind of research is still lacking in case of pulses.

6.1.6 Utilisation of native soil P (organic and inorganic)

It is a well-documented fact that prior applied P-fertiliser reduces the P-sorption capacity of the soils and escalates the use efficiency of current fertiliser (Burkitt *et al.*, 2008) and practically highly correlated in the long run systems. Pulses should be incorporated in the long run cereal-cereal cropping systems to break the disease-pest cycle and utilise native P. Generally, organic-P present in the soil is very important for maintaining the equilibrium of available P content in the soil. Soil organic matter is generally a store house of different nutrients but, harnessing this resource is not an easy task. There has been reports that pulses are excellent utilisers of organic P in the soil and helpful for the next crop too (Simpson *et al.*, 2011).

6.1.7 Modern practices for improving PUE

Agronomic interventions are highly successful and with development of new technologies it's become more user-friendly and sustainable for the farming community. The new technologies for improving PUE are listed below:

- Discarding age old practices and promote next-gen targeted approach
- Development of new fertilisers particularly liquid fertilisers
- Intercropping and phase farming
- Precision agriculture- development of GPS maps and zone specific management
- Understanding the nutrient translocation and rooting behaviour

6.2 Microbiological interventions

Microorganism plays an important role in agriculture because of its eco-friendly nature, cheap and easy to apply. In the present scenario when the agriculture is highly input intensive microbial culture proved as an very promising option for increasing agricultural yield without hampering nature. Phosphate solubilising micro-organisms (solubilising bacteria and vesicular arbuscular mycorrhizae) are promising options for increasing solubility of native soil-P and it also explores the possibilities of direct application of rock phosphate in neutral and alkaline soils (Tagore *et al.*, 2013). Besides, certain group of micro-organisms, beneficial organisms residing in the rhizosphere zone secrets different organic acids, enzymes, sugar, amino-acids which in turn promote the plant growth (Patel *et al.*, 2015). Understanding the role of micro-organisms in close vicinity to roots is one of the challenging and interesting area of research which can unfold multiple mysteries related to nutrient transformation, plant defensive mechanism, and abiotic stress tolerance so on.

6.2.1 Micro-organisms for phosphorus solubilisation

Importance of phosphorus solubilising micro-organisms (PSM) in solubilisation of insoluble and sparingly soluble-P is well documented. Most notable bacterial species are *Bacillus megatherium,* and *Pseudomonas striata* and *Aspergillus awamori* among fungal species is typically important and fixes around 30-35 kg P_2O_5 ha^{-1} under optimum condition, although researchers found multiple organisms in promoting P-nutrition in pulses (Table 5).

Unlike bacteria the mode of activity of VAM is quite different. VAM basically helps plant acquire P in two ways: (i) mycelia of VAM act as pseudo root system, helping the plants to explore greater soil volume and (ii) roots infected by VAM are more efficient in absorbing P in low P soils.

Table 5. Important micro-organisms helping pulses in P-nutrition

Crop	Microorganism	Reference
Chickpea	*Rhizobium, Bacillus megaterium* subsp. *Phospaticum, T. harzianum*	Rudresh *et al.* (2005)
Chickpea	*Azospirillum*	Rokhzadi *et al.* (2008)
Chickpea	*Pseudomonas, Azotobacter, Bacillus, M. ciceri*	Wani *et al.* (2007)
Soybean	*Glomus mosseae* and *Acaulospora laevis, Pseudomonas fluorescens*	Fattah (2013)
Greengram	*Pseudomonas* and *Rhizobium*	Kumar *et al.* (2015)
Greengram	*Funneliformis mosseae+ T. viride*	Sharma *et al.* (2016)
Blackgram	*Trichoderma hamatum*	Badar and Qureshi (2012)
Cowpea	*Glomus* sp.	Yaseen *et al.* (2011)

Micro-organisms are highly susceptible to external environment. So, following points may always to be considered while applying PSM:

- **Soil temperature:** PSMs are basically mesophilic so, soil temperature >35°C during July-August and <10°C during winters is not suitable for micro-organisms to grow and work.
- **Agro-ecology:** PSMs are not suitable of arid and semi-arid regions due to very high soil temperature, poor soil moisture and low SOC content.
- **Soil organic carbon:** Higher SOC content always congenial for the micro-organisms because it acts as a food source and improves soil physicochemical condition. So, it is always better to apply microbial culture with farm yard manure in soils with poor SOC content (Wani and Lee, 1992).
- **Culturing:** In case of bacterial strains sub-culturing for multiple times is prohibited whereas, the same is not true for fungal strains.
- **Relative effectiveness:** Solubilising fungal groups are more effective the fungal species because of higher production of acidifying agents.
- **Storage:** Packets containing PSMs should always be kept in cool place and not under direct sunlight.
- **Commercialisation:** Large scale use particularly in the perennial crops is restricted in case of VAM because it can be grown in synthetic medium.

6.2.2 Soil microbial biomass-P and organic matter solubilisation

Soil micro-organisms are very important for a sustainable soil system by taking part in P-cycle. The prime role of micro-organism is supplying inorganic P to the plants through soil organic matter solubilisation. Soil micro-organisms represent about 0.5% - 7.5%

and 0.4%-2.4% of total P in grassland and arable soils respectively (Oberson and Joner, 2005). Activity of soil micro-organisms depends on a lot of factors like soil moisture, aeration, soil temperature, food source, interaction with other micro-organisms etc. For example, if we incorporate huge amount of labile soil organic matter to the soil, rapidly the content of bioavailable P decreases and leading to temporary immobilisation of microbial P (Oehl *et al.*, 2001; Bünemann *et al.*, 2004a). Micro-organisms live in close symbiotic relationship with plants by helping each other such as plant roots secrets different root mediated labile –C products which in turn promote microbial growth and microbes supply available P to the plants (Wichern *et al.*, 2007). The recovery rate of microbial P (inorganic orthophosphate, polyphosphates and a range of organic compounds primarily as nucleic acids and phospholipids) from the added legume residue is about 15-28% depending on the residue composition where it is only 5% from mineral fertilisers, because in intensive agricultural systems soils are low in organic carbon and available N (McLaughlin *et al.*, 1988; Bünemann, 2008; Ehlers *et al.*, 2010). In stress situation, like fluctuation of soil moisture regimes or temperature and poor soil organic carbon content, the microbial cells got disrupted and release of microbial P in the form of inorganic P in turn available to plants through rapid mineralisation (Oehl *et al.*, 2001; Turner *et al.*, 2003). Inorganic P is highly reactive and getting sorbed easily with different soil constituents. In the soil with moderate P-sorption capacity microbial P directly increase the Pi through desorption while, in the highly weathered soils of the tropics where the sorption is very high, Pi can't be available like the former unless mineralisation in the rhizosphere (Oehl *et al.*, 2001). In a research, Oberson *et al.* (2001) showed that incorporation of legume in the pastures increase the build-up of soil organic P, microbial activity vis-à-vis increase in the bioavailable P through greater P cycling compared to sole pasture cropping system and native savanna. Similar results also found in the cereal cropping rotation too.

7. BREEDING FOR P-USE EFFICIENCY

Combination of advanced agronomic and microbiological approach along with improved breeding techniques for developing cultivars with higher PUE is the need of the hour (Cordell *et al.*, 2009). Earlier, breeding programme mainly focused on increasing the phosphorus acquisition efficiency (PAE) of crops but nowadays the concept of PUE is coming forward because improving traits for PUE would adjunct the PAE traits for obvious reasons (Wissuwa *et al.*, 2009). Although, breeding programme for PUE is sluggish because of mostly two reasons: firstly, lack of genotypic difference based on yield, harvest index (HI), P- uptake and secondly, higher genotypic differences among the genotype in case of PAE than PUE (Parentoni and Junior, 2008). But, there is a lot of ambiguity regarding the mechanisms as these assessments failed to show individual impacts rather than cumulating impact in a crop cycle. For example, differences in P-uptake by several folds after a period of 3 months does not justify one genotype has better acquisition efficiency over other rather than PUE is an amalgamation of multiple plant above and below ground traits (Lynch and Ho, 2005). Entire genetic basis is really important to work out as every plant part is having specific role in P-translocation and root attributes and modifications could be targeted for developing low cost below ground system (Lynch and Ho, 2005). Apart from root, grain P content is also an important targeted site for PUE. Since, P concentration in the grains is comparatively higher in the grains than root or shoot, so, apart from normal physiological redistribution, some P-loading and translocation factor is expected to involve in P-distribution (Raboy, 2009; Rose *et al.*, 2010). Nonetheless, quantitative trait loci (QTL) factors have been identified for grain P-concentration or P-uptake by plants which alternately expresses the content of available-P pool in the soil translocated to the grains (Stangoulis *et al.*, 2007; Zhao *et al.*, 2008). Addressing, this topic two future aspect have been come into picture which needs through investigation. These are: (i) critical concentration of grain/seed-P content related to maximum yield for optimum yield and higher seed germination and (ii) identification of P-transporter involved in loading P into the grains and its molecular characterisation. Thus, project on screening higher PUE genotype can't be done unless we get lines with low seed P content or mutants. Therefore, while screening for higher use efficient genotype we have to consider many important parameters and give equal weightage for both PAE and PUE. In general, PUE and PAE are inversely proportional to each other for that, higher tissue P concentration makes confusion regarding that actually related to internal PUE (Rose *et al.*, 2011). So, as a way out, exact quantification of tissue-P concentration would led to identification of QTL linked with crop PUE. One of the important traits for screening genotypes for PUE is root morphology and rhizosphere activity like root exudates secretion, enzymes, etc. It has been found that lower grain yield or seed P content directly linked with high PUE genotypes (Rose *et al.*, 2011). Indirectly, lower grain-P content linked with better accumulation of micro-nutrients like Fe and Zn (Rose and Wissua, 2012). Experiments have been tried regarding enhancement of PAE of pulses through genetic amplification but, results are not totally acceptable. Like, transgenic plants in the lab condition can excess the organic-P by phytase release but, the results are not encouraging (George *et al.*, 2005). So, lastly we can conclude that breeding crops for higher PAE/PUE, we need diverse genotypes to exploit the natural variation of a particular crop species (Lynch, 2007; Wissuwa *et al.*, 2009). Crop physiological behaviour under P-depleted condition is a well-known fact but, the intra-specific variation is still to be investigated. While, the conventional breeding strategies is suitable up to a certain limit, identification of exact QTLs and molecular approaches like marker assisted selection (MAS) is the need of the hour.

8. MOLECULAR INTERVENTIONS

Identification of numerous traits associated with PUE has been found in multiple crop varieties. These variations can be examined through discerning numerous genetic trait loci scientifically known as quantitative trait loci (QTL) and this identification could only be possible through genetic improvement programme, genetic identification or molecular engineering or combination of fore mentioned processes. Most of the work done so far, concentrates majorly on efficient internal PAE not better PUE (White *et al.*, 2012). However, identification of potential QTL related to PUE in pulses done in several crops (Vance, 2010; Rose *et al.*, 2011; White *et al.*, 2012). Present day, apart from identification of QTL, marker assisted selection (MAS) gives enough opportunity to the scientific community to identify and introgress particular traits difficult to examined and at the same time eliminate the undesirable traits (Septiningsih *et al.*, 2009). So, not only yield potential of the donor parent but also, breeder can make full use of the genetic variations. Genomic data where information about the marker along with data regarding genebank accessions in combination with phenotypic data to identify the specific loci associated with phenotype, is typically used to identify loci controlling PURE in multiple tissues. Recent molecular techniques together with advanced crop production technologies are still lacking soil-plant P relation studies. Transcriptomic expression and genome wide association studies will allow the researches to identify novel loci related to plant P relation including PUE (Vance, 2010; Morrell *et al.*, 2012). Thus, in conclusion it can be said that identification of superior alleles for a particular traits followed by transferred with MAS to the targeted variety with high yield potential in combination with promising PUE and PAE will result variety with maximum use efficiency.

9. CONCLUSION

Phosphorus is a key to optimum plant growth and yield but this precious resource is highly limiting. So, increase in PUE will not only help the eco-system but also reduce the economic burden on the farmers. Utilisation of P inside plant body is combination of optimum physiological condition and genetics of the crop plant. Pulses are the important source of proteins and suitable for diverse ecosystems. Pulses have a wonderful rhizosphere system which allows them to grow in sub-optimal P nutrition as they can harness the native soil P more efficiently than other crops and thus, open avenues for the researchers to increase the PUE. Therefore, a multidisciplinary team including agronomists, physiologist, breeders, and molecular biologists is needed to target this very aspect of PUE in pulses. The ultimate target would be coming out with a variety which requires low P and have potential to use native soil –P with higher grain P content.

10. FUTURE RESEARCH

- Legumes can be excellent component of CA as they are potent cover crops with small duration which can fit easily in the crop rotation cycle. Thus, there is need to identify the CA practices that lead to the higher P-use efficiency under diverse agro-ecosystems.
- In the present input intensive agriculture system, adaptation of modern ecosystem based approach rather than age old method is highly recommended for hitting the target of increased PUE. The ecosystem based approach is highly acceptable for nutrients like N but, for P more research work is needed.
- Understanding the dynamics of different P-fractions and site specific use of different P-fertilisers rather than focusing on only conventional soluble sources like DAP or MAP.
- Climate change is posing high threat to our agriculture and addressing this challenge with potent agronomic and breeding strategies is effective in increasing crop yield vis-à-vis increasing PUE.
- Time has come to move into advanced agricultural practices like biotechnology and molecular interventions. Our main task is to take large number of genotypes for particular PUE traits and identify the specific loci using molecular markers. One important question arises regarding performance of selected genotypes in the field condition. Improving root: shoot PUE in the high P-content condition is also need of the hour and need serious interventions from the breeders (Rose and Wissuwa, 2012).

- Intervening policy regarding the importance of pulses as a healthy and high remunerative crop and balanced application of nutrients like N, P and other micronutrient is very important. Supplying valuable inputs like improved planting materials with microbial consortia and its way of use should be provided to the resource poor farmers.

REFERENCES

Ahmad, Z., Gill, M.A. and Qureshi, R.H. (2001) Genotypic variations of phosphorus utilization efficiency of crops. *Journal of Plant Nutrition* 24(8), 1149-1171.

Akram, M., Hussain, S., Hamid, A., Majeed, S., Chaudary, S.A., Shah, Z.A., Yaqoob, A., Kayani, F., Arif, U., Fareed, K. and Jamil, F. (2017) Interactive effect of phosphorus and potassium on growth, yield, quality and seed production of chili (*Capsicum annuum* L.). *Journal of Horticulture* 4(1), 2-5.

Ali, M., Mishra, J.P., Ahlawat, I.P.S., Kumar, R. and Chauhan, Y.S. (1998) Effective management of legumes for maximizing biological nitrogen fixation and other benefits. pp. 107-128. In: Residual Effects of Legumes in Rice and Wheat Cropping Systems in Indi-Gangetic Plain (Eds. JVDK Kumar Rao, C Johansen and TJ Rego), International Crop Research Institute for the Semi-Arid Tropics (ICRISAT), Patancheru, India.

Annual Report (2019) Ministry of statistics and Programme Implementation (http://mospi.gov.in/), Government of India.

Badar, R. and Qureshi, S.A. (2012) Comparative effect of *Trichoderma hamatum* and host-specific *Rhizobium* species on growth of *Vigna mungo*. *Journal of Applied Pharmaceutical Science* 2(4), 128.

Bana, R.S., Gautam, R.C. and Rana, K.S. (2012) Effect of different organic sources on productivity and quality of pearlmillet (*Pennisetum glaucum*) and their residual effect on wheat (*Triticum aetivum*). *Annals of Agricultural Research* 33(3), 126-30.

Batjes, N.H. (1997) A world dataset of derived soil properties by FAO–UNESCO soil unit for global modelling. *Soil Use and Management* 13(1), 9-16.

Bray, R.H. and Kurtz, L.T. (1945) Determination of total, organic, and available forms of phosphorus in soils. *Soil Science* 59(1), 39-46.

Bünemann, E.K. (2008) Enzyme additions as a tool to assess the potential bioavailability of organically bound nutrients. *Soil Biology and Biochemistry* 40(9), 2116-2129.

Bünemann, E.K., Bossio, D.A., Smithson, P.C., Frossard, E. and Oberson, A. (2004) Microbial community composition and substrate use in a highly weathered soil as affected by crop rotation and P fertilization. *Soil Biology and Biochemistry* 36(6), 889-901.

Burkitt, L.L., Sale, P.W.G. and Gourley, C.J.P. (2008) Soil phosphorus buffering measures should not be adjusted for current phosphorus fertility. *Soil Research* 46(8), 676-685.

Cabeza, R.A., Liese, R., Lingner, A., von Stieglitz, I., Neumann, J., Salinas-Riester, G., Pommerenke, C., Dittert, K. and Schulze, J. (2014) RNA-seq transcriptome profiling reveals that *Medicago truncatula* nodules acclimate N2 fixation before emerging P deficiency reaches the nodules. *Journal of Experimental Botany* 65(20), 6035-6048.

Chan, K.Y., Oates, A., Li, G.D., Conyers, M.K., Prangnell, R.J., Poile, G., Liu, D.L. and Barchia, I.M. (2010) Soil carbon stocks under different pastures and pasture management in the higher rainfall areas of south-eastern Australia. *Soil Research* 48(1), 7-15.

Chaudhary, M.I., Adu-Gyamfi, J.J., Saneoka, H., Nguyen, N.T., Suwa, R., Kanai, S., El-Shemy, H.A., Lightfoot, D.A. and Fujita, K. (2008) The effect of phosphorus deficiency on nutrient uptake, nitrogen fixation and photosynthetic rate in mashbean, mungbean and soybean. *ActaPhysiologiaePlantarum* 30(4), 537-544.

Chen, J., Xu, L., Cai, Y. and Xu, J. (2009) Identification of QTLs for phosphorus utilization efficiency in maize (*Zea mays* L.) across P levels. *Euphytica* 167(2), 245-252.

Chien, S.H., Prochnow, L.I. and Cantarella, A.H. (2009) Recent developments of fertilizer production and use to improve nutrient efficiency and minimize environmental impacts. *Advances in Agronomy* 102, 267-322.

Colwell, J.D. (1963) The estimation of the phosphorus fertilizer requirements of wheat in southern New South Wales by soil analysis. *Australian Journal of Experimental Agriculture* 3(10), 190-197.

Cordell, D., Drangert, J.O. and White, S. (2009) The story of phosphorus: global food security and food for thought. *Global Environmental Change* 19(2), 292-305.

Cornish, P.S. (2009) Research directions: Improving plant uptake of soil phosphorus, and reducing dependency on input of phosphorus fertiliser. *Crop and Pasture Science* 60(2), 190-196.

Correll, D.L. (1998) The role of phosphorus in the eutrophication of receiving waters: A review. *Journal of Environmental Quality* 27(2), 261-266.

Delhaize, E., Taylor, P., Hocking, P.J., Simpson, R.J., Ryan, P.R. and Richardson, A.E. (2009) Transgenic barley (*Hordeum vulgare* L.) expressing the wheat aluminium resistance gene (TaALMT1) shows enhanced phosphorus nutrition and grain production when grown on an acid soil. *Plant Biotechnology Journal* 7(5), 391-400.

Dey, P., Santhi, R., Maragatham, S. and Sellamuthu, K.M. (2017) Status of phosphorus and potassium in the Indian soils vis-à-vis world soils. *Indian Journal of Fertilisers* 13(4), 44-59.

Ehlers, K., Bakken, L.R., Frostegård, Å., Frossard, E. and Bünemann, E.K. (2010) Phosphorus limitation in a Ferralsol: impact on microbial activity and cell internal P pools. *Soil Biology and Biochemistry* 42(4), 558-566.

Evans, J. and Condon, J. (2009) New fertiliser options for managing phosphorus for organic and low-input farming systems. *Crop and Pasture Science* 60(2), 152-162.

Farias, V.L.D.S., Martins Filho, M.V., Paula, D.T.D. and Siqueira, D.S. (2018) Modeling of phosphorus losses by water erosion. *EngenhariaAgrícola* 38(1), 149-157.

Fattah, O.A. (2013) Effect of mycorrhiza and phosphorus on micronutrients uptake by soybean plant grown in acid soil. *International Journal of Agronomy and Plant Production* 4(3), 429-437.

George, T.S., Richardson, A.E., Smith, J.B., Hadobas, P.A. and Simpson, R.J. (2005) Limitations to the potential of transgenic *Trifolium subterraneum* L. plants that exude phytase when grown in soils with a range of organic P content. *Plant and Soil* 278(1-2), 263.

Gordon, B. and Tindall, T. (2006) Fluid P performance improved with polymers. *Fluid Journal* 14, 12-13.

Górny, A.G. (1999). Inheritance of nitrogen and phosphorus utilization efficiency in spring barley at the vegetative growth stages under high and low nutrition. *Plant Breeding* 118(6), 511-516.

Hammond, J.P., Broadley, M.R., White, P.J., King, G.J., Bowen, H.C., Hayden, R., Meacham, M.C., Mead, A., Overs, T., Spracklen, W.P. and Greenwood, D.J. (2009) Shoot yield drives phosphorus use efficiency in *Brassica oleracea* and correlates with root architecture traits. *Journal of Experimental Botany* 60(7), 1953-1968.

Hart, M.R., Quin, B.F. and Nguyen, M.L. (2004) Phosphorus runoff from agricultural land and direct fertilizer effects: A review. *Journal of Environmental Quality* 33(6), 1954-1972.

Hettiarachchi, G.M., Lombi, E., McLaughlin, M.J., Chittleborough, D. and Self, P. (2006) Density changes around phosphorus granules and fluid bands in a calcareous soil. *Soil Science Society of America Journal* 70(3), 960-966.

JD, T.S.N.W.B. and Havlin, J.L. (1993) Soil fertility and fertilizers Macmillan Publishing New York.

Jin, J., Tang, C. and Sale, P. (2015) The impact of elevated carbon dioxide on the phosphorus nutrition of plants: a review. *Annals of Botany* 116(6), 987-999.

Jones, G.P.D., Jessop, R.S. and Blair, G.J. (1992) Alternative methods for the selection of phosphorus efficiency in wheat. *Field Crops Research* 30(1-2), 29-40.

Karamanos, R.E. and Puurveen, D. (2011) Evaluation of a polymer treatment as enhancer of phosphorus fertilizer efficiency in wheat. *Canadian Journal of Soil Science* 91(1), 123-125.

Khan, F.N., Lukac, M., Turner, G. and Godbold, D.L. (2008) Elevated atmospheric CO2 changes phosphorus fractions in soils under a short rotation poplar plantation (EuroFACE). *Soil Biology and Biochemistry* 40(7), 1716-1723.

Kumar, M., Singh, D.P., Prabha, R. and Sharma, A.K. (2015) Rolc of cyanobacteria in nutrient cycle and use efficiency in the soil. In *Nutrient Use Efficiency: from Basics to Advances* (pp. 163-171). Springer, New Delhi.

Laliberté, E., Lambers, H., Burgess, T.I. and Wright, S.J. (2015) Phosphorus limitation, soil-borne pathogens and the coexistence of plant species in hyperdiverse forests and shrublands. *New Phytologist* 206(2), 507-521.

Lauer, M.J., Blevins, D.G. and Sierzputowska-Gracz, H. (1989) 31P-nuclear magnetic resonance determination of phosphate compartmentation in leaves of reproductive soybeans (*Glycine max* L.) as affected by phosphate nutrition. *Plant Physiology* 89(4), 1331-1336.

Lynch, J.P. (2007) Roots of the second green revolution. *Australian Journal of Botany* 55(5), 493-512.

Lynch, J.P. and Ho, M.D. (2005) Rhizoeconomics: carbon costs of phosphorus acquisition. *Plant and Soil* 269(1-2), 45-56.

Ma, Q., Rengel, Z. and Rose, T. (2009) The effectiveness of deep placement of fertilisers is determined by crop species and edaphic conditions in Mediterranean-type environments: a review. *Soil Research* 47(1), 19-32.

Manske, G.G.B., Ortiz-Monasterio, J.I., Van Ginkel, M., Gonzalez, R.M., Fischer, R.A., Rajaram, S. and Vlek, P.L.G. (2001) Importance of P uptake efficiency versus P utilization for wheat yield in acid and calcareous soils in Mexico. *European Journal of Agronomy* 14(4), 261-274.

Manske, G.G.B., Ortiz-Monasterio, J.I., Van Ginkel, R.M., Rajaram, S. and Vlek, P.L.G. (2002) Phosphorus use efficiency in tall, semi-dwarf and dwarf near-isogenic lines of spring wheat. *Euphytica* 125(1), 113-119.

Marschner, H. (2011) Marschner›s mineral nutrition of higher plants. Academic press.

McLaughlin, M.J., Alston, A.M. and Martin, J.K. (1988) Phosphorus cycling in wheat pasture rotations. II. The role of the microbial biomass in phosphorus cycling. *Soil Research* 26(2), 333-342.

McLaughlin, M.J., McBeath, T.M., Smernik, R., Stacey, S.P., Ajiboye, B. and Guppy, C. (2011) The chemical nature of P accumulation in agricultural soils—implications for fertiliser management and design: an Australian perspective. *Plant and Soil* 349(1-2), 69-87.

Mehlich, A. (1953) Soil test division mimeo. *Determination of P, K, Na, Ca, Mg and NH4; North Carolina Department of Agriculture: Raleigh, North Carolina.*

Mehlich, A. (1984) Mehlich 3 soil test extractant: A modification of Mehlich 2 extractant. *Communications in Soil Science and Plant Analysis* 15(12), 1409-1416.

Mines, I. B. O. (2016) Indian Minerals Yearbook, 2016. Government of India, Ministry of Mines, Nagpur.

Morrell, P.L., Buckler, E.S. and Ross-Ibarra, J. (2012) Crop genomics: advances and applications. *Nature Reviews Genetics* 13(2), 85-96.

Niu, Y.F., Chai, R.S., Jin, G.L., Wang, H., Tang, C.X. and Zhang, Y.S. (2013) Responses of root architecture development to low phosphorus availability: a review. *Annals of Botany* 112(2), 391-408.

Noack, S.R., McBeath, T.M. and McLaughlin, M.J. (2011) Potential for foliar phosphorus fertilisation of dryland cereal crops: a review. *Crop and Pasture Science* 61(8), 569-669.

Oberson, A. and Joner, E.J. (2005) Microbial turnover of phosphorus in soil. In *Organic phosphorus in the environment* (pp. 133-164). CABI Publishing.

Oberson, A., Friesen, D.K., Rao, I.M., Bühler, S. and Frossard, E. (2001) Phosphorus transformations in an Oxisol under contrasting land-use systems: the role of the soil microbial biomass. *Plant and Soil* 237(2), 197-210.

Oehl, F., Oberson, A., Probst, M., Fliessbach, A., Roth, H.R. and Frossard, E. (2001) Kinetics of microbial phosphorus uptake in cultivated soils. *Biology and Fertility of Soils* 34(1), 31-41.

Olsen, S.R., Cole, C.V., Watambe, F.S. and Dean, L.A. (1954) Estimation of available phosphorus in soil by extraction with NaHCO3, USDA Ciraza (Quoted from, Method of soil Analysis, CA Black 2nd ed.) 1165 Am. *Soc. Agron., Inc. Medision Wisconsin, USA.*

Oracka, T. and Łapiński, B. (2006) Nitrogen and phosphorus uptake and utilization efficiency in D (R) substitution lines of hexaploid triticale. *Plant Breeding* 125(3), 221-224.

Parentoni, S.N. and Souza Júnior, C.L.D. (2008) Phosphorus acquisition and internal utilization efficiency in tropical maize genotypes. *PesquisaAgropecuáriaBrasileira* 43(7), 893-901.

Parker, F.W., Nelson, W.L., Winters, E. and Miles, I.E. (1951) The broad interpretation and application of soil test information. *Agronomy Journal* 43(3), 105-112.

Patel, J.S., Singh, A., Singh, H.B. and Sarma, B.K. (2015) Plant genotype, microbial recruitment and nutritional security. *Frontiers in Plant Science* 6, 608.

Pooniya, V. and Shivay, Y.S. (2013) Enrichment of Basmati rice grain and straw with zinc and nitrogen through ferti-fortification and summer green manuring under Indo-gangetic plains of India. *Journal of Plant Nutrition* 36(1), 91-117.

Pooniya, V., Choudhary, A.K., Dass, A., Bana, R.S., Rana, K.S., Rana, D.S., Tyagi, V.K. and Puniya, M.M. (2015) Improved crop management practices for sustainable pulse production: An Indian perspective. *Indian Journal of Agricultural Sciences 85*(6), 747-758.

Prasad, R. (2002) Textbook of field crops production, In *Textbook offield crops production.* Vol I, 248–319.

Prochnow, L.I., Chien, S.H., Carmona, G., Dillard, E.F., Henao, J. and Austin, E.R. (2008) Plant Availability of Phosphorus in Four Superphosphate Fertilizers Varying in Water-Insoluble Phosphate Compounds. *Soil Science Society of America Journal* 72(2), 462-470.

Quinton, J.N., Strauss, P., Miller, N., Azazoglu, E., Yli-Halla, M. and Uusitalo, R. (2003) The potential for soil phosphorus tests to predict phosphorus losses in overland flow. *Journal of Plant Nutrition and Soil Science* 166(4), 432-437.

Raboy, V. (2009) Approaches and challenges to engineering seed phytate and total phosphorus. *Plant Science* 177(4), 281-296.

Rokhzadi, A., Asgharzadeh, A., Darvish, F., Nour-Mohammadi, G. and Majidi, E. (2008) Influence of plant growth-promoting rhizobacteria on dry matter accumulation and yield of chickpea (*Cicer arietinum* L.) under field conditions. *American-Eurasian Journal of Agricultural and Environmental Science* 3(2), 253-257.

Römer, W. and Schenk, H. (1998) Influence of genotype on phosphate uptake and utilization efficiencies in spring barley. *European Journal of Agronomy* 8(3-4), 215-224.

Rose, T.J. and Wissuwa, M. (2012) Rethinking internal phosphorus utilization efficiency: a new approach is needed to improve PUE in grain crops. *Advances in Agronomy* 116, 185-217.

Rose, T.J., Pariasca-Tanaka, J., Rose, M.T., Fukuta, Y. and Wissuwa, M. (2010) Genotypic variation in grain phosphorus concentration, and opportunities to improve P-use efficiency in rice. *Field Crops Research* 119(1), 154-160.

Rose, T.J., Rose, M.T., Pariasca Tanaka, J., Heuer, S. and Wissuwa, M. (2011) The frustration with utilization: why have improvements in internal phosphorus utilization efficiency in crops remained so elusive?. *Frontiers in Plant Science* 2, 73.

Rudresh, D.L., Shivaprakash, M.K. and Prasad, R.D. (2005) Effect of combined application of Rhizobium, phosphate solubilizing bacterium and *Trichoderma* spp. on growth, nutrient uptake and yield of chickpea (*Cicer aritenium* L.). *Applied Soil Ecology* 28(2), 139-146.

Saeid, A., Labuda, M., Chojnacka, K., and Górecki, H. (2014) Valorization of bones to liquid phosphorus fertilizer by microbial solubilization. *Waste and Biomass Valorization* 5(2), 265-272.

Sanchez, C.A., Porter, P.S. and Ulloa, M.F. (1991) Relative efficiency of broadcast and banded phosphorus for sweet corn produced on histosols. *Soil Science Society of America Journal* 55(3), 871-875.

Sanyal, S.K., Dwivedi, B.S., Singh, V.K., Majumdar, K., Datta, S.C., Pattanayak, S.K. and Annapurna, K. (2015) Phosphorus in relation to dominant cropping sequences in India: chemistry, fertility relations and management options. *Current Science* 108(7), 1262-1270.

Schröder, J.J., Smit, A.L., Cordell, D. and Rosemarin, A. (2011) Improved phosphorus use efficiency in agriculture: a key requirement for its sustainable use. *Chemosphere* 84(6), 822-831.

Sepehr, E., Malakouti, M.J., Khold, B.B., Samadi, A. and Karimian, N. (2009) Genotypic variation in P efficiency of selected Iranian cereals in greenhouse experiment. *International Journal of Plant Production* 3(3), 17-28.

Septiningsih, E.M., Pamplona, A.M., Sanchez, D.L., Neeraja, C.N., Vergara, G.V., Heuer, S., Ismail, A.M. and Mackill, D.J. (2009) Development of submergence-tolerant rice cultivars: the Sub1 locus and beyond. *Annals of Botany* 103(2), 151-160.

Sharma, N., Yadav, K. and Aggarwal, A. (2016) Growth response of two *Phaseolus mungo* L. cultivars induced by arbuscular mycorrhizal fungi and *Trichoderma viride*. *International Journal of Agronomy* 2016: 1524304. doi:10.1155/2016/1524304

Shen, J., Yuan, L., Zhang, J., Li, H., Bai, Z., Chen, X., Zhang, W. and Zhang, F. (2011) Phosphorus dynamics: from soil to plant. *Plant Physiology* 156(3), 997-1005.

Siddique, K.H., Johansen, C., Turner, N.C., Jeuffroy, M.H., Hashem, A., Sakar, D., Gan, Y. and Alghamdi, S.S. (2012) Innovations in agronomy for food legumes.A review. *Agronomy for Sustainable Development*, *32*(1), 45-64.

Simpson, R.J., Stefanski, A., Marshall, D.J., Moore, A.D. and Richardson, A.E. (2010) November. The farm-gate phosphorus balance of sheep grazing systems maintained at three contrasting soil fertility levels. In *Food Security from Sustainable Agriculture. Proc 15th AustSocAgronConf* (pp. 15-18).

Soltanpour, P.N. and Schwab, A.P. (1977) A new soil test for simultaneous extraction of macro-and micro-nutrients in alkaline soils. *Communications in Soil Science and Plant Analysis 8*(3), 195-207.

Sulieman, S., Ha, C.V., Schulze, J. and Tran, L.S.P. (2013) Growth and nodulation of symbiotic *Medicago truncatula* at different levels of phosphorus availability. *Journal of Experimental Botany* 64(10), 2701-2712.

Sulieman, S., Schulze, J. and Tran, L.S.P. (2014) N-feedback regulation is synchronized with nodule carbon alteration in *Medicago truncatula* under excessive nitrate or low phosphorus conditions. *Journal of Plant Physiology* 171(6),407-410.

Suzaki, T., Yoro, E. and Kawaguchi, M. (2015) Leguminous plants: inventors of root nodules to accommodate symbiotic bacteria. In *International review of cell and molecular biology* (Vol. 316, pp. 111-158). Academic Press.

Tachibana, S. (1982) Comparison of effects of root temperature on the growth and mineral nutrition of cucumber cultivars and figleaf gourd. *Journal of the Japanese Society for Horticultural Science* 51(3), 299-308.

Tagore, G.S., Namdeo, S.L., Sharma, S.K. and Kumar, N. (2013) Effect of Rhizobium and phosphate solubilizing bacterial inoculants on symbiotic traits, nodule leghemoglobin, and yield of chickpea genotypes. *International Journal of Agronomy* Article ID: 581627.

Turner, B.L., Driessen, J.P., Haygarth, P.M. and Mckelvie, I.D. (2003) Potential contribution of lysed bacterial cells to phosphorus solubilisation in two rewetted Australian pasture soils. *Soil Biology and Biochemistry* 35(1), 187-189.

Turner, N.C. (2004) Agronomic options for improving rainfall-use efficiency of crops in dryland farming systems. *Journal of Experimental Botany* 55(407), 2413-2425.

Valizadeh, G.R., Rengel, Z. and Rate, A.W. (2003) Response of wheat genotypes efficient in P utilisation and genotypes responsive to P fertilisation to different P banding depths and watering regimes. *Australian Journal of Agricultural Research* 54(1), 59-65.

Vance, C.P. (2010) Quantitative trait loci, epigenetics, sugars, and microRNAs: quaternaries in phosphate acquisition and use. *Plant physiology* 154(2), 582-588.

Veneklaas, E.J., Lambers, H., Bragg, J., Finnegan, P.M., Lovelock, C.E., Plaxton, W.C., Price, C.A., Scheible, W.R., Shane, M.W., White, P.J. and Raven, J.A. (2012) Opportunities for improving phosphorus-use efficiency in crop plants. *New Phytologist* 195(2), 306-320.

Veneklaas, E.J., Stevens, J., Cawthray, G.R., Turner, S., Grigg, A.M. and Lambers, H. (2003) Chickpea and white lupin rhizosphere carboxylates vary with soil properties and enhance phosphorus uptake. *Plant and Soil* 248(1-2), 187-197.

Wani, P.A., Khan, M.S. and Zaidi, A. (2007) Synergistic effects of the inoculation with nitrogen-fixing and phosphate-solubilizing rhizobacteria on the performance of field-grown chickpea. *Journal of Plant Nutrition and Soil Science* 170(2), 283-287.

Wani, S.P. and Lee, K.K. (1992). Role of biofertilizers in upland crop production. *Fertilisers, organic manures, recyclable wastes and biofertilisers'.(Ed. HLS Tandon)pp.* 91-112.

White, P.J., Broadley, M.R. and Gregory, P.J. (2012) Managing the nutrition of plants and people. *Applied and Environmental Soil Science* 2012: Article ID 104826.

Wichern, F., Mayer, J., Joergensen, R.G. and Müller, T. (2007) Release of C and N from roots of peas and oats and their availability to soil microorganisms. *Soil Biology and Biochemistry* 39(11), 2829-2839.

Wissuwa, M., Mazzola, M. and Picard, C. (2009) Novel approaches in plant breeding for rhizosphere-related traits. *Plant and Soil* 321(1-2), 409.

Wolf, B. (1982) An improved universal extracting solution and its use for diagnosing soil fertility. *Communications in Soil Science and Plant Analysis*, 13(12), 1005-1033.

Yadav, G.S., Babu, S., Meena, R.S., Debnath, C., Saha, P., Debbaram, C. and Datta, M.(2017). Effects of godawariphosgold and single supper phosphate on groundnut (*Arachis hypogaea*) productivity, phosphorus uptake, phosphorus use efficiency and economics. *Indian Journal of Agricultural Sciences* 87(9), 1165-1169.

Yaseen, M. and Malhi, S.S. (2009a) Variation in yield, phosphorus uptake, and physiological efficiency of wheat genotypes at adequate and stress phosphorus levels in soil. *Communications in Soil Science and Plant Analysis* 40(19-20), 3104-3120.

Yaseen, M. and Malhi, S.S. (2009b) Differential growth response of wheat genotypes to ammonium phosphate and rock phosphate phosphorus sources. *Journal of plant nutrition* 32(3), 410-432.

Yaseen, T., Burni, T. and Hussain, F. (2011) Effect of arbuscular mycorrhizal inoculation on nutrient uptake, growth and productivity of cowpea (*Vigna unguiculata*) varieties. *African Journal of Biotechnology* 10(43), 8593-8598.

Zhang, Y., Chen, X., Zhang, C., Pan, G. and Zhang, X. (2014) Availability of soil nitrogen and phosphorus under elevated [CO_2] and temperature in the Taihu Lake region, China. *Journal of Plant Nutrition and Soil Science* 177(3), 343-348.

Zhang, Z., Liao, H. and Lucas, W.J. (2014) Molecular mechanisms underlying phosphate sensing, signaling, and adaptation in plants. *Journal of Integrative Plant Biology* 56(3), 192-220.

CHAPTER 8

Response of pulse crops to zinc application

Dharmendra Singh Yashona[1] and Satish Bhagwatrao Aher[2]*

1. *ICAR-Indian Institute of Soil Science, Nabibagh, Bhopal 462 038, Madhya Pradesh, India*

2. *ICMR-National Institute for Research in Environmental Health, Bhauri, Bhopal 462 030, Madhya Pradesh, India*

*Corresponding author email: satishbaher@yahoo.com

Abstract

Pulses are important food crops contributing to healthy diets. Zinc has been the micronutrient needed by crops especially pulses in large quantity. Unfortunately, zinc deficiency in Indian soils has been continuously increasing. Zn plays a major role in plant physiological processes which influences growth, yield and quality of crops. Zinc deficiency in plants causes typical symptoms; however, up to 50% reduction in crop growth can result due to Zn deficiency without the appearance of visual symptoms. The studies involving the assessment of pulse crop performance under the application of different form and rate of zinc has been synthesized and response of pulse crop to zinc application is presented. The studies revealed that, zinc plays a vital role in growth, physiology, metabolism, yield, and quality of pulses. The pulse crop responds positively to the applied zinc which reflected in terms of better vegetative growth, yield and quality of the pulse crops.

Keywords: Produce quality, Pulse crop, Yield, Zinc, Zinc nutrition, Zinc fertilization

1. INTRODUCTION

Pulses are important food crops that can play a major role in addressing future global food security and environmental challenges, as well as in contributing to healthy diets. In a country where vegetarianism is promoted, pulses form the indispensable constituent of the daily dining plate of the poorest Indian. Pulses are an important group of food crops that can play a vital role to address national food and nutritional security. Pulses are an important source to provide high quality protein complementing cereal proteins for pre-dominantly substantial vegetarian population of the country. In India, pulses can be produced with a minimum use of resources and hence, it becomes less costly even than animal protein. In comparison to other vegetables, pulses are rich in protein which are less expensive and can be cultivated as an inter-crop and also as mixed crop. Pulses are mostly cultivated under rainfed conditions and do not require intensive irrigation facility and this is the reason why pulses are grown in areas left after satisfying the demand for cereals/cash crops. Even in such conditions, pulses give better returns. Unfortunately, the zinc deficiency in Indian soils is continuously increasing. It is inducing Zn deficiency in human and animal due to reduction in concentration of zinc in edible plant parts. Recent research revealed that one third of the world population under the risk of zinc malnutrition. Zinc plays an important role in metabolism both in plants as well as animals by acting as essential component of enzyme, RNA, electron carrier etc. Soil is the only source for availability of zinc to plants and animals naturally but the intensive cropping system involving high yielding varieties have led to depletion of soil zinc.

2. ZINC: AN ESSENTIAL PLANT NUTRIENT

2.1 Role of zinc in plant metabolism

Zinc is directly and indirectly involved in the synthesis and metabolism in living organisms and plants. Zinc serves as an essential component of enzymes and acts as a functional, structural and/or regulatory cofactor of a large number of enzymes. The proteinases, peptidases, carbonic, anhydrase, dehydrogenase, etc. are the examples metalloenzymes in which zinc is the integral part. Besides enzymes, zinc also associated with the proteins and plays an important role. The plants exhibited lower rate of protein synthesis and protein accumulation under zinc deficiency. Zinc also plays important role in physiological process of plants through synthesis of hormones essential for growth and reproduction. Zinc is an essential component of RNA polymerase and provides structural integrity to ribosomes. It also has a significant role in plant metabolism and synthesis of auxins, carbohydrate, phosphate and nucleic acid (Latef *et al.,* 2017). The high concentration of Zn indicates the role of Zn in physiological processes *viz.*, protein synthesis, cell elongation, membrane function and resistance to abiotic stresses in early seedling development. Marschner (1995) reported that higher seed Zn content during germination and seedling development stage expressed greater resistance to soil borne pathogens, thus ensured good crop stand and better yield. Pulses are a good source of several micronutrients, in particular zinc and some B vitamins, compared to cereal crops and vegetables. It also plays a vital role in stomatal regulation and maintaining an ionic balance in plant system (Baybordi, 2006). Zinc is also involved in chlorophyll production, pollen function, fertilization and germination (Pandey *et al.,* 2006; Cakmak, 2008).

2.2 Zinc availability, deficiency and critical concentration

Application of acid producing amendments on alkaline and calcareous soils could decrease soil pH and consequently increase plant-available Zn (Singh *et al.,* 1989). The trace element zinc (Zn) is essential to the normal growth of plant. Only a small proportion of the total zinc in soil is available. The mobility and availability of zinc is controlled by chemical and biochemical processes including precipitation-dissolution, adsorption- desorption, complexation-dissolution and redox processes (Hursthouse, 2001). The zinc is relatively insoluble in soils. This insolubility is especially marked in soils where pH is greater than 5, as in many areas with low rainfall. Under these conditions, micronutrient cations react with hydroxyl ions, precipitating hydrous metal oxides. In order to hold these cations in solution, they must bond with an organic ligand, or chelating agent, which donates electrons to the cation (Salisbury and Ross, 1992). As for zinc deficiency is common throughout the world, particularly in soils with high pH, and is thought to be the most widespread micronutrient deficiency in cereals (Ruel and Bouis, 1998). Zinc deficiency in plants causes typical symptoms; however, up to 50% reduction in crop growth can result due to Zn deficiency without the appearance of visual symptoms. Deficiency of Zn causes chlorosis, sterility, reduction in leaf size and reduction in spikelet number (Cakmak, 2000). Zinc deficiency symptoms common to many crops normally appear in four-week-old plants on older and emerging leaves.

These are light green yellow or bleached spots in interveinal areas of older leaves. The emerging leaves become smaller in size and often termed as 'little leaf'. During severe deficiency, intermodal distance becomes too short so that all leaves appear to come out from the same point, and is termed as 'rosetting'. Major factors responsible for increase in incidences of Zn deficiency include large Zn removal due to high crop yields and intensive cropping system, lesser application of organic manures, use of high analysis fertilizers, increased use of phosphatic fertilizers resulting in phosphorus (P)-induced Zn deficiency and the use of constraint for crop production, especially in calcareous soils. Zinc is usually present in soil in adequate to excess amounts, but deficiency is caused by its presence in an unavailable form rather than by its lack (Rengel, 2001). In general, low Zn deficiency has been recorded in soils having acidic pH as compared to soils having high pH; however, soils of northern India, except Rajasthan, also displayed medium deficiency range as compared to previous studies due to regular use of $ZnSO_4$ fertilizer (Sadana *et al.*, 2010). On the other hand, increase in Zn deficiency in areas where low deficiency was recorded earlier has resulted from intensification of agricultural systems, faster depletion rate of available Zn pools (Shukla *et al.*, 2016). Zinc deficiency is the major cause of low productivity of the crops. The critical concentration of Zn in different pulse crop plants is presented in Table 1. ICAR-AICRP-MSN, Lucknow centre established the critical concentration of Zinc of various pulses crops. The values for each category varied among different crops and plant parts.

Table 1. Critical concentration of Zn (mg/kg) in different pulses

Crop	Growth period DAS	Plant part	Plant part	Threshold (deficiency)	Sufficiency
Chickpea	60	Middle leaf	<7	15	17
Pea	42	Middle leaf	<12	20	22-80
Lentil	55	Middle leaf	–	10	11-50
Mungbean	28	Middle leaf	<15	20	22
Urdbean	30	Middle leaf	<12	25	27-45
Cowpea	32	Lower bud	<20	45	50-150
French bean	75	Younger leaf	36	50	60-120

Source: Shukla and Tiwari (2014)

2.3 Zinc content and uptake in major pulses

The zinc concentration and uptake in major pulse crops is shown Table 2. The pigeonpea has highest Zn uptake potential whereas the lentil accumulates maximum zinc in grain.

The zinc concentration in pulse seed/grain generally ranges 20-80 mg kg^{-1} among various pulses. Similarly, the uptake of zinc varies between 100 and 400 g ha^{-1} among different pulses.

Table 2. Zinc content and uptake of major pulses in India

Crops	Seed Zn (mg/kg)	Zn uptake (g/ha)
Chickpea	35-50	150-250
Pigeonpea	30-50	125-400
Green gram	25-40	100-200
Black gram	20-60	100-200
Lentil	40-80	100-250
Field peas	35-65	100-250

3. RESPONSE OF PULSE CROPS TO ZINC APPLICATION

The application of graded level of soil zinc application on performance of different pulse crops has been widely studied since long. The response of different crops to the applied zinc through different modes alone or in combination has been reviewed with respect to growth parameters, yield attributes, yield and nutritional quality (Yashona *et al.,* 2018a). Performance of the crop is measured in terms of plant height, leaf area, primary and secondary branches, biomass accumulation, chlorophyll content, yield etc.

3.1 Plant height, branching, leaf area and chlorophyll content

Plant height is one of the important morphological growth parameter influenced by the applied nutrients and growth regulators. The zinc nutrition always proved as a promoter for crop growth. The positive results of zinc application through various modes in various pulse crops are presented in Table 3. Similar to the soil application, the application of zinc in combination with FYM is known for imparting favorable changes in the plant height of the crop. The application through soil or in combination with the FYM becomes difficult when the standing crop shows the zinc deficiency. The foliar application of nutrients in standing crops in order to avoid the deficiency had been introduced. The application of zinc through foliar application of zinc salts proved beneficial in eliminating the Zn deficiency in many crops especially pulses. The increment in plant height of different pulse crops has been documented by many researchers. The foliar Zn application at flowering and podding stages has been effective in prevention of flower and premature abscission and acceleration of assimilate translocation in pulses (Tekale *et al.,* 2009). The importance of appropriate time of application (*i.e.* flowering and panicle initiation) of Zn could alter the physiological events of crop. Increase in plant height was mainly attributed due to higher shoot growth through cell elongation, cell differentiation and apical dominance promoted by zinc. Zinc were also supposed to be involved in the hormone synthesis, hence indirectly related to translocation and metabolism of carbohydrate finally contributing to additional growth compared to control (Padma *et al.,* 1989; Deotale *et al.,* 1998).

Number of main branch and number of sub branch plays an important role in determining the yield of the crop. The positive effect of soil zinc application on branching in pulse crops has been reported by many researchers throughout the globe (Table 3). The studies in Table 3 showed that Zn had significant effects on branching in the studied crops. The effect of application of soil zinc in combination with FYM also found beneficial with respect to branching in the different crops. Similarly, positive effect of foliar application of Zn on enhanced branching in pulse crops has also been reported which was mainly attributed to promotion of bud and branch development by the auxins whereas Zn application ultimately increased the availability of other nutrients and accelerated the translocation of photo assimilates (Guhey, 1999; Barclay and Mcdavid, 1980). The application of zinc greatly influences the leaf area and leaf area index in pulse crop. The studies mentioned in table 3 are few examples of positive effect of zinc application on leaf area of crop (Thamke, 2017; Mondal *et al.*, 2011). The effects of zinc application on leaf area mainly attributed to more availability of zinc both during seedling and subsequent stages of plant growth which has been known to increase photosynthates and 'N' fixation (Hegazy *et al.*, 1990; Nayak, 1989).

Table 3. Response of zinc application to crop growth parameters in pulses

Crop parameter	Crop	Zinc form and dose	Mode of application	Reference
Plant height	Chickpea	0.2% $ZnSO_4$	Foliar	Habbasha *et al.* (2013)
		0.5% $ZnSO_4$	-do-	Hidoto *et al.* (2017)
		15 kg Zn/ha	Soil	Sangwan and Raj (2004)
		20 kg $ZnSO_4$/ha	-do-	Khrogamy and Farnia (2009)
	Pigeonpea	5 mg Zn/kg	-do-	Dube *et al.* (2001)
		20 kg Zn/ha	-do-	Shah *et al.* (2016)
		15 kg $ZnSO_4$/ha	-do-	Thamke (2017); Sharma *et al.* (2009); Rathod *et al.* (2017)
		20 kg $ZnSO_4$/ha	-do-	Puste and Jana (1988)
	Cowpea	Zn 100 ppm	Foliar	Fouda and Abd-Elhamied (2017)
		0.1% Zn spray	-do-	Salehin and Rahman (2012)
		12.5 kg $ZnSO_4$/ha	Soil	Nagaraju and Yadahalli (1996)
		25 kg $ZnSO_4$/ha	-do-	Patel *et al.* (2011)
	Mungbean	2 µM Foliar	Foliar	Tayyeba *et al.* (2017)
		10 kg Zn/ha	Soil	Ram and Kattiyar (2013)
	Cluster bean	5 kg Zn/ha	-do-	Kuniya *et al.* (2018)

Branching	Chickpea	0.5 % $ZnSO_4$	Foliar	Hidoto *et al.* (2017)
		5 kg Zn/ha	Soil	Kuldeep *et al.* (2018)
		15 kg Zn/ha	-do-	Sangwan and Raj (2004)
		20 kg $ZnSO_4$/ha	-do-	Khrogamy and Farnia (2009)
	Pigeonpea	5 mg Zn/kg	-do-	Dube *et al.* (2001)
		15 kg $ZnSO_4$/ha		Sharma *et al.* (2009); Rathod *et al.* (2017)
	Cowpea	ZnSO4 0.05%	Seed treatment	Raj (2019)
		Zn 100 ppm	Foliar	Fouda and Abd-Elhamied (2017)
		25 kg $ZnSO_4$/ha	Soil	Patel *et al.* (2011)
	Cluster bean	5 kg Zn/ha	-do-	Kuniya *et al.* (2018)
	Mungbean	10 kg Zn/ha	-do-	Ram and Kattiyar (2013)
Leaf area	Pigeonpea	15 kg $ZnSO_4$/ha	-do-	Thamke (2017)
		20 kg $ZnSO_4$/ha	-do-	Puste and Jana (1988)
	Mungbean	0.1% Zn	Foliar	Mondal *et al.* (2011)

3.2 Chlorophyll content, nodulation, test weight and harvest index

The application of zinc improves the chlorophyll content in plant leaf. The effects of zinc application on chlorophyll and leaf area mainly attributed to more availability of zinc both during seedling and subsequent stages of plant growth which has been known to increase photosynthates and 'N' fixation (Hegazy *et al.,* 1990; Nayak, 1989). The zinc have important role in chlorophyll formation which enhanced chlorophyll content in leaf of the plants (Sharma *et al.,* 2010). Chickpea, cluster bean, mungbean, soybean and pigeonpea showed positive response to applied zinc in terms of nodulation (Table 4). The various modes and rates of zinc application in pulse crop results in significantly higher number of root nodules and nodule fresh weight. Hundred grain weight/seed index is one of the most important yield components in crop.

Table 4. Response of zinc application on chlorophyll content, nodulation, test weight and harvest index in pulse crops

Crop parameter	Crop	Zinc form and dose	Mode of application	Reference
Chlorophyll	Mungbean	2 µM Zn	Foliar	Tayyeba *et al.* (2017)
	Soybean	200 µM Zn	-do-	Rahdari *et al.* (2013)
	Cowpea	100 ppm Zn	-do-	Fouda and Abd-Elhamied (2017)
	Pigeonpea	0.5% $ZnSO_4$	-do-	Purushottam *et al.* (2018)
	Chickpea	1.5 kg Zn/ha	Soil	Akay (2011)

Nodulation	Cowpea	0.05% $ZnSO_4$	Seed	Raj (2019)
		7.5 kg Zn/ha	Soil	Debnath *et al.* (2018)
		15 kg Zn/ha	-do-	Upadhyay and Singh (2016)
	Cluster bean	5.0 kg Zn/ha	-do-	Kuniya *et al.* (2018)
	Soybean	5 kg Zn/ha	-do-	Chauhan *et al.* (2013)
	Mungbean	10 kg Zn/ha	-do-	Ram and Kattiyar (2013)
	Chickpea	20 kg $ZnSO_4$/ha	-do-	Khorgamy and farina (2009)
Test weight	Pigeonpea	0.5% $ZnSO_4$	Foliar	Channabasavanna *et al.* (2017)
		20 kg Zn/ha	Soil	Shah *et al.* (2016)
		12.5 kg $ZnSO_4$/ha	-do-	Umesh and Shankar (2013)
		15 kg $ZnSO_4$/ha	-do-	Thamke (2017); Rathod *et al.* (2017)
		20 kg $ZnSO_4$/ha	-do-	Srikanth Babu *et al.* (2012)
		25 kg $ZnSO_4$/ha	-do-	Sharma *et al.* (2010)
	Chickpea	0.5% $ZnSO_4$	Foliar	Hidoto *et al.* (2017)
		15 kg Zn/ha	Soil	Sangwan and Raj (2004)
		20 kg $ZnSO_4$/ha	-do-	Khrogamy and Farnia (2009)
	Mungbean	500 ppm Zn		Ali and Mahmoud (2013)
		5.5 kg Zn/ha	Soil	Roy *et al.* (2017)
		10 kg Zn/ha	-do-	Ram and Katiyar (2013)
	Cluster bean	0.5% $ZnSO_4$	Foliar	Prasanna *et al.* (2014)
		5.0 kg Zn/ha	Soil	Kuniya *et al.* (2018)
	Cowpea	100 ppm Zn	Foliar	Fouda and Abd-Elhamied (2017)
		25 kg $ZnSO_4$/ha	Soil	Patel *et al.* (2011)
	Soybean	Zn (116 ppm)	Foliar	Heidarian *et al.* (2011)
Harvest index	Pigeonpea	0.5% $ZnSO_4$	-do-	Purushottam *et al.* (2018)
		5 mg Zn/ha	Soil	Dube *et al.* (2001)
		Vermicompost + 5 kg Zn/ha	-do-	Kumawat *et al.* (2015)
	Chickpea	0.5% $ZnSO_4$	Foliar	Hidoto *et al.* (2017)
	Mungbean	0.1% Zn	-do-	Mondal *et al.* (2011)

The application of zinc showed significant effect on the size and weight of the seeds. The studies mentioned in Table 4 concluded that the application of zinc in different forms and rates results in significantly higher test weight. Besides sole inorganic and combined with FYM application, the foliar application with different magnitudes and at different growth stages significantly alters the test weight in various pulse crops. Harvest index (HI) is the genetic character of the crop and varies with cultivar. The harvest index of the crop generally remains unchanged but some crucial management practices make some changes in HI. The studies involving the application of the zinc showed favorable results with respect to the harvest index of crop (Table 4).

3.3 Seed and pod number

Zinc application either alone or in combination with FYM through soil and/or foliar application improves the seed/pod or pods/plant in pulse crops. The studies mentioned in Table 5 indicated the enhancement of number of pods per plant and number of seeds per plant upon application of zinc. The enhancement effect on seed/pod and pods/plant attributed to the favorable influence of the Zn application to crops on nutrient metabolism, biological activity and growth parameters and hence applied zinc resulted in taller plant and higher enzyme activity which in turn encourage vegetative branches and pods/plant (Michail *et al.,* 2004).

3.4 Seed/grain Zn and protein content

The soil available nutrients, applied nutrients and their accumulation in the plant have significant positive relationships. The studies mentioned in Table 6 shows the positive response of crop towards zinc application with respect to the seed/grain zinc concentration. These studies showed positive response towards accumulation of Zn in plant tissues at different developmental stages. The relationship between the bio-accumulation of zinc and the zinc concentration in the nutrient solution has been noted earlier by Cui and Wang (2005) and Sharma and Agrawal (2006). The increased Zn content in seed/grain upon zinc fertilization offers a practical and useful option towards eliminating the Zn deficiency through biofortification. Plant nutrient increases assimilation, production and photosynthesis efficiency at seed formation stage (Taliee and Sayadian, 2000). The micronutrients especially Zinc have important role in chlorophyll formation, carbohydrate metabolism, synthesis of proteins and activation of oxidation process and enzymes. Zn is required for the biosynthesis of plant growth regulator (IAA) and for carbohydrate and N metabolism which leads to improvement in seed quality components (Taliee and Sayadian, 2000). The work mentioned in Table 6 revealed the fact that, the application of zinc improved the protein content in pulse crops. Zn fertilizer ($ZnSO_4$) decreases pH of soil in drylands and increases root absorption of minerals (Taliee and Sayadian, 2000). Thus, good and correct management of macronutrients and zinc (both rate and type of application) improves soil fertility which can lead to high protein content in seed. Calhor (2006) and Yilmaz (1997) reported that Zn deficiency caused low protein content in seed of pulse and cereal. Ved *et al.* (2002) stated that foliar applied zinc enhances photosynthesis, early growth of plants, improves nitrogen fixation, grain protein and yields.

Table 5. Response of zinc application on pod formation of seed numbers in pulse crops

Crop parameter	Crop	Zinc form and dose	Mode of application	Reference
Pods per plant	Pigeonpea	0.5% $ZnSO_4$	Foliar	Channabasavanna *et al.* (2017)
		5 mg/kg Zn	Soil	Dube *et al.* (2001)
		20 kg Zn/ha	-do-	Shah *et al.* (2016)
		12.5 kg $ZnSO_4$/ha	-do-	Umesh and Shankar (2013)
		15 kg $ZnSO_4$/ha	-do-	Thamke (2017); Rathod *et al.* (2017)

		20 kg $ZnSO_4$/ha	-do-	Puste and Jana (1988); Srikanth Babu *et al.* (2012)
		25 kg $ZnSO_4$/ha	-do-	Sharma *et al.* (2010)
	Mungbean	20 ppm Zn	Foliar	Malik *et al.* (2015)
		500 ppm Zn	-do-	Ali and Mahmoud (2013)
		0.1% Zn	-do-	Mondal *et al.* (2011)
		5.5 kg Zn/ha	Soil	Roy *et al.* (2017)
		10 kg Zn/ha	-do-	Ram and Katiyar (2013)
	Chickpea	0.2% $ZnSO_4$	Foliar	Habbasha *et al.* (2013)
		0.5% $ZnSO_4$	-do-	Hidoto *et al.* (2017)
		0.5% Zn-EDTA	-do-	Shivay *et al.* (2015)
		Zn at 15 kg/ha	Soil	Sangwan and Raj (2004)
	Cowpea	Zn 100 ppm	Foliar	Fouda and Abd-Elhamied (2017)
		0.1% Zn spray	-do-	Salehin and Rahman (2012)
		25 kg $ZnSO_4$/ha	Soil	Patel *et al.* (2011)
	Cluster bean	0.5% $ZnSO_4$	Foliar	Prasanna *et al.* (2014)
		5 kg Zn/ha	Soil	Kuniya *et al.* (2018)
	Moth bean	0.5% ZnSO4	Foliar	Ramesh (2002)
	Soybean	116 ppm Zn	-do-	Heidarian *et al.* (2011)
Seeds per pod	Pigeonpea	0.5% $ZnSO_4$	-do-	Channabasavanna *et al.* (2017)
		5 mg/kg Zn	Soil	Dube *et al.* (2001)
		20 kg Zn/ha	-do-	Shah *et al.* (2016)
		20 kg $ZnSO_4$/ha	-do-	Srikanth Babu *et al.* (2012)
		25 kg $ZnSO_4$/ha	-do-	Sharma *et al.* (2010)
	Mungbean	20 ppm zinc	Foliar	Malik *et al.* (2015)
		5.5 kg Zn/ha	Soil	Roy *et al.* (2017)
		10 kg Zn/ha	-do-	Ram and Katiyar (2013)
	Cowpea	Zn 100 ppm	Foliar	Fouda and Abd-Elhamied (2017)
		0.1% Zn spray	-do-	Salehin and Rahman (2012)
		25 kg $ZnSO_4$/ha	Soil	Patel *et al.* (2011)
	Cluster bean	0.5% $ZnSO_4$	Foliar	Prasanna *et al.* (2014)
		5 kg Zn/ha	Soil	Kuniya *et al.* (2018)
	Chickpea	0.5% Zn-EDTA	Foliar	Shivay *et al.* (2015)
	Soybean	116 ppm Zn	-do-	Heidarian *et al.* (2011)

Table 6. Response of zinc application on seed/grain zinc and protein content in pulse crops

Crop parameter	Crop	Zinc form and dose	Mode of application	Reference
Zn content grain	Chickpea	0.5% Zn-EDTA	Foliar	Shivay *et al.* (2015)
		0.5% $ZnSO_4$	-do-	Hidoto *et al.* (2017)
		20 kg $ZnSO_4$/ha	Soil	Khorgamy and Farnia (2009)
		25 kg+0.5% $ZnSO_4$	Soil+ foliar	Sharafi (2015)
	Mungbean	2 μM Zn	Foliar	Tayyeba *et al.* (2017)
		5.5 kg Zn/ha	Soil	Roy *et al.* (2017)
		10 kg $ZnSO_4$/ha	-do-	Ranpariya *et al.* (2017)
		5.5 kg Zn/ha + 0.1% Zn	Soil+ foliar	Roy *et al.* (2014)
	Pigeonpea	0.5% $ZnSO_4$	Foliar	Purushottam *et al.* (2018); Hanumanthappa *et al.* (2018)
		5 mg Zn/kg	Soil	Dube *et al.* (2001)
		7.5 kg Zn/ha	-do-	Rao and Sresty (2000)
	Cowpea	2 ppm Zn	Foliar	Salih (2013)
	Urdbean	0.5% $ZnSO_4$	-do-	Pandey and Gupta (2012)
	Pea	16 kg Zn/ha	Soil	Rafique *et al.* (2015)
Protein	Pigeonpea	20 kg Zn/ha	-do-	Shah *et al.* (2016)
		15 kg $ZnSO_4$/ha	-do-	Thamke (2017)
		25 kg $ZnSO_4$/ha	-do-	Sharma *et al.* (2010)
	Chickpea	0.2% $ZnSO_4$	Foliar	Habbasha *et al.* (2013)
		10 kg Zn/ha	Soil	Singh and Singh (2012)
		20 kg $ZnSO_4$/ha	-do-	Khrogamy and Farnia (2009)
		25 kg+0.5 % $ZnSO_4$	Soil+ foliar	Sharafi (2015)
	Mungbean	2 μM Zn.	Foliar	Tayyeba *et al.* (2017)
		5.5 kg Zn/ha	Soil	Roy *et al.* (2017)
		10 kg Zn/ha	-do-	Ram and Kattiyar (2013)
		5.5 kg Zn/ha + 0.1% Zn	Soil+ foliar	Roy *et al.* (2014)
	Cowpea	0.05% $ZnSO_4$	Seed treat.	Raj (2019)
		Zn 100 ppm	Foliar	Fouda and Abd-Elhamied (2017)
		Zn 20 kg/ha	Soil	Chavan *et al.* (2012)
	Cluster bean	0.5 % $ZnSO_4$	Foliar	Prasanna *et al.* 2014
		5.0 kg Zn/ha	Soil	Kuniya *et al.* (2018)
		20 kg+0.5% $ZnSO_4$	Soil+ foliar	Selvaraj and Prasanna (2012)

3.5 Zinc uptake and crop yield

The nutrient uptake in any crop is the resultant of crop yield and nutrient concentration in plant tissue/grain. Many researchers found positive influence of zinc application on zinc uptake by crop especially pulses (Table 7). The relationship between the bio-accumulation of zinc and the zinc concentration in the nutrient solution has been noted earlier by Cui and Wang (2005) and Sharma and Agrawal (2006). The zinc concentration in plant tissues increases with the increase in time and in the intensity of treatment. Leaf shows greater accumulation of zinc in the treatments receiving foliar application of zinc. The higher accumulation of the zinc in the plant tissues *viz*., leaf, stalk and grain results in the higher total zinc uptake. It is the compound effect of grain and stalk yield of their content. Grain yield is the ultimate economic produce of the crop which is determined by grain weight, number of grains/unit land area as governed by the management practices and its native genetic potential. Studies on response of Zn fertilization to crop yield showed positive effect. The combined application of Zn with FYM or foliar spray with different magnitude and time to various crops showed significant increment in yield (Table 7). The various pulse crops viz., urdbean (18%), chickpea (24-37%), cluster bean (40-54%), cowpea (15-43%), mungbean (18-57%), pigeonpea (23-67%) and soybean (29-43%) recorded higher yields upon zinc fertilization (Table 7). The foliar application of zinc helps standing crop to eliminate the zinc deficiency. The crop response is more prompt in case of foliar application than any other mode as the zinc is readily assimilated by the crop through leaves. Among these studies, the treatments involving application of soil zinc in combination with foliar zinc and FYM found most beneficial with respect to improvement in growth and yield of crops (Yashona *et al.,* 2019). Zn is required for the biosynthesis of plant growth regulator (IAA) and for carbohydrate and N metabolism which leads to high yield and yield components (Taliee and Sayadian, 2000). Overcoming limitations to plant nutrient through the application of appropriate fertilizers increased assimilate production and photosynthesis efficiency at the seed filling stage (Yilmaz *et al.,* 1997; Ali *et al.,* 2004; Calhor, 2006). High harvest index indicates a high seed yield (economic yield) relative to total biomass production. Zn fertilizer ($ZnSO_4$) decreases pH of soil in dry lands and increases root absorption of minerals (Taliee and Sayadian, 2000). The positive crop response to zinc fertilization either through soil or foliar with and without FYM might be due to the Zn fertilizer (as $ZnSO_4$) decreases pH of soil and increases root absorption of minerals and improved Zn nutrition of plants that improves biosynthesis of the plant growth regulator IAA, carbohydrate and N-metabolism which lead to high yield components and yield. The enhanced plant nutrition increases photosynthesis efficiency, assimilation and production (Taliee and Sayadian, 2000; Jakson *et al.,* 2003; Calhor, 2006; Amjad *et al.,* 2004 and Ali *et al.,* 2004; Yashona *et al.,* 2020). Dry matter accumulation in the plant at progressive stages is a justified assessment of growth as a cumulative expression of different growth parameters. Further, it was observed that crop productivity is not only dependent on accumulation of total amount of dry matter but its effective partitioning into economic sink seems to be key to increase the yield. Auxin is known to maintain the higher rate of photosynthesis which contributed to higher dry matter which was an indicator of current photosynthesis (Bangla *et al.,* 1983; Puste and Jana, 1988; Shinde *et al.,* 1991 and Upadhyay, 2002).

Table 7. Response of zinc application on zinc uptake and grain/seed yield in pulse crops

Crop parameter	Crop	Zinc form and dose	Mode of application	Reference
Zn uptake	Mungbean	5 kg Zn/ha	Soil	Meena *et al.* (2017)
		10 kg $ZnSO_4$/ha	-do-	Ranpariya *et al.* (2017)
		5.5 kg Zn/ha + 0.1% Zn	Soil+ foliar	Roy *et al.* (2014)
	Pigeonpea	0.5% $ZnSO_4$	Foliar	Purushottam *et al.* (2018)
		Vermicompost + 5 kg Zn/ha	Soil	Kumawat *et al.* (2015)
		12.5 kg $ZnSO_4$/ha	-do-	Umesh and Shankar (2013)
	Chickpea	0.5% Zn-EDTA	Foliar	Shivay *et al.* (2015)
	Pea	16 kg Zn/ha	Soil	Rafique *et al.* (2015)
Yield	Pigeonpea	0.5% $ZnSO_4$	Foliar	Channabasavanna *et al.* (2017); Purushottam *et al.* (2018)
		5 kg Zn/ha	Soil	Mali *et al.* (2003)
		15 kg ZnSO4/ha	-do-	Rathod *et al.* (2017)
		15 kg ZnSO4+ 5 t FYM/ha	Soil+ FYM	Sharma *et al.* (2009)
	Chickpea	0.2% $ZnSO_4$	Foliar	Habbasha *et al.* (2013)
		0.5% $ZnSO_4$	-do-	Hidoto *et al.* (2017)
		0.5% Zn-EDTA	-do-	Shivay *et al.* (2015)
		15 kg Zn/ha	Soil	Sangwan and Raj (2004)
		25 kg + 0.5% $ZnSO_4$	Soil + foliar	Sharafi (2015)
	Mungbean	500 ppm Zn	Foliar	Ali and Mahmoud (2013)
		5 kg Zn/ha	Soil	Srinivasarao (2012); Meena *et al.* (2017)
		5.5 kg Zn/ha	-do-	Roy *et al.* (2017)
		10 kg Zn/ha	-do-	Ram and Kattiyar (2013)
		5.5 kg Zn/ha + 0.1% Zn	Soil+ foliar	Roy *et al.* (2014)
	Cowpea	Zn 100 ppm	Foliar	Fouda and Abd-Elhamied (2017)
		0.1% Zn	-do-	Salehin and Rahman (2012)
		0.5% $ZnSO_4$	-do-	Anitha *et al.* (2005)
		25 kg $ZnSO_4$/ha	Soil	Patel *et al.* (2011)
	Culaster bean	5 kg Zn/ha	-do-	Kuniya *et al.* (2018)
		0.5% $ZnSO_4$	Soil+ foliar	Prasanna *et al.* 2014
		20 kg + 0.5% $ZnSO_4$	-do-	Selvaraj and Prasanna (2012)
	Blackgram	0.5% $ZnSO_4$	Foliar	Pandey and Gupta (2012)
	Pea	16 kg Zn/ha	Soil	Rafique *et al.* (2015)
	Soybean	1.0% $ZnSO_4$	Foliar	Gowthami and Rao (2014)
		5 kg Zn/ha	Soil	Chauhan *et al.* (2013)

4. RATE AND MODES OF ZINC APPLICATION AND PERFORMANCE OF PIGEONPEA: A TWO YEARS STUDY

The rate and mode of zinc application and response of pigeonpea was studied at Mahatma Gandhi Chitrakoot Gramodaya Vishwa Vidyalaya, Chitrakoot during 2013-14 and 2014-15. The data pertaining to the plant height of pigeonpea as influenced by sole and combined mode of zinc nutrition is presented in Table 8. The plant height of pigeonpea found 3-14% higher under the treatments receiving different mode of zinc application and their combination as compared to the control (no zinc application). The average increment in plant height over control was 9%. The application of 12.5 kg $ZnSO_4$ either alone or in combination with FYM and/or foliar application registered 3-12% higher plant height as compared to control. Similarly, the application of 25 kg $ZnSO_4$ either alone or in combination with FYM and/or foliar zinc increased plant height of pigeonpea by 7-14% over control (Table 8). In general, the plant height responded to the combined application of soil zinc, foliar zinc and FYM as the zinc application proved beneficial effects of combined method of application of zinc on growth of pigeonpea. The number of pods per plant in pigeonpea at harvest was found 1-16% higher under the treatments receiving different mode of zinc application and their combination as compared to the control. The application of zinc either alone or in combination with FYM and/or foliar application registered significantly higher pods in pigeonpea plant as compared to control. Similarly, the number of seeds per pod in pigeonpea found 1-6% higher under the treatments receiving different mode of zinc application and their combination as compared to the control. However, the application of zinc either alone or in combination had no significant effect on seeds per pod in pigeonpea. The test weight of pigeonpea found 1-5% higher under the treatments receiving different mode of zinc application and their combination as compared to the control. Among these treatments, the treatments involving application of soil zinc in combination with foliar zinc and FYM found most beneficial with respect to improvement in test weight of pigeonpea (Table 8).

Table 8. Response of rate and modes of zinc application on performance of pigeonpea

Treatment	Plant height (cm)	Pods per plant	Test weight (g)	Yield (t/ha)	Grain protein (%)	Grain zinc (mg/kg)
Control	195	46.8	90.8	1.91	18.7	29.1
25 kg $ZnSO_4$/ha	208	48.6	91.4	2.06	20.3	32.1
25 kg $ZnSO_4$/ha +FYM @ 5 t/ha	217	53.0	93.4	2.26	20.8	35.1
25 kg $ZnSO_4$/ha +FYM @ 5 t/ha + 0.5% foliar $ZnSO_4$	222	53.8	95.4	2.38	21.9	51.5
12.5 kg $ZnSO_4$/ha	200	47.2	91.0	2.04	20.2	30.0
12.5 kg $ZnSO_4$/ha +FYM @ 5 t/ha	214	52.4	93.2	2.22	20.5	33.1
12.5 kg $ZnSO_4$/ha +FYM @ 5 t/ha + 0.5% foliar $ZnSO_4$	218	54.1	94.9	2.34	21.7	48.9

Source: Yashona *et al.* (2018b); Yashona *et al.* (2018c)

The grain yield of pigeonpea found 7-25% higher under the treatments receiving different mode of zinc application and their combination as compared to the control (no zinc application). The application of 12.5 kg $ZnSO_4$ either alone or in combination with FYM and/or foliar application registered 7-23% higher grain yield as compared to control. Similarly, the application of 25 kg $ZnSO_4$ either alone or in combination with FYM and/or foliar zinc increased grain yield of pigeonpea by 8-25% over control. The application of 0.5% $ZnSO_4$ as foliar spray at flower initiation and/or pod initiation stage in combination with different soil application (12.5 or 25 kg $ZnSO_4$) with or without FYM 5 t/ha showed 15-25% higher grain yield over control. Similarly, zinc fertilization through soil (with or without foliar application) in combination with FYM 5 t/ha increased grain yield of pigeonpea by 16-25% as compared to the control. Among these treatments, the treatments involving application of soil zinc in combination with foliar zinc and FYM found most beneficial with respect to improvement in grain yield of pigeonpea. The protein contents in pigeonpea grain ranged from 18.67% in treatment control to 21.9% in treatment receiving 25 kg $ZnSO_4$ + FYM 5 t/ha+ foliar Zn application. The protein content in pigeonpea found 8-17% higher under the treatments receiving different mode of zinc application and their combination as compared to the control. Similarly, the zinc content in pigeonpea grain varied from 29.0 in Control to 51.5 mg/kg in treatment receiving 25 kg $ZnSO_4$ + 5 t FYM and two foliar application of 0.5% $ZnSO_4$ at flowering and pod initiation stage (Table 8). The treatments receiving the application of 5 t FYM along with 0.5% $ZnSO_4$ foliar application both at flowering and pod initiation stage found significantly higher Zn content in pigeonpea grain as compared to rest other treatments. The increment was 3-77% higher as compared to the control. Among these treatments, the treatments involving application of soil zinc in combination with foliar zinc and FYM found most beneficial with respect to improvement in grain Zn content in pigeonpea (Table 8).

5. CONCLUSION

The comprehensive review of the studies involving the assessment of pulse crop performance under the application of different form and rate of zinc revealed that, the zinc plays a vital role in growth, physiology, metabolism, yield, and quality of pulses. The pulse crop responds positively to the applied zinc which reflects in terms of vegetative growth, yield and quality of the pulse crops.

REFERENCES

Akay, A. (2011) Effect of zinc fertilizer applications on yield and element contents of some registered chickpeas varieties. *African Journal of Biotechnolog* 10(60), 12890-12896.

Ali, E.A. and Mahmoud, A.M. (2013) Effect of foliar spray by different salicylic acid and zinc concentrations on seed yield and yield components of mungbean in sandy soil. *Asian Journal of Crop Science* 5, 33-40.

Ali, H., Khan, M.A. and Randhawa, S.A. (2004) Interactive effects of seed inoculation and phosphorous application on growth and yield of chick pea (*Cicer arietinum* L.). *International Journal of Agriculture and Biology* 6(1), 110-112.

Anitha, S., Sreenivasan, E. and Purushothaman, S.M. (2005) Response of cowpea (*Vigna unguiculata* (L.) Walp.) to foliar nutrition of zinc and iron in the oxisols of Kerala. *Legume Research* 28(4), 294-296.

Bangla, D.B., Deshmukh, S.N, and Patil, V.A. (1983) Contribution of pod wall in grain development of Chickpea (*Cicer arientanum* L.) as influenced by growth promoter. *Indian Journal of Plant Physiology* 26, 292-295.

Barclay, G.F. and McDavid, C.R. (1980) Effect of benzylaminopurine on fruit set and seed development in pigeon pea (*Cajanus cajan*). *Scientia Horticulturae* 72(2), 81-86.

Baybordi, A. (2006) Effect of Fe, Mn, Zn and Cu on the quality and quantity of wheat under salinity stress. *Journal of Water and Soil Science* 17, 140-150.

Cakmak, I. (2000) Possible roles of zinc in protecting plant cells from damage by reactive oxygen species. *New Phytologist* 146(2), 185-205.

Cakmak, I. (2008) Enrichment of cereal grains with zinc: Agronomic or genetic biofortification. *Plant and Soil* 302, 1-17.

Cakmak, I. (2009) Enrichment of fertilizers with zinc: An excellent investment for humanity and crop production in India. *Journal of Trace Elements in Medicine and Biology* 23, 281-289.

Calhor, M. (2006) Effect of nitrogen and zinc on yield of durum wheat in Khoramabad Region. Thesis, Agricultural Research Institute, Lorestan, Iran.

Channabasavanna, A.S., Kitturmath, M.S. and Rajakumar, H. (2017) Effect of soil and foliar application of micro nutrients and fertilizers on growth and yield of pigeon pea [*Cajanus cajan* (L.) Millsp.]. *Journal of Farm Sciences* 30(3), 424-425.

Chavan, A.S., Khafi, M.R., Raj, A.D. and Parmar, R.M. (2012) Effect of potassium and zinc on yield, protein content and uptake of micronutrients on cow-pea (*Vigna unguiculata* (L.) Walp. *Agricultural Science Digest* 32, 175-177.

Cui, Y. and Wang, Q. (2005) Interaction effect of zinc and elemental sulfur on their uptake by spring wheat. *Journal of Plant Nutrition* 28, 639-649.

Debnath, P., Pattanaaik, S.K., Sah, D., Chandra, G. and Pandey, A.K. (2018) Effect of boron and zinc fertilization on growth and yield of cowpea (*Vigna unguiculata* Walp.) in Inceptisols of Arunachal Pradesh. *Journal of Indian Society of Soil Science* 66(2), 229-234.

Deotale, R.D., Maske, V.G., Sorte, N.V., Chimurkar, B.S. and Yerne, A.Z. (1998) Effect of GAa and NAA on morphological parameters of soybean. *Journal of Soils and Crops* 8(1), 91-94.

Dube, B.K., Sharma, C.P. and Chatterjee, C. (2001) Response of pigeon pea to applied zinc in Ustifluvent soils of Western, Uttar Pradesh. *Journal of Indian Society of Soil Science* 49(3), 471-475.

Fouda, K.F. and Abd-Elhamied, A.S. (2017) Integrated effect of foliar fertilization of Fe, Zn and rates of P fertilization on growth and yield of cowpea. *Journal of Soil Sciences and Agricultural Engineering, Mansoura Univ.* 8(12), 733-740.

Gowthami, P. and Rao, R.G. (2014) Effect of foliar application of potassium, boron and zinc of growth analysis and seed yield in soybean. *Journal of Agriculture and Veterinary* Science 4(3), 73-80.

Guhey, A. (1999) Physiological studies on chickpea in relation to drought tolerance. Ph.D. Thesis, Institute of Agriculture Sciences, BHU, Varanasi, India.

Habbasha, S.F., Mohamed, M.H., Abd El-Lateef, E.M., Mekki, B.B. and Ibrahim, M.E. (2013) Effect of combined zinc and nitrogen on yield, chemical constituents and nitrogen use efficiency of some chickpea cultivars under sandy soil conditions. *World Journal of Agricultural Sciences* 9(4), 354-360.

Hanumanthappa, D., Vasudevan, S.N., Maruthi, J.B., Shakuntala, N.M., Muniswamy and Macha, S.I. (2018) Enrichment of iron and zinc content in pigeon pea genotypes through agronomic biofortification to mitigate malnutrition. *International Journal of Current Microbiology and Applied Sciences* 7, 4334-4342.

Hehazy, M.H., El-Hawary, F.I. and Ghobrial, W.N. (1990) Effect of micronutrients application and Brady rhizobium japonium inoculation on soybean. *Annals of Agricultural Sciences* 1, 381-398.

Heidarian, A.R., Kord, H., Mostafavi, K., Lak, A.P. and Mashhadi, F.A. (2011) Investigating Fe and Zn foliar application on yield and its components of soybean (*Glycine max* (L.) Merr.) at different growth stages. *Journal of Agricultural Biotechnology and Sustainable Development* 3(9), 189-197.

Hidoto, L., Worku, W., Mohammed, H. and Taran, B. (2017) Effects of zinc application strategy on zinc content and productivity of chickpea grown under zinc deficient soils. *Journal of Soil Science and Plant Nutrition* 17(1), 112-126.

Hursthouse, A.S. (2001) The relevance of speciation in the remediation of soils and sediments contaminated by metallic elements an overview and examples from Central Scotland, UK. *Journal of Environmental Monitoring* 3(1), 46-60.

Khorgamy, A. and Farina, A. (2009) Effect of phosphorus and zinc fertilisation on yield and yield components of chick pea cultivars. *African Crop Science Conference Proceedings* 9, 205-208.

Kuldeep, Kumavat, P.D,, Bhadu, V., Sumeriya, H.K. and Kumar, V. (2018) Effect of iron and zinc nutrition on growth and yield of chickpea (*Cicer arietinum* L.). *International Journal of Current Microbiology and Applied Sciences* 7(8), 2837-2841.

Kumawat, N., Singh, R.P., Kumar, R., Yadav, T.P. and Hari Om. (2015) Effect of integrated nutrient management on productivity, nutrient uptake and economics of rainfed pigeon pea (*Cajanus cajan*) and blackgram (*Vigna mungo*) intercropping system. *Indian Journal of Agricultural Sciences* 85(2), 23-28.

Kuniya, N., Chaudhary, N. and Patel, S. (2018) Effect of sulphur and zinc application on growth, yield attributes, yield and quality of summer cluster bean [*Cyamopsis tetragonoloba* (L.)] in light textured soil. *International Journal of Chemical Studies* 6(1), 1529-1532.

Latef, A.A.H.A., Alhmad, M.F.A. and Abdelfattah, K.E. (2017) The possible roles of priming with ZnO nanoparticles in mitigation of salinity stress in lupine (*Lupinus termis*) plants. *Journal of Plant Growth Regulation* 36(1), 60-70.

Mali, G.C., Sharma, N.N., Acharya, H.K., Gupta, S.K. and Gupta, P.K. (2003) Response of pigeon pea to S and Zn fertilization on vertisols in south-eastern plain of Rajasthan. Proc. National Symposium on Arid Legumes, for Food Nutrition Security and Promotion of Trade, Hisar, 15-16 May 2002. pp. 267-271.

Malik, K., Kumar, S. and Arya, K.P.S. (2015) Effect of zinc, molybdenum and urea on growth and yield of mung bean (*Vigna radiate* L.Wilczek). *Advance Research Journal of Crop Improvement* 6(1), 58-62.

Marschner, H. (1995) Mineral nutrition of higher plants. Academic Press, San Diego, USA. pp. 379-396.

Meena, N.R., Meena, M.K., Sharma, K.K. and Meena, M.D. (2017) Effect of zinc enriched farm yard manures on yield of mung bean and Physico-chemical properties of soil. *Legume Research* 41(5), 734-739.

Michail, T., Walter, T., Astrid, W., Walter, G., Dieter, G., Maria, S.J. and Domingo, M. (2004) A survey of foliar mineral nutrient concentrations of *Pinus canariensis* at field plots in Tenerife. *Forest Ecology and Management* 189, 49-55.

Mondal, M., Rahman, M.A., Akter, M.B. and Fakir, M.S.A. (2011) Effect of foliar application of nitrogen and micronutrients on growth and yield in mung bean. *Legume Research* 34(3), 166-171.

Nagaraju, A.P. and Yadahalli. (1996) Response of cowpea (*Vigna unguiculata*) to sources and levels of phosphorus and zinc. *Indian Journal of Agronomy* 41(1), 88-90.

Nayak, B.K. (1989) Response of soybean to molybdenum and fertility levels. *Indian Journal of Agronomy* 34, 454-455.

Padma, M., Reddy, S.A. and Babu, R.S. (1989) Effect of foliar sprays of molybdenum (Mo) and boron (B) on the vegetative growth and dry matter production of Frenchbean (*Phaseolus vulgaris* L.). *Journal of Research APAU* 17(1), 87-89.

Pandey, N., Pathak, G.C. and Sharma, C.P. (2006) Zinc is critically required for pollen function and fertilization in lentil. *Journal of Trace Elements in Medicine and Biology* 20, 89- 96.

Pandey, N. and Gupta, B. (2012) Improving seed yield of Black Gram (*Vigna Mungol. var* DPU-88-31) through foliar fertilization of zinc during the reproductive phase. *Journal of Plant Nutrition* 35,1683-1692.

Patel, M.M., Patel, I.C., Patel, R.I. and Acharya, S. (2011) Effect of zinc and iron on yield and yield attributes of rainfed cowpea (*Vigna unguiculata* (L.) Walp). *Annals of Arid Zone* 50(1), 17-19.

Prasanna, K.L., Selvaraj, S. and Reddy, P.M. (2014) Dry matter production, yield attributes, yield and quality of cluster bean [*cyamopsis tetragonoloba* (L.) taub.] as influenced by nitrogen and zinc application. *Indian Journal of Agricultural Sciences* 48(1), 9-15.

Purushottam, B.K., Puhup CSK Kumar and Sodi B. 2018. Effect of irrigation scheduling and zinc application on chlorophyll content, zinc content, uptake and yield of chickpea (*Cicer arietinum* L.). *Journal of Pharmacognosy Phytochemistry* 7(1), 1834-1837.

Puste, A.N. and Jana, P.K. (1988) Effect of phosphorus and zinc on growth patterns of pigeon pea (*Cajans Cajan* (L.) Millsp.) growth during winter season. *Indian Journal of Plant Physiology* 31(3), 243-247.

Rafique, E., Yousra, M., Mahmood-Ul-Hassan, M., Sarwar, S., Tabassam, T. and Choudhary, T.K. (2015) Zinc application affects tissue zinc concentration and seed yield of pea (*Pisum sativum* L.). *Pedosphere* 25(2), 275-281.

Rahdari, P., Hoseini, S.M. and Movafegh, S. (2013) Alteration in metabolic process of *Glycine max* (L.) following Zn rate changes. *International Journal of Agronomy and Plant Production* 4(3), 589-594.

Raj, A.B. (2019) Seed invigouration for yield en-hancement in grain cowpea (*Vigna unguiculate* L. Walp). M.Sc. (Ag) thesis, Kerala Agricultural University, Thrissur, India. pp. 155

Ram, S. and Katiyar, T.P.S. (2013) Effect of sulphur and zinc on the seed yield and protein content of summer mung bean under arid climate. *International Journal of Science & Nature* 4(3), 563-566.

Ramesh, S. (2002) Effect of plant growth regulators, chemicals and nutrients on morphophysiological, biochemical and yield and yield attributes in mothbean [*Vigna aconitifolia* (Jacq.) Marchel]. M.Sc.(Agri.) Thesis, Univ. Agric. Sci. Dharwad, India.

Ranpariya, V.S., Polara, K.B., Hirpara, D.V. and Bodar, K.H. (2017) Effect of potassium, zinc and FYM on content and uptake of nutrients in seed of summer green gram (*Vigna radiata* L.) and post harvest soil fertility under medium black calcareous soil. *International Journal of Chemical Studies* 5(5), 1055-1058.

Rao, K.V.M. and Sresty, T.V.S. (2000) Antioxidative parameters in the seedlings of pigeon pea (*Cajanus cajan* (L.) Millspaugh) in response to Zn and Ni stresses. *Plant Science* 157, 113-128.

Rathod, P.S., Patil, D.H., Rachappa, V., Bellad, S.B. and Dodamani, B.M. (2017) Response of late sown pigeon pea (*Cajanus cajan* (L.) Mill Sp.) to trace elements. *Green Farming* 8(1), 164-167.

Rawal, V. and Navarro, D.K. eds. (2019) The Global Economy of Pulses. Rome, FAO.

Roy, P.D., Narwal, R.P., Malik, R.S., Saha, B.N. and Kumar, S. (2014) Impact of zinc application methods on green gram (*Vigna radiata* L.) productivity and grain zinc fortification. *Journal of Environmental Biology* 35(5), 851-855.

Roy, P.D., Lakshman, K., Narwal, R.P., Malik, R.S. and Saha, S. (2017) Green gram (*Vigna radiata* L.) productivity and grain quality enrichment through zinc fertilization. Int. J. Curr. Microbiol. *Applied Sciences* 6(6), 643-648.

Ruel, M.T. and Bouis, H.E. (1998) Plant breeding: a long-term strategy for the control of zinc deficiency in vulnerable populations. *The American Journal of Clinical Nutrition* 68(2), 488S-494S.

Sadana, U.S., Manchanda, J.S., Khurana, M.P.S., Dhaliwal, S.S. and Singh, H. (2010) The current scenario and efficient management of zinc, iron, and manganese deficiencies. *Better Crops South Asia* 5, 24-26.

Salehin, F. and Rahman, S. (2012) Effect of zinc and nitrogen fertilizer and their application method on yield and yield components of *Phaseolus vulgaris* L. *Agricultural Sciences* 3(1), 9-13.

Salih, H.O. (2013) Effect of foliar fertilization of Fe, B and Zn on nutrient concentration and seed protein of cowpea (*Vigna unguiculata*). *Journal of Agriculture and Veterinary Science* 6(3), 42-46.

Salisbury, F.B. and Ross, C.W. (1992) Hormones and growth regulators: auxins and gibberellins. *Plant Physiology* 4(18.5), 401-405.

Sangwan, P.S. and Raj, M. (2004) Effect of zinc nutrition on yield of chickpea (*Cicer arietinum* l.) under dryland conditions. *Indian Journal of Dryland Agricultural Research and Development* 19(1), 01-03.

Selvaraj, S. and Prasanna, K.L. (2012) Dry matter production, yield attributes, yield and quality of cluster bean (*Cyamopsis tetragonoloba* L.) as influenced by nitrogen and zinc application. *Indian Journal of Plant Sciences* 1, 167-176.

Shah, K.A., Gurjar, R., Parmarand, H.C. and Sonani, V.V. (2016) Effect of sulphur and zinc fertilization on yield and quality of pigeon pea in sandy loam soil. *Green Farming* 7(2), 495-497.

Sharafi, S. (2015) Effect of sowing season and zinc sulfate application methods on quantity and quality characteristics of *Cicer arietinum*. *Journal of Biological & Environmental Sciences* 9(25), 41-45.

Sharma, A., Nakul, H.T., Jelgeri, B.R. and Surwenshi, A. (2010) Effect of micronutrients on growth, yield and yield components in pigeon pea (*Cajanus cajan* L. Millsp.). *Journal of Agricultural Sciences* 1(2), 142-144.

Sharma, A., Kumar, A. and Potdar, M.P. (2009) Response of pigeon pea to conjunctive use of organic and inorganic source of fertilizers under rainfed conditions. *Karnataka Journal of Agricultural Sciences* 22(1), 8-10.

Shinde, A.K., Jamadagni, B.M. and Birari, S.P. (1991) Effect of foliar spray of growth regulators and KNO_3 on growth and yield of cowpea (*Vigna unguiculata* L.) Var. VCM-8. *Indian Journal of Plant physiology* 34(4), 392-395.

Shivay, Y.S., Prasad, R. and Pal, M. (2015) Effects of source and method of zinc application on yield, zinc biofortification of grain, and zn uptake and use efficiency in chickpea (*Cicer arietinum* L.). *Communications in Soil Science and Plant Analysis* 46(17), 2191-2200.

Shukla, A.K., Behera, S.K., Lenka, N.K. *et al.* (2016) Spatial variability of soil micronutrients in the intensively cultivated Trans-Gangetic Plains of India. *Soil and Tillage Research* 163, 282-289.

Singh, D. and Singh, H. (2012) Effect of phosphorus and zinc nutrition on yield, nutrient uptake and quality of chickpea. *Annals of Plant and Soil Research* 14(1), 71-74.

Singh, G., Abrol, I.P. and Cheema, S.S. (1989) Effects of gypsum application on mesquite (*Prosopis julitlora*) and soil properties in an abandoned sodic soil. *Forest Ecology and Management* 29, 1-14.

Srikanth Babu, P.N., Koppalkar, B.G., Desai, B.K., Nagalikar, V.P. and Katti, P. (2012) Yield and yield components and economics of pigeon pea cultivation as influenced by organic manures and graded levels of zinc sulphate. *Karnataka Journal of Agricultural Sciences* 25(4), 527-530.

Srinivasarao, C. (2012) Impacts of participatory site specific potassium management in several crops in rainfed regions of Andhra Pradesh, India. International Potash Institute. e-ifc (Electronic International Fertilizer Correspondent) 30, 7-25.

Taliee, A. and Sayadan, K. (2000) Effect of supplemental irrigation and plant nutrition chickpea (dry farming). *Journal of Agronomy and Crop Science* 2, 12-19.

Tayyeba, S., Humaira, H.U.S., Saleem, U. and Muhammad, J. (2017) Zinc effect on growth rate, chlorophyll, protein and mineral contents of hydroponically grown mung beans plant (*Vigna radiata*). *Arabian Journal of Chemistry* 10, 1802-1807.

Tekale, R.P., Guhey, A. and Agrawal, K. (2009) Impact of boron, zinc and IAA on growth, dry matter accumulation and sink potential of pigeon pea (*Cajanus Cajan* L.). *Agricultural Science Digest* 29(4), 246-249.

Thamke, S.S. (2017) Studies on effect of graded levels of potassium and zinc on growth, yield, nutrient uptake and quality of pigeon pea. M.Sc. Ag Thesis, Vasantrao Naik Marathwada Krishi Vidyapeeth, Parbhani (M.S.) 431402, India.

Umesh, M.R. and Shankar, M.A. (2013) Yield performance and profitability of pigeon pea (*Cajanus cajana* L.) varieties under different nutrient Supply levels in dryland alfisols of Karnataka. *Indian Journal of Dryland Agricultural Research and Development* 28(1), 63-69.

Upadhyay RG and Singh A. 2016. Effect of nitrogen and zinc on nodulation, growth and yield of cowpea (*Vigna unguiculata*). *Legume Research* 39(1): 149-151.

Upadhyay, R.G. (2002) Response of growth regulators on flower drop, fruit setting, biochemical constituents and yield of chickpea under mid hill conditions of H.P. *Legume Research* 25(3), 211-214.

Ved, R., Misra, S.K. and Upadhyay, R.M. (2002) Effects of sulphur, zinc and biofertilizers on the quality characteristics of mung bean. *Indian Journal of Pulses Research* 2, 139-141.

Yilmaz, A., Ekiz, A. and Torun, B. (1997) Effect of different zinc application methods on grain yield and zinc concentration in wheat cultivars grown on zinc deficient calcareous soils. *Journal of Plant and Nutrition* 20(4&5), 461-471.

Yashona, D.S., Mishra, U.S. and Aher, S.B. (2018a) Response of pulse crops to sole and combined mode of zinc application: A review. *Journal of Soils and Crops* 28(2), 249-258.

Yashona, D.S., Mishra, U.S. and Aher, S.B. (2018b) Response of pigeon pea (*Cajanus cajan*) to sole and combined modes of zinc fertilization. *Journal of Pharmacognosy and Phytochemistry* 7(4), 2703-2710.

Yashona, D.S., Mishra, U.S., Aher, S.B., Tripathi, A. and Sirothia, P. (2018c) Protein and zinc concentration in pigeon pea (*Cajanus cajan*) under various mode of zinc application. *Indian Journal of Agricultural Biochemistry* 31(2), 186-194.

Yashona, D.S., Mishra, U.S. and Aher, S.B. (2019) Effect of rate and mode of zinc application on zinc dynamics in typic haplustalfs under rainfed conditions. *Journal of the Indian Society of Soil Science* 67(4), 450-457.

Yashona, D.S., Mishra, U.S. and Aher, S.B. (2020) Nutrient uptake, zinc use efficiency and yield of pigeon pea as influenced by various modes of zinc application under rainfed condition. International conference on "Pulses as the Climate Smart Crops: Challenges and Opportunities" at 10-12 February 2020, Bhopal (M.P.) India.

CHAPTER 9

Management strategies for micronutrients deficiency in pulses

Ranabir Chakraborty[1], Abhishek Das[1] and Asik Dutta[2]*

1. *ICAR- Indian Agricultural Research Institute, New Delhi-110012*

2. *ICAR-Indian Institute of Pulses Research, Kanpur-208024, Uttar Pradesh*

*Corresponding author email: asikdutta975@gmail.com

Abstract

Pulses being an integral component of daily diet are store house of proteins and different mineral elements. India is the cultivating ground for all types of pulses and in recent years the popularity of pulses gained significantly due to availability of quality seeds, precision management practices and government support. Micronutrients or trace elements represent few essential elements which are required in minute amount but, have an important role in various physiological and biochemical processes and most importantly in N-fixation in pulses. Among different micronutrients 49% and 13% of total analysed soil samples from all around India is deficient in zinc (Zn) and iron (Fe). Pulses are well responsive to micronutrients especially in the reproductive stages but, application of micronutrients in pulses is still not in practise. In India, most of the cationic micronutrient is available in the market in granulated sulphate salt form. Anionic micronutrients like molybdenum (Mo) and boron (B) is available in molybdate and borate form and easily available. Research has been done in various locations to highlight the importance of micronutrient application in pulses and found that with micronutrient supplementation crop growth, yield attributes and yield increased significantly over control. Since the requirement of micronutrient in pulses is very specific and interlinked with other nutrients in their functional relationship it is highly difficult to make a generalise soil management practise for management of micronutrient deficiency in soil and crops.

Keywords: Deficiency, Indian soil, Phenology, Productivity, Pulses, Micronutrient

1. INTRODUCTION

Pulses are not only a chief source of protein in vegetarian diets but also provide most of the essential mineral nutrients (Wang *et al.*, 2003) and it is an integral ingredient of breakfast grains and specialty diets. Pulses have multi-dimensional role in agriculture like nitrogen fixing, green manure and cover crops, catch crops and so on, it is often scientists' first choice for agricultural, environmental and biotechnological research. A wide range of pulses are grown in India, of which the major contributors are chickpea (41%), pigeonpea (15%), urdbean (10%), mungbean (9%), cowpea (7%) lentil (5%) and field pea (5%).

Popularity of pulses among the farmers is gaining more and more importance in recent years. India is witnessing an upward trend of production which has remained constantly over 18 Mt since 2010. Among the micronutrients iron, zinc, boron and molybdenum mostly influenced the production of pulse crops. Foliar application of micronutrient along with biofertilizer or sulphur can enhance the production. Aslam *et al.* (2002) reported that boron nutrition leads to better pollination and seed setting which essentially contributes to higher grain yield. Productions of pulses are often limited to relatively poor and low fertility lands where other crops do not perform well. Cultivation in poor, micronutrient deficient soils without any external application of micronutrient fertilizers is the often-major driver for unsatisfactory pulse productivity. Moreover, after green revolution, due to intensive cultivation, exhaustive variety and adopting straight fertilizers instead of organic manure aggravated micronutrient deficiency.

2. MICRONUTRIENT STATUS IN INDIA

Till eighties, zinc (Zn) deficiency was the major micro-nutrient production constrain. But due to intensive cultivation, popularization of chemical fertilizers, introduction of high yielding varieties, deficiencies of other micronutrients are also being reported (Fig 1). Among cationic micro-nutrients, Zn is the most deficient (49%), followed by Fe, Mn and Cu, currently deficient in 12%, 4% and 3% soils, respectively. Solubility of micro-nutrients is highly dependent on soil conditions and hence deficiency of Zn, Fe and Mn are most extensive in calcareous soil of arid and semi-arid regions. Deficiencies of Cu and Mn are not widespread, henceforth sporadic crop responses are reported. The anionic micronutrients e.g. boron and molybdenum are indispensable for pulses. Soils with high rainfall are generally deficient in B, similarly Mo is deficient in acidic soils. Currently about 33% and 13% samples all over India are having sub-optimum level of B and Mo, respectively, which could severely affect crop production specially, pulses. A summary of percent deficient samples for different micro-nutrients in different Indian states are tabulated in table 1 (Behra *et al.* 2009).

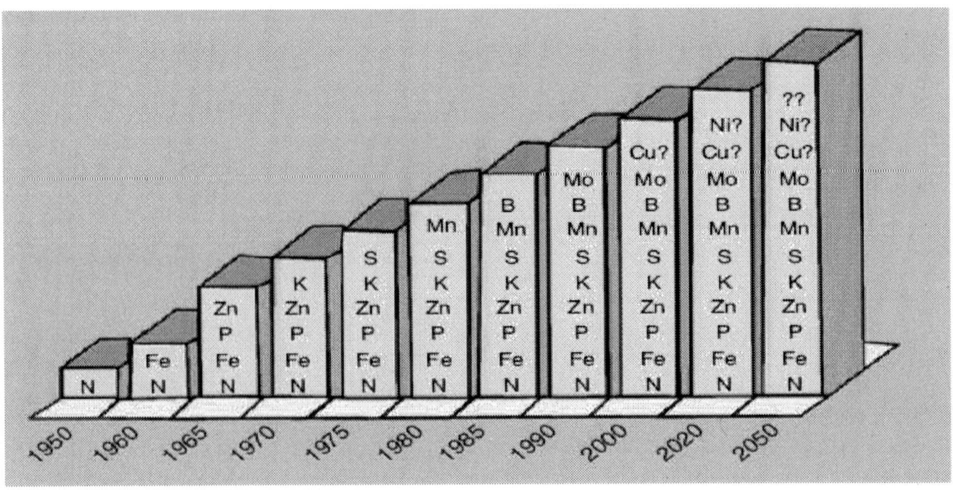

Fig. 1. Emergence of micronutrient deficiencies in crops in India (Singh, 2008)

Table 1. Extent of micro-nutrient deficiencies in soils of India

States	Percent deficient samples (PSD)					
	Zn	**Cu**	**Fe**	**Mn**	**B**	**Mo**
Andhra Pradesh	46.8	<1.0	2.8	1.2	53	49
Assam	34.0	—	2.0	20.0	17	—
Bihar	54.0	3.0	6.0	2.0	1.0	1.0
Gujarat	23.9	4.0	8.0	4.0	—	—
Haryana	60.5	2.0	20.0	4.0	—	—
Himachal Pradesh	42.0	0.0	27.0	5.0	32	5.0
Karnataka	72.8	5.0	35.0	17.0	53	49
Kerala	34.0	3.0	<1.0	0.2	17	—
Madhya Pradesh	44.2	<1.0	7.3	0.2	49	30
Maharashtra	83.0	0.0	24.0	0.4	—	—
Meghalaya	57.0	2.0	0.0	23.0	—	—
Orissa	52.5	<1.0	0.0	0.6	69	—
Pondicherry	8.0	4.0	2.0	3.0	—	—
Punjab	46.1	1.1	14	2.3	—	—
Rajasthan	21.0	—	—	—	14.0	—
Tamil Nadu	58.6	6.0	17.0	6.0	68.0	—
Uttar Pradesh	45.7	1.0	6.0	3.0	45	12
West Bengal	36.0	0.0	0.0	3.0	49	30
All India	48.8	3.0	11.9	4.4	33.0	13.0

*For cations, 2.52 lakh samples were analysed and B and Mo data are calculated on the basis of 50,000 and 1850 samples

3. IMPORTANCE OF MICRONUTRIENT APPLICATION IN PULSES

Micronutrients have immense important in production of pulse crops. Iron is absorbed by roots as ferrous ions (Fe^{2+}). Its concentration in the range of 100-500 mg/kg in mature leaf tissues is regarded sufficient for optimum crop production. Iron is a constituent of two groups of protein besides activating number of enzymes and deficiency of Fe leads to interveinal chlorosis. Another important micronutrient is manganese which is absorbed by root as manganous ions (Mn^{2+}). Mn sufficient mature plant contains 20 to 300 ppm of Mn. It plays an important role in the photosynthesis. Manganese activates several enzymes linked to synthesis of several amino acid and phenols important for lignin production. Deficiency of Mn leads to reduction in root and shoot growth which leads to accumulation of nitrogen (N) and phosphorus (P). It increases potential for root and leaf diseases (e.g. Marshy spot of pea). Zinc also plays an important role in pulses growth and it absorbed by roots as Zn^{2+}. It has an imperative role in production of protein and nucleic acid in plants and it also aids in nitrogen and phosphorus metabolism. Zinc encourages root nodulation in pulses and thereby plays a crucial role in nitrogen fixation. In pulses, formation of starch and improving protein content were observed with Zn application (Khalil *et al.*, 2014). It influences the synthesis of auxin in plant by encouraging the synthesis of tryptophane, a precursor of auxin. Usually a healthy plant contains 27 to 150 ppm Zn in mature tissues. Poor growth, interveinal chlorosis and necrosis of lower leaves are the common symptoms of Zn deficiency in field crops. Like other cationic micronutrients copper is absorbed by plant roots as cupric ions (Cu^{2+}). The concentration of Cu in Cu-sufficient plants varies from 5 to 30 ppm. Cu imparts disease resistance to the plants and it also enhances the fertility of male flower. Nickel (Ni) concentration in plant tissue is critical for plant development, it is relatively low in comparison to other micronutrients (0.1 mg/kg, dry mass basis). Deficiency of Ni inhibits urease activity leading to accumulation of urea related N-compounds, which results in toxicity and decreased plant growth.

Molybdenum plays an imperative role in nitrogen assimilation. It is a fundamental component of two very important enzymes- nitrogenase and nitrate reductase. Mo directly influences nitrogen fixation from atmosphere and its assimilation in pulses. Boron plays a wide range of important functions in plant metabolism including cell division, protein synthesis and carbohydrate transport, uptake of calcium and potassium, and activity of certain enzymes, hence ultimately enhance pod and seed formation (Janaki *et al.*, 2018). Molybdenum also participates in structural interring of cell wall and cell membrane. In plants, Mo is mostly found in the envelope of chloroplasts in leaves where it takes part in synthesis of ascorbic acid thereby made Fe physiologically available to plant. Among all the micronutrient fertilizers, Mo is often required in the smallest amount, but its absence could produce significant reduction in production and quality of pulses (Flemming, 1980)

Fig. 2. Deficiency symptoms of some micronutrient in pulses a. Zn deficiency in field pea b. molybdenum deficiency in pulse c. Fe deficiency in red gram d. Mn deficiency in pea (marshy spots on pea)

3.1 Response of pulses to cationic micronutrients

3.1.1 Iron (Fe)

Iron influences the growth, yield and quality of pulse crops. Application of iron fertilizer increases nodulation, nodules dry weight and dry matter accumulation (Bhanavase *et al.*, 1994). Kumawat *et al.* (2006) reported that application of $FeSO_4$ @ 25 kg/ha resulted higher chlorophyll content of leaves, shoot weight and root nodules over control and it also increases grain and straw yields. Sahu *et al.* (2009) reported that application of $FeSO_4$ @ 2 kg/ha along with bio-fertilizer inoculation in chickpea led to higher grain and straw yields over control. Jamal *et al* (2018) also reported positive effect of Fe and Zn application on mungbean yield (Fig 2).

Meena *et al.* (2013) conducted a field experiment on loamy sand soil during kharif season to assess the impact of Fe on plant growth and development and the results are summarised in table 2. In conclusion, application of 25 kg $FeSO_4$/ha as basal dose and foliar applied treatments, viz. 0.5% $FeSO_4$, 0.5% $FeSO_4$ + 0.1% citric acid has consistent effect on yield attributing character and yield of mungbean.

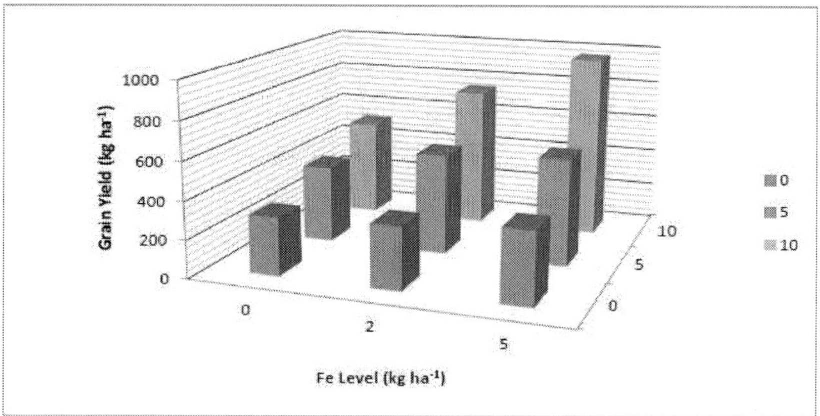

Fig. 3. Grain yield as (kg/ha) of mungbean as affected by different levels of iron and zinc (Jamal *et al.*, 2018).

Table 2. Effect of iron fertilization on yield attributes and harvest index of mungbean

Treatment	Yield (kg/ha)			Harvest index (%)
	Seed	Straw	Biomass	
Control	990.5	2148.6	3139.1	31.5
$FeSO_4$ 0.5% foliar spray at 25 and 40 DAS	1058.8	2282.0	3340.4	31.7
$FeSO_4$ 0.5% + 0.1% citric acid foliar spray at 25 and 40 DAS	1037.7	2236.0	3273.3	31.7
$FeSO_4$ 25 kg/ha	1081.4	2382.7	3464.6	31.2
SEm±	11.4	30.6	32.5	0.4
CD (P=0.05)	32.5	87.1	92.4	NS

NS: Non-significant; DAS: days after sowing.

Kumawat *et al.* (2006) revealed uptake of N, P, S and Fe by the mungbean crop increased significantly with both soil application of $FeSO_4$ and foliar spray treatments compared to control. Nasar *et al.* (2017) conducted a study assess the effect of iron (Fe) and molybdenum (Mo) on yield and nodulation of lentil (Table 3). Iron was applied at the rate of 0.5 and 1.0 kg/ha in the form of ferrous sulphate ($FeSO_4.7H_2O$) and molybdenum was applied at the rate of 0.05 and 0.10 kg/ha in the form of ammonium molybdate $\{(NH_4)_6Mo\ O_{24}.4H_2O)\}$ as foliar spray. They have found that application of iron and molybdenum significantly increased the grain yield, biomass yield, harvest index (%) and 1000 seed weight. Further, the combined application of Fe and Mo significantly produced higher crop yields than the sole application of Fe or Mo. These results suggested that combined application of iron @ 1.0 kg/ha and molybdenum @ 0.10 kg/ha as foliar spray significantly enhanced the crop yields.

Table 3. Effect of iron and molybdenum on yield and yield parameters of lentil

Treatment	Grain yield (kg/ha)	Biomass yield (kg/ha)	1000 seed weight (g)	Harvest index (%)
Control	1293	4163	28.95	31.09
Fe 0.5 kg/ha	1693	4577	30.95	34.52
Fe 1.0 kg/ha	1757	4827	31.80	36.41
Mo 0.05 kg/ha	1747	4850	32.39	36.02
Mo 0.1 kg/ha	1753	4860	32.95	36.27
Fe 0.5 kg/ha + Mo 0.05 kg/ha	1750	4810	32.54	36.38
Fe 0.5 kg/ha + Mo 0.1 kg/ha	1753	4867	32.98	36.04
Fe 1.0 kg/ha + Mo 0.05 kg/ha	1720	4853	33.54	35.36
Fe 1.0 kg/ha + Mo 0.0.1 kg/ha	1767	4930	34.72	38.36
LSD (0.05)	182	292	1.09	3.170

3.1.2 Zinc (Zn)

Zinc is an important micro-nutrient for plant growth and development. Tripathi *et al.* (1999) reported significantly higher leaf area index (LAI) in soybean with soil application of Zn @ 25 kg/ha + B 10 kg/ha. In mungbean foliar application of 1% Zn recorded significantly higher LAI (Mondal *et al.*, 2011). Usman *et al.* (2014) reported that seed treatment with $ZnSO_4$ significantly increased the pod bearing branches in mungbean. Kuldeep *et al.* (2018) observed that Zn nutrition had positive effect on growth attributes of chickpea and it was observed that application of Zn @ 5 kg/ha recorded higher number of branches per plant. Zinc fertilization had positive effect on the yield of pulses. Application of Zn @ 5 kg/ha along with S @ 60 kg/ha recorded 67 per cent higher seed yield over control in mungbean (Mali *et al.*, 2003). Shivay *et al.* (2015) conducted a study in Zn deficient soils during the rainy season and found that application of Zn not only increased above ground Zn concentration in rice but also increased protein content of rice kernels due to the overall improvement in crop growth. Foliar application of Zn was better from the viewpoint of Zn biofortification of rice kernels. However, foliar application of Zn at later stage is not as effective as soil application in increasing yield attributes. This study brought out that Zn coated urea applying less than half the amount of Zn as applied through soil + foliar application was very close to it and is quite promising. Oktem (2013) conducted an experiment to determine the effects of different Zn levels on the grain yield and some phenological characteristics of the red lentil variety (Table 4). The Zn levels used were control (0 kg/ha Zn), 5 kg/ha Zn, 10 kg/ha Zn, 15 kg/ha Zn, 20 kg/ha Zn, and 25 kg/ha Zn. According to anova analysis it was observed that harvest index was significantly increased in both the years and the highest harvest index values were obtained from 15 kg/ha Zn. 1000 kernel weight were positively affected by increased rate of Zn application. It was observed that the 1000-kernelweight increased with increasing Zn levels from the control application to 15 kg/ha Zn, but after that it was seen to decrease in both years. The highest grain yield was obtained with 15 kg/ha Zn in both years. A field experiment was conducted by Singh *et al.* (2012) to study the effect of Zn on yield and protein content of chickpea (Table 5). They observed that the grain and straw yields increased significantly with increasing dose of Zn and most notably interaction with other nutrients like N and P which positively impacted yield and protein content of chickpea.

Table 4. Harvest index, 1000-kernel weight and grain yield of lentil at different Zn levels

Zn level (kg/ha)	Harvest index (%)		1000 kernel weight (g)		Grain yield (kg/ha)	
	2013-14	2014-15	2013-14	2014-15	2013-14	2014-15
Control	25.0 cd	26.6 e	37.8 d	38.9 d	899 e	1093 d
5	25.8 c	28.4 d	39.1 c	39.9 cd	942 de	1153 d
10	26.2 c	31.9 bc	40.6 b	41.4 b	1133 c	1273 c
15	31.9 a	36.0 a	42.0 a	42.7 a	1398 a	1485 a
20	30.5 ab	32.7 b	40.3 b	40.8 bc	1268 b	1463 ab
25	29.7 b	30.9 c	40.2 b	40.8 bc	1049 cd	1370 bc
LSD	1.60	1.51	0.97	1.06	127.3	112.7

There is no significant difference between averages with the same letter as compared by LSD test at $P \leq 0.05$

Table 5. Effects of zinc levels on yield and protein content of chickpea

Treatment (kg/ha)	Yield (kg/ha)		Protein (%)	
	Grain	Straw	Grain	Straw
0	1702	2023	20.21	9.18
2.5	1824	2174	20.49	9.31
5.0	1869	2254	20.55	9.52
10.0	1826	2160	20.65	9.62
CD (P = 0.05)	90	140	0.16	0.17

3.1.3 Manganese (Mn)

The role of Mn in pulse physiology is very typical and depends on soil and crop management practices. The availability of Mn to crops could be limited to high pH soils. Halvin *et al.* (1999) reported that soil application of Fe by Fe-EDDH may reduce availability of manganese (Mn). Parker *et al.* (1981) concluded that treatment of manganese sulphate (11.2-22.4 kg/ha) leads to 27% increase in seed yield of legume crops comparing to control due to higher 100-seed weight. Fasaei *et al.* (2005) conducted a pot experiment to study the effect of solo Fe and Mn and their interaction on the dry matter yield (DMY) of chickpea (Table 6). Results showed that both foliar and soil application of Fe decreased mean shoot DMY, but Mn addition had no significant effect.

Table 6. Effects of Fe and Mn on shoot dry weight (g/pot) in chickpea

Fe levels (mg/kg)	Mn levels (mg/kg)			Mean
	0	15	30	
0	3.68[a]	3.58[ab]	3.51[abc]	3.59[A]
4	2.74[d]	3.24[abcd]	2.8 [cd]	2.95[B]
8	2.81[d]	2.94[bcd]	2.96[abcd]	2.94[B]
2	2.99[bcd]	3.15[abcd]	3.06[bcd]	3.03[B]
Mean	3.05[A]	3.23[A]	3.10[A]	

N.B. Analysis was being performed by Duncan's multiple-range test (p=0.05)

3.1.4 Nickel (Ni)

Nickel is the latest addition in the list of essentiality and recent studies showed Ni has important role in pulses production particularly in India. Levy (2019) conducted a study to evaluate the effect of Ni at different rates of application in two different soil types. Ni applied directly in the soil by using a solution were equivalent to 0, 0.25, 0.5 and 1 mg/kg Ni. He found that the absorption of Ni by the plants and its availability depend on soil texture. The rate of Ni 0.25 mg/kg increased the soybean dry matter production by 25% in the sandy soil (Table 7).

Table 7. Effect of Ni dose on grain mass (g) and number of pods per plant of soybean

Dose (mg/kg)	Grain (g) per plant		Pods per plant	
	Sandy	Clayey	Sandy	Clayey
0.0	10	13	21	22
0.25	10	13	25	23
0.50	9.0	13	23	24
1.0	9.0	13	21	22
Mean	9.5	13	22.5	22.7

3.2 Response of pulses to anionic micronutrients

3.2.1 Boron (B)

Many of the Indian states are inherently deficient in B and positive responses on B application on pulses was found in Bihar, Orissa, West Bengal, Assam, and Punjab (Takkar *et al.*, 1997). The rate and method of application of these micronutrient fertilizers largely depend on crop species and genotype, and B may become deficient or toxic to different genotypes at same dose (Ceyhan and Onder, 2007). For instance, in frenchbean, when B was applied at a lower dose of 1 kg/ha, it reportedly produced an additional pod yield of 7.38 q/ha, but its application over this level expressed detrimental signs in coarse textured highly calcareous soils (Singh and Singh, 1990). Addition of B maximized the light interception ratio, leaf area index, net assimilation rate, seed and biomass production in pulses (Renukadevi *et al.*, 2002). Several reports are available in literature where application of boron increased crop yield. Ross *et al.* (2003) reported 8.2-11.8% yield increase over the control due to boron application in soybean. Similarly, application of B at 6 kg/ha and 25 kg Zn/ha expressively enhanced the seed yield of mungbean over control (Patil *et al.*, 2006). In mungbean maximum leaf area, plant height, seeds per pod and 1000 grain weight was obtained at 4 kg B/ha (Nabi *et al.*, 2006). Similar results were also reported by Chowdhury *et al.* (2010) where all the yield attributing characteristics and production were improved as a consequence of B application. Jabeen and Ahmad (2011) in their study found that B and Mn when applied singly or in combination imparted beneficial results on different growth parameters and biochemical activities under saline or non-saline condition. Furthermore, the growth parameters and yield were more significantly improved with combination of B and Mn as compared to separate application. Boron might have some negative effects on shoot and root fresh and dry weights as reported in the study by Muhammad *et al* (2013). Similar findings were also found by Metwally *et al* (2012) where shoot and root fresh and dry matter decreased in a sand culture media with higher B application. Over application of B in pulses might initiate toxicity symptoms, a critical limit of 0.25 mg/L was developed by Ashagre *et al* (2014) beyond which germination percentage, seedling vigour, index shoot and root lengths, fresh and dry weights, root - shoot ratio were decreased and the level of phyto-toxicity increased with rise in B concentration. Boron plays an indispensable role in legumes nodule formation and activity, B deficiency radically affect nodulation process. B deficient pulses cannot supply adequate carbohydrates to bacteria in the root nodules and causing poor hydrolyzation of starch to soluble sugars which ultimately hinders proper growth and yield of legumes (Tripathy *et al.*, 1999). A reduction in seed yield of blackgram to the extent of 40-50 per cent is recorded as a result of boron deficiency in soils (Rerkasem *et al.*, 1988). Blackgram is more sensitive to boron deficiency than greengram, in B deficient soils of Thailand, only 21% reduction in yield was recorded for greengram whereas, in blackgram 70% yield loss was observed (Rerkasem, 1991). The quality of pulses also depends on B content. A study confirmed that unsaturated fatty acids e.g. palmitic and stearic augmented by the application of sulphur and boron (Abd El-Wahab, 2008). Boron also affect soil microbial dynamics and enzymatic activity, urease, de-hydrogenase and phosphatase is highly correlated with B application and maximum microbial activity was recorded at 3 kg B/ha (Bilen *et al.*, 2011). However, different enzyme activity varied with B dose.

3.2.2 Molybdenum (Mo)

Many authors have reported effect of Mo on nodulation of pulses, for instance, Karpagam and Rajesh (2014) reported Mo helped to boost nodulation in greengram and after decomposition, it gets mineralized and contribute toward available nitrogen. Molybdenum plays a very significant role in increasing yield of pulses through directly affecting N and P nutrition. Many others study also reported a very close association between Mo fertilization and nitrogen availability (Bhattacharya *et al.*, 2004; Laltlanmawia *et al.*, 2004; Singh *et al.*, 2008). The increased nodulation due to incremental dose of Mo and subsequent decomposition of N rich nodules was identified as the possible reason for higher N availability. They also reported that incremental levels of Mo have correspondingly increased number of nodules which assisted in N-uptake of soybean plants and resulted in higher yield. Like N, Mo also shows a synergistic relation with P. Higher levels of molybdenum increased the available phosphorous content through formation of phosphomolybdate complex, which is also a readily available form of Mo (Barshad, 1951). Another reason could be the release of huge amount of organic acids from decomposition of vast root biomass under Mo application as it is a well-known fact that organic acids made P soluble through chelation of Fe, Mn and Ca.

4. CONCLUSION

Pulses and cereals are complimentary protein sources, pulse protein is deficient in methionine but has abundant lysine whereas cereals are poor in lysine and rich in methionine. Together cereals and pulses are equivalent to animal protein. To spread awareness among the people about the nutritional importance of pulses, 2016 was declared as international year of pulses by FAO. Pulse production in India is mostly adopted by small and marginal farmers primarily as subsistence farming. Poor soils conditions with minimum inputs and care attributes to severe yield losses. The increasing deficiencies of micro-nutrients in soil in different parts of the country have further limited the yield of pulse crops. Thus, based on soil test values, site specific micro-nutrient management may play bigger role in increasing pulses production in the country.

REFERENCES

Abd El-Wahab, A.M. and Mohamed, A. (2008) Effect of some trace elements on growth, yield and chemical constituents of *Trachyspermum ammi* L. plants under Sinai conditions. *Research Journal of Agriculture and Biological Sciences* 4, 717-724.

Aslam, M., Mahmood, I.H., Qureshi, R.H., Nawaz, S. and Akhtar, J. (2002) Salinity tolerance of rice as affected by boron nutrition. *Pakistan Journal of Soil Science (Pakistan)* 21, 110-118.

Barshad, I. (1951) Factors affecting the molybdenum content of pasture plants. I. Nature of soil molybdenum, growth of plants and soil pH. *Soil Science* 71, 297.

Bhanavase, D.B., Jadhav, B.R., Kshirsagar, C.R. and Patil, P.L. (1994) Studies on chlorophyll, nodulation, nitrogen fixation, soybean yield and their correlation as influenced by micronutrient. *Madras Agriculture Journal* 81(6), 325-328.

Bhattacharya, S.S., Mandal, D., Chattopadhyay, G.N.. and Majumdar, K. (2004) Effect of balanced fertilization on pulse crop production in red and lateritic soils. *Better Crop* 88(4), 25-27.

Bilen, S., Bilen, M. and Bardhan, S. (2011) The effect of boron management on soil microbial population and enzyme activities. *African Journal of Biotechn*ology 10, 5311-5319.

Ceyhan, E. and Onder, M. (2007) Response of chickpea cultivars to application of boron in boron- deficient calcareous soils. *Communications in Soil Science Plant Analysis* 38, 2381-2399.

Chowdhury, A.R., Parbhakarysetty, T.K. and Nagarathna, T.K. (2010) Growth and yield of mungbean as influenced by micronutrients. *Karnataka Journal of Agricultural Sciences* 23, 495-496.

Flemming, G.A. (1980) Essential micronutrients. I. Boron and molybdenum. In: Davies, B. E. ed., Applied soil trace elements. Chichester, John Wiley & Sons Ltd. pp. 155-197.

Fasaei, G.R., Ronaghi, A., Maftoun, M., Karimian, N.A. and Soltanpour, P.N. (2005) Iron, manganese interaction in chickpea as affected by foliar and soil application of iron in a calcareous soil. *Communications in Soil Science and Plant Analysis* 36(13-14), 1717-1725.

Jamal, A., Khan, M.I., Tariq, M. and Fawad, M. (2018). Response of mung bean crop to different levels of applied iron and zinc. *Journal of Horticulture and Plant Research* 3, 13-22.

Kuldeep, K. and PD, B. V., Sumeriya, H.K. and Kumar, V. (2018) Effect of iron and zinc nutrition on growth and yield of chickpea (*Cicer arietinum* L.). *International Journal of Current Microbiology and Applied Sci*ences 7(8), 2837-2841.

Kumawat, R.N., Rathore, P.S. and Pareek, N. (2006) Response of mungbean to S and Fe nutrition grown on calcareous soils of western Rajasthan. *Indian Journal of Pulses Research* 19(2), 228.

Laltlanmawia, L., Singh, A.K. and Sharma, S.K. (2004) Effect of phosphorous and molybdenum on yield, protein content and nutrient uptake by soybean on acid soils of Nagaland. *Journal of Indian Society of Soil Science* 52(2), 199-202.

Levy, C.D.C.B., Mellis, E.V., Murrer, M.K., Inglés, C.R., Daynes, C.N., Cavalli, E. and Chiba, M.K. (2019) Effects of nickel fertilization on soybean growth in tropical soils. *Bragantia* 78(3), 432-443.

Mali, G.C., Sharma, N.N., Acharya, H.K., Gupta, S.K. and Gupta, P.K. (2003) Response of pigeon pea to S and Zn fertilization on *Vertisols* in South eastern plain of Rajasthan. Proceedings of National symposium on Arid Legumes for Food Nutrition Security and Promotion Trade, Hisar, India, 15-16 May 2002. Pp. 267-271.

Meena, K.K., Meena, R.S. and Kumawat, S.M. (2013) Effect of sulphur and iron fertilization on yield attributes, yield and nutrient uptake of mungbean (*Vigna radiata*). *Indian Journal of Agricultural Science* 83(4), 472-476.

Metwally, A., El-Shazoly, R. and Hamada, A.M. (2012) Effect of boron on growth criteria of some wheat cultivars. *Journal of Biology and Earth Sciences* 2(1),1-9.

Mondal, M., Rahman, M.A., Akter, M.B. and Fakir, M.S.A. (2011). Effect of foliar application of nitrogen and micronutrients on growth and yield in mung bean. *Legume Research* 34 (3), 166-171

Janaki, M.A., Parmar, K.B. and Vekaria, L.C. (2018) Effect of boron and molybdenum on yield and yield attributes of summer green gram (*Vigna radiata* L.) under medium black calcareous soils. *International Journal of Chemical Studies* 6(1), 321-323

Muhammad, H.R.S, Tasveer, Z.B. and Uzma, Y. (2013) Boron irrigation effect on germination and morphological attributes of *Zea mays* cultivars (*Cv.* Afghoee & Cv. Composite). *International Journal of Scientific Engineering Research* 4(8),1563-1569.

Nabi, G., Rafique, E. and Salim, M. (2006) Source, level and methods of boron application on the dry matter production, yield attributes and yields of mungbean crop. *Journal of Plant Nutrition* 29, 717-725.

Nasar, J. and Shah, Z. (2017) Effect of iron and molybdenum on yield and nodulation of lentil. *Journal of Agriculture and Biological Sciences* 12(11), 332-339.

Oktem, A.G. (2019) Effects of different zinc levels on grain yield and some phenological characteristics of red lentil (*Lens culinaris* Medic.) under arid conditions. *Turkish Journal of Agriculture and Forestry*, 43(3) 360-367.

Parker, D. R. (1997) Responses of six crop species to solution zinc^{2+} activities buffered with HEDTA. *Soil Science Society of America Journal* 61(1), 167-176.

Patil, S.B., Vyakaranahal, B.S., Deshpande, V.K. and Shekhargouda, M. (2006) Effect of boron and zinc application on seed yield and quality of mungbean. *Karnataka Journal of Agricultural Sciences* 19, 708-710.

Renukadevi, A., Savithri, P. and Andi, K. (2002) Evaluation of B fertilizer for sunflower-greengram sequence in Inceptisols. *Acta Agronomica Hungarica* 50(2), 163-168.

Rerkasem, B. (1991) Comparison of green gram (*Vigna radiata* L.) and black gram (*Vigna mungo* L.) in boron deficiency. In Proceedings of the Mungbean Meeting 90, Chiang Mai, Thailand, Feb. 23–24, 1990. Edited by Thavarasook, C., Srinives, R., Boonkerd, N., Imai, H., Pookpadki, A., Laosuwan, P. and Pupipat, U. 167–174. Japan: Bangkok Office of Tropical Agriculture Research Center.

Ross, J.R., Slaton, N.A., DeLong, R.E., Brye, K.R., Golden, B.R., Thompson, R., Wimberly, R., Klerk, R., Hamilton, M., Mozaffari, M. and Espinoza, L. (2003) Soybean grain yield response to foliar boron application rate and time. Wayne E Sabbe Arkansas Soil Fertility Studies, 61-65.

Sahu, S., Lidder, R.S. and Singh, P.K. (2008) Effect of micronutrients and biofertilizers on growth, yield and nutrients uptake by chickpea (*Cicer aeritinum* L.) in vertisol of Madhya Pradesh. *Plant Science* 21, 501-503.

Shivay, Y.S., Prasad, R., Singh, R.K. and Pal, M. (2015) Relative efficiency of zinc-coated urea and soil and foliar application of zinc sulphate on yield, nitrogen, phosphorus, potassium, zinc and iron biofortification in grains and uptake by basmati rice (*Oryza sativa* L.). *Journal of Agricultural Science* 7(2), 161.

Singh, B.P., and Singh, B. (1990) Response of French bean to phosphorus and boron in acid alfisols in Meghalaya. *Journal of the Indian Society of Soil Science* 38, 769-771.

Singh, D. and Singh, H. (2012) Effect of phosphorus and zinc nutrition on yield, nutrient uptake and quality of chickpea. *Annals of Plant and Soil research* 14(1) 71-4.

Singh, M.V. (2008) Micronutrient deficiencies in crops and soils in India. In: Alloway B.J. (eds) Micronutrient Deficiencies in Global Crop Production. Springer, Dordrecht. pp. 93-125.

Singh, R.P., Bisen, J.S., Yadav, P.K., Singh, S.N., Singh, R.K. and Singh, J. (2008) Integrated use of sulphur and molybdenum on growth, yield and quality of blackgram (*Vigna mungo* L). *Legume Research* 31(3), 214-217.

Takkar, P.N., Singh, M.V. and Ganeshamurthy, A.N. (1997) A critical review of plant nutrient supply needs, efficiency and policy issue for Indian agriculture for the year

2000 In: Proceedings of a Seminar on Plant nutrient needs, supply, efficiency and policy issues: 2000-2025 (Eds.) J. S. Kanwar and J. C. Katyal, National Academy of Agricultural Sciences, New Delhi. 238-265

Tripathy, S.K., Patra, A.K. and Samui, S.C. (1999) Effect of micronutrient on nodulation, growth, yield and nutrient uptake by groundnut (*Arachis hypogea*). *Indian Journal of Plant Physiology* 4, 207-209.

Usman, M., Tahir, M. and Majeed, M.A. (2014) Effect of zinc sulphate as soil application and seed treatment on green gram (*Vigna radiata* L.). *Pakistan Journal of Life and Social Science* 12(2), 87-91.

Wang, T.L., Domoney, C., Hedley, C.L., Casey, R. and Grusak, M.A. (2003) Can we improve the nutritional quality of legume seeds? *Plant Physiology* 131(3), 886-891.

CHAPTER 10

Nutrient and weed management in summer pulses in IGP

Harpreet Kaur Virk[1]* and Guriqbal Singh
Department of Plant Breeding and Genetics
Punjab Agricultural University, Ludhiana-141004, Punjab
*Corresponding author email: hkmand@pau.edu

Abstract

The Indo-Gangetic Plains, including most of northern and eastern India, the eastern parts of Pakistan, almost all Bangladesh and southern plains of Nepal, are dominated by rice-wheat and rice-based cropping systems. Summer pulses (mungbean and urdbean) fit well in rice-wheat and rice-based cropping systems being short duration crops. Nutrient and weed management are major factors affecting the productivity of summer pulses. Application of organic manures [FYM (farmyard manure)/ vermicompost/ compost/ biofertilizers)] improves soil physical properties and enhances plant nutrients. Being leguminous crops, though summer pulses can fix atmospheric nitrogen but they also require balanced fertilizers (20-45 kg N, 40-60 kg P_2O_5, 80-100 kg K and 20-40 kg S ha^{-1}) for enhancing nodulation, productivity and profitability. Apart from macronutrients, micronutrients (zinc, molybdenum, boron) also enhance the productivity and quality of summer pulses. Furthermore, integrated nutrient management is the best approach to improve the productivity as well as soil properties through the application of organic nutrients, biofertilizers and chemical fertilizers in an integrated manner for agricultural sustainability. Importantly, weeds cause reduction in grain yield of mungbean and urdbean to an extent of 22.5-79.0% and 41.2-53.1%, respectively. Weeds can be controlled by two hand weedings (20-25 and 40 DAS) and using herbicides. Some herbicides such as fluchloralin (pre-plant incorporation), pendimethalin (pre-emergence) or pre-mix pendimethalin 30 EC + imazethapyr 2 EC (pre-emergence) or imazethapyr/quizalofop-p-ethyl/fluazifop-p-butyl (post-emergence) were found to be effective in controlling weeds and improving the grain yield over weedy check. Furthermore, depending upon the weed flora and intensity, one or more methods can be used in an integrated manner for effective weed management, productivity and profitability.

Keywords: Grain yield, Mungbean, Nutrients, Urdbean, Weeds

1. INTRODUCTION

The Indo-Gangetic Plains (IGP), also known as Indus-Ganga Plain and the North Indian River Plain, is a 630 million acre long stretch including most of northern and eastern India, the eastern parts of Pakistan, almost all Bangladesh and southern plains of Nepal (Taneja *et al.*, 2014). In the IGP, 13.5 M ha area is occupied by the rice-wheat cropping system (Ladha *et al.*, 2003). Rice-wheat and rice-based cropping systems are being practiced in the IGP after green revolution. These two cereal crops have replaced the area under pulses. In Punjab and West Bengal, more than 95% of the area of food grain production is now under rice and wheat. In the IGP, there is a huge potential exist for cultivation of summer crops i.e. mungbean [*Vigna radiata* (L.) Wilczek] and urdbean [*Vigna mungo* (L.) Hepper] after harvest of mustard, potato, pea and wheat. Being short duration crops, these fit well in various multiple and intercropping systems. Summer pulses, being short duration crops (60-70 days) can be easily accommodated in irrigated rice-wheat cropping system. Apart from the yield advantage, the summer crop being a legume, provides additional benefits of maintenance of soil health, system diversification and often used as a source of organic nutrients as a green manure crop. Inclusion of legume in cereal-cereal rotation enhances soil quality and results in 6% increase in organic carbon level in soil and 85% increase in soil microbial biomass carbon as compared with the conventional rice-wheat system (Ghosh *et al.*, 2012). Moreover, addition of summer pulses to the cropping system has the potential to increase farm income, improve human health and soil productivity, save irrigation water, and promotes long-term sustainability of agriculture (Kumar *et al.*, 2018b).

Pulses are important leguminous crops that provide high quality protein (20-24%), essential amino acids, vitamins and minerals for vegetarian population of the country. Pulses provide significant nutritional and health benefits. The cultivation of pulses helps to fix atmospheric nitrogen in their root nodules and thus meet their nitrogen (N) requirements to a great extent. Pulses can play a significant role in maintaining soil fertility through nitrogen fixation and thus contribute significantly to sustainability and profitability of cereal based cropping systems. Inclusion of a summer pulse in cereal-based cropping system helps to provide the nutritional security, system productivity and environmental sustainability.

Mungbean and urdbean are the most important legume crops for IGP under cereal-cereal cropping system. Nutrient and weed management are very important strategies to increase production of pulse crop. Weed control has been found to be the single most important input followed by fertilizers in influencing the grain yield of mungbean (Singh and Sekhon, 2002; Singh and Sekhon, 2008b). Appropriate nutrients, such as phosphorus (P), sulphur (S) and zinc (Zn) help in improving plant biomass for pulses and result in better yields. Application of fertilizer had significant influence on the grain yield of mungbean and urdbean.

2. NUTRIENT MANAGEMENT

Nutrient management means management of all nutrient sources: chemical fertilizers, organic manures, waste materials, biological nitrogen fixation (BNF) and biofertilizers efficiently by minimizing the loss of nutrients to environment and maintenance of soil fertility and enhancing crop productivity. Different sources of nutrients affect the productivity of summer pulses (Table 1). Moreover, the emphasis is on balanced fertilizer use i.e., application of fertilizers in right proportion, right time and appropriate method and in an integrated manner for a higher use efficiency of applied fertilizers sustaining the productivity of cropping systems.

Table 1. Effect of different nutrients on productivity of summer pulses in IGP.

Type of nutrients	Nutrients	Reference
Organic nutrients	Biofertilizers	Khan and Prakash (2014); Rani *et al.* (2016)
	Organic manures	Shukla and Tyagi (2009); Hussain *et al.* (2017)
Macro nutrients	Nitrogen	Singh *et al.* (2011); Manoj *et al.* (2014); Hossen *et al.* (2015); Hussain *et al.* (2017)
	Phosphorus	Bhat *et al.* (2005); Mandal *et al.* (2005); Hayat *et al.* (2008); Sultana *et al.* (2009); Asaduzzaman *et al.* (2010); Singh *et al.* (2011); Dharwe *et al.* (2019)
	Potassium	Kumar *et al.* (2014); Hussain *et al.* (2016); Mazed *et al.* (2016)
	Sulphur	Nath *et al.* (2010); Rani *et al.* (2016); Dharwe *et al.* (2019)
Micronutrients	Zinc	Singh *et al.* (2008); Sharma *et al.* (2013); Khan and Prakash (2014)
	Boron	Singh and Sekhon (2008a); Choudhary *et al.* (2017)
	Molybdenum	Roy *et al.* (2006); Khan and Prakash (2014)
Integrated nutrient management		Jat *et al.* (2012); Amruta *et al.* (2015); Singh *et al.* (2017); Bilkis *et al.* (2018)

2.1 Organic nutrients

Application of organic nutrients such as FYM, vermicompost, biofertilizers and compost helps to enhance the productivity and improve the soil fertility. Application of vermicompost @ 2 t/ha and compost @ 2 t/ha improved the soil physical properties and enhanced the plant nutrients (N, P and K) for growth of shoots, roots and nodulation (Shukla and Tyagi, 2009). Application of FYM produced higher grain yield of mungbean at 10 t/ha^{-1} as compared to 5 t/ha at Peshawar in Pakistan (Hussain *et al.*, 2017).

Seed inoculation of *Rhizobium* recorded significantly higher growth attributes, number and dry weight of nodules, grain and straw yield, N, Zn and molybdenum (Mo) uptake, net return and B:C ratio over uninoculation (Khan and Prakash, 2014). Similarly, seed inoculation with phosphate solubilizing bacteria (PSB) recorded the highest growth and yield attributes and grain yield of mungbean, nutrient uptake and net returns (Rani *et al.*, 2016). Further, dual inoculation of *Rhizobium* and plant growth promoting rhizobacteria (PGPR) also recorded significantly higher yield, N and P content and their uptake as compared to individual biofertilizer inoculation and uninoculated control in mungbean in Punjab (Kaur and Sharma, 2016).

2.2 Macronutrients

Nitrogen as well as phosphorus are essential nutrients for normal growth and development of crops. N is the most important nutrient element among the major essential elements. Being the main component of amino acids as well as protein, N is more useful in pulses. Besides, P promotes early root formation and formation of lateral, fibrous and healthy roots, which are very important for nodule formation and atmospheric N_2 fixation. K regulates the opening and closing of stomata, improves drought resistance, enhances biological nitrogen fixation and protein synthesis. Sulphur plays an important role in chlorophyll formation, protein synthesis (especially sulphur containing amino acids *viz.* cystine, cysteine and methionine) and activation of various enzymes.

Pulses are generally grown on low fertile soils or with application of low quantities of organic and inorganic sources of plant nutrients, which has resulted in low productivity. Though pulses fix atmospheric nitrogen, but application of nitrogenous fertilizers becomes helpful in increasing the yield. Research revealed that grain yield of mungbean and urdbean improved by the use of balanced fertilizers (Singh *et al.*, 2011). Application of 30 kg N/ha produced higher grain yield of mungbean as compared to 15 kg N/ha at Peshawar in Pakistan (Hussain *et al.*, 2017). Similarly, application of 30 kg N/ha as basal + one irrigation at flower initiation stage recorded the highest yield attributes and grain yield of mungbean in Uttar Pradesh (Manoj *et al.*, 2014). Application of 45 kg N/ha recorded significantly higher grain yield of mungbean than 30, 60, 75 and 0 kg N/ha in Bangladesh (Hossen *et al.*, 2015).

Application of 60 kg P_2O_5/ha recorded the highest grain yield of mungbean and nutrient uptake in West Bengal (Mandal *et al.*, 2005), Bangladesh (Asaduzzaman *et al.*, 2010) and Uttar Pradesh (Rani *et al.*, 2016). Application of 90 kg P_2O_5/ha and 20 kg S/ha to mungbean crop resulted in the highest grain yield and straw yield (Dharwe *et al.*, 2019). Application of 60 kg P_2O_5/ha provided the highest grain yield of mungbean (Sultana *et al.*, 2009). However, application of 90 kg P_2O_5/ha produced the highest grain yield and was at par with 60 kg P_2O_5/ha, and both were significantly superior to 30 kg P_2O_5/ha (Bhat *et al.*, 2005). Application of 80 kg P_2O_5/ha with inoculation increased N_2-fixation by 47.3% and 13.8% in mungbean and urdbean, respectively and P-fixation by 15.3% and 31.7% in mungbean and urdbean, respectively over control (Hayat *et al.*, 2008).

Application of 80 kg (Kumar *et al.*, 2014), 90 kg (Kumar *et al.*, 2018a) in Uttar Pradesh and 100 kg K/ha in Pakistan (Hussain *et al.*, 2016) improved the grain yield of mungbean. However, application of potassium (25 kg K/ha) and sulphur (6 kg S/ha) recorded higher grain yield of mungbean compared to their individual application and also improved organic carbon, available N, P, K and S status of soil in Bangladesh (Mazed *et al.*, 2016). Application of gypsum @ 40 kg S/ha recorded the highest nutrient uptake, grain yield, seed protein and NPK content in mungbean grains in IGP of Uttar Pradesh (Nath *et al.*, 2010). Similarly, application of 40 kg S/ha provided the highest growth attributes, yield attributes and grain yield of mungbean and uptake of N, P and S (Rani *et al.*, 2016).

Application of 12.5 kg N + 60 kg P_2O_5/ha resulted in the highest grain yield of mungbean which was on par with 12.5 kg N + 40 kg P_2O_5/ha but significantly higher than control, 12.5 kg N, 40 kg P_2O_5 and 60 kg P_2O_5/ha in Punjab (Singh *et al.*, 2011). Though application of 12.5 kg N + 40 kg P_2O_5 + 15 kg $ZnSO_4$/ha resulted in the highest nodulation, plant growth and grain yield of mungbean was on par with 12.5 kg N + 40 kg P_2O_5/ha (Singh *et al.*, 2008). Application of 40 kg P_2O_5/ha recorded significantly higher grain yield, yield attributing characters, harvest index, attraction index, net returns, B:C ratio and nutrient uptake of mungbean compared to control and 20 kg P_2O_5/ha in Haryana (Singh *et al.*, 2019).

2.3 Micronutrients

Micronutrients play an important role in improving grain yield of mungbean (Raj and Raj, 2019). Micronutrients (B, Cu, Fe, Mn, Mo, Zn, Ni and Cl) are essential for plant growth and play an important role in balanced crop nutrition. Iron is essential nutrient for crop growth and is involved in chlorophyll synthesis and chloroplast development (Saini and Singh, 2017) and is an important part of nitrogenase, leghaemoglobin and ferredoxin. Cobalt and molybdenum are essential for the growth of *Rhizobium* and nitrogen fixation. Zinc plays an important role in chlorophyll production, pollen function, fertilization and germination (Sharma *et al.*, 2013). Boron enhances flowering blooms and develops uniform ripening process and it is essential in sugar transport, cell division, and amino acid production. Manganese performs an important role in photosynthesis, chloroplast production, a cofactor in many plant reactions and activates enzymes. Copper stimulates enzymes required for photosynthesis. Molybdenum application plays a vital role in increasing the nitrogen fixation process by *Rhizobium* and, is responsible for the formation of nodule tissue and increase in N fixation (Roy *et al.*, 2006). Cobalt is an important constituent of cobalamine coenzyme and required for formation of leghaemoglobin in nitrogen fixation. Micronutrients can be applied as seed treatment, basal or foliar application. However, foliar application of micronutrients at reproductive stages is more beneficial than basal. Seed inoculation with *Rhizobium*, zinc application @ 7.5 kg/ha and molybdenum @ 1.0 kg/ha recorded the highest number and dry weight of nodules, grain and stover yield, seed protein content, nitrogen, zinc and molybdenum uptake, which was significantly higher than control in urdbean in Uttar Pradesh (Khan and Prakash, 2014). Application of 20:60:20 NPK + 0.2% foliar spray of boron at 35 DAS recorded the highest grain yield of mungbean (Choudhary *et al.*, 2017). Supplemental use of zinc sulphate, borax and sodium molybdate tended to increase the grain yield of mungbean over sole application of nitrogen and phosphorus (Singh and Sekhon, 2008a).

2.4 Integrated nutrient management

The chemical fertilizers are the important source that can meet the nutrient requirement, however, continuous use lead to environmental pollution and deterioration of soil health. Under these circumstances, one should not depend on single source of plant nutrients like chemical fertilizers. Therefore, the need of the hour is to evolve an integrated plant nutrient supply system comprising balanced use of chemical fertilizers, organic manures and biofertilizers. Integrated nutrient management refers to meeting the nutrient demand of the crop through different organic and inorganic sources of nutrients in an integrated manner to maintain the soil fertility and for sustainable agricultural production. Application of vermicompost (2.0 t/ha) along with inorganic fertilizer (100 kg/ha DAP) and *Rhizobium* inoculation recorded the highest grain yield, protein yield and net returns of mungbean and furthermore improved the soil status by increasing soil organic carbon, available N, available P and available K content at Kanpur (Jat *et al.*, 2012). Application of 50% RDF (recommended dose of fertilizer i.e. 20 kg N + 40 kg P/ha) + 50% RDN (recommended dose of nitrogen as vermicompost) + PSB (phosphate solubilizing bacteria) produced significantly higher growth attributes, yield and economics of mungbean than control and 100% RDF (Kumar and Kumawat, 2014). Seed inoculation of biofertilizer (*Rhizobium* + PSB) + Mo 1.0 + Co 1.0 kg/ha increased growth, yield attributes, nodule number & dry weight, and recorded higher grain yield, protein content, protein yield and nutrient uptake than control in mungbean (Singh *et al.*, 2017). Application of 50:100:100 NPK kg/ha+ rhizobia (250 g/ha) + *Bacillus megaterium* (250 g/ha) increased the productivity of urdbean (Amruta *et al.*, 2015). Application of vermicompost or trichocompost in combination with inorganic fertilizers improved the grain yield and nutritional quality in mungbean in Bangladesh (Bilkis *et al.*, 2018).

3. WEED MANAGEMENT

Weeds are a major biotic constraint to crop production globally (Sardana *et al.*, 2017). Weeds compete with plants for sunlight, nutrients, moisture and space. Weed competition depends greatly on nature and intensity of weed flora, soil type, agroclimatic conditions and management practices. Pulses, being poor competitor to weeds especially during initial growth stages, suffer considerable yield loss. Summer pulses, being short duration crops, are a poor competitor of weeds. Their critical crop-weed competition period varies from 15-30 days after sowing. Critical period of crop-weed competition lies between 10 to 40 days after sowing in urdbean (Kumar and Tiwari, 2004b).

3.1 Losses due to weeds

Worldwide, weeds causes the highest economic losses to the tune of 34% followed by animal pests (18%) and pathogens (16%) (Oerke, 2006). The magnitude of yield losses caused by weeds depends upon weed species, their densities and crop weed competition period. Weeds cause reduction in grain yield of mungbean and urdbean to the tune of 22.5-79.0% and 41.2-53.1%, respectively (Table 2). Moreover, weeds deteriorate the quality of the crop produce. Weeds compete for nutrients with the crop plants and the highest nutrient removal by weeds was recorded in weedy check (Sahu *et al.*, 2019; Singh and Singh 2020). In an another study also, the highest nutrient removal by weeds was recorded in unweeded control i.e. 68.90, 19.29 and 77.17 kg/ha of N, P and K, respectively and the lowest in treatment of pendimethalin 0.75 kg/ha i.e. 8.70, 3.17 and 11.57 kg/ha of N, P and K, respectively in mungbean (Kaur *et al.*, 2010). In weedy check, weeds removed 6 kg N, 2.8 kg P and 7.0 kg K/ha in urdbean (Choudhary *et al.*, 2012). Weedy check also reduced the economic returns in mungbean (Singh and Singh, 2017; Sahu *et al.*, 2019) and urdbean (Singh 2011). Weed control measures increased the crop production costs (Oerke, 2006). Moreover, weeds also caused negative effects on the symbiotic parameters. Weedy check recorded the lowest number and dry weight of nodules and leghaemoglobin content of mungbean, which was significantly lower than the treatments of two hand weedings and pendimethalin alone or integrated with hand weeding (Singh and Singh, 2020).

Table 2. Yield loss due to weeds in summer pulses in IGP.

Crop	Yield loss	Reference
Mungbean	65.4%	Shuaib (2001)
	79.0%	Dungarwal *et al.* (2003)
	44.2%	Kaur *et al.* (2009)
	60.1%	Sahu *et al.* (2019)
	52.5%	Tamang *et al.* (2015)
	22.5%	Ram *et al.* (2016)
	38.6%	Kumar *et al.* (2016)
Urdbean	45.2%	Bhandari *et al.* (2004)
	41.2%	Singh (2011)
	40.1%	Kumar and Tiwari (2004b)

3.2 Weed flora

Major weeds associated with summer pulses included annual grasses like *Cynodon dactylon, Digitaria sanguinalis, Eleusine indica, Setaria glauca, Panicum maximum,* sedges like *Cyperus rotundus* and broadleaf weeds like *Trianthema portulacastrum, Portulaca quadrifida, Physalis minima and Solanum nigrum.* However, weed flora differ from region to region with soil conditions in different crops (Table 3).

Table 3. Major weed flora during summer season in IGP areas.

Crop	Name of weed	Area	Reference
Mungbean	*Echinochloa colona, Echinochloa crussgalli, Digitaria sanguinalis, Eleusine indica, Cyperus rotundus, Physalis minima, Alternanthera sessilis, Euphorbia hirta, Cleome viscosa, Chenopodium album*	West Bengal	Kundu *et al.* (2009)
	Cyperus rotundus, Trianthema portulacastrum and *Eragrostis tenella*	Punjab	Kaur *et al.* (2009)
	Eleusine indica, Dactyloctenium aegyptium, Digitaria ciliaris, Commelina benghalensis, Digera arvensis and Trianthema portulacastrum	Punjab	Ram *et al.* (2016)
	Cynodon dactylon, Dactyloctenium aegyptium, Digitaria sanguinalis, Panicum repens, Cyperus rotundus, Amaranthus viridis, Celosia argentea, Commelina benghalensis, Digera arvensis, Euphorbia hirta and *Trichoderma indicum*	Bihar	Sahu *et al.* (2019)
	Digitaria sanguinalis, Cynodon dactylon, Eleusine indica, Echinochloa colona, Cyperus rotundus, Cleome viscosa, Chenopodium album, Euphorbia hirta, Digeria arvensis, Physalis minima and *Amaranthus viridis.*	West Bengal	Tamang *et al.* (2015)

Urdbean	*Trianthema portulacastrum, Eleusine aegyptiacum, Digitaria sanguinalis* and *Cyperus rotundus*	Punjab	Singh (2011)
	Cynodon dactylon, Trianthema monogyna, Amaranthus viridis, Medicago denticulata, Vicia sativa, Lepidium sativum and *Cyperus rotundus*	Punjab	Bhandari *et al.* (2004)
	Trianthema monogyna, Sorghum halepense, Commelina benghalensis and *Cyperus rotundus*	Kanpur	Kumar and Tiwari (2004)

3.3 Methods of weed management

Weeds cause huge losses to agricultural crop production in terms of yield, economics and quality. Crop-weed competition is very high initially. Therefore, there is need to control weeds during this period to encourage the growth of crop plants by reducing the crop-weed competition and thereby improve productivity. For increasing the productivity of crops, there are many approaches by which weeds can be effectively and economically controlled in pulses. Weeds can be controlled by mechanically, chemically or integrated weed management method (Table 4).

Table 4. Weed management practices in summer pulses.

Crop	Weed management	Reference
Mungbean	Quizalofop-p-ethyl 50 g a.i./ha at 21 day after emergence (DAE) + hand weeding (HW) at 28 DAE	Kundu *et al.* (2009)
	Pendimethalin 0.75 kg/ha as pre-emergence	Ram *et al.* (2016)
	Pendimethalin 30 EC at 0.45 kg/ha + HW and pendimethalin 30 EC + imazethapyr 2 SL (pre-mix) at 0.45 kg/ha + HW	Singh and Singh (2020)
	Pendimethalin (1 kg/ha) 2 DAS + one hand weeding at 20 days after sowing (DAS)	Sahu *et al.* (2019)
	Pendimethalin 30 EC + imazethapyr 2 EC @ 1.00 kg a.i./ha	Tamang *et al.* (2015)
Urdbean	Pendimethalin 1.0-2.0 kg, pendimethalin 1.0 kg/ha + HW 25 DAS and fluchloralin 0.5-1.5 kg/ha	Bhandari *et al.* (2004)
	Two HW 25 & 40 DAS and pendimethalin 0.45 kg/ha + HW 25 DAS	Singh (2011)
	Pre-emergence application of pendimethalin @ 1.5 kg/ha + one hand weeding 25 DAS	Choudhary *et al.* (2012)
	Pre-plant incorporation of imazethapyr and pre-emergence application of pendimethalin.	Mishra and Bhanu (2006)
	Pendimethalin (1 kg/ha) as pre-emergence followed by fluazifop-p-butyl (0.375 kg/ha) as post-emergence	Kumar and Tiwari (2004a)

3.3.1 Mechanical method

Mechanical weed control is the safest, but costly method of weed control. Mechanical weed control involves removal of weeds with various tools and implements including hand weeding and hand pulling. Inter-culture operations are performed primarily to destroy the weeds present in the field and create favorable soil conditions for plant growth. Hand weeding during critical stage of crop-weed competition provides satisfactory control of weeds in all the crops. Two hand weedings improved the grain yield in mungbean and urdbean to the tune of 60.1 (Sahu *et al.*, 2019) and 70.2% (Singh, 2011) over weedy check. Weeds can be effectively controlled by hand weeding in mungbean (Singh, 2011; Singh and Singh, 2020) and urdbean (Bhandari *et al.*, 2004; Sahu *et al.*, 2019). Two hand weedings at 20 and 40 DAS recorded significantly lower weed density and dry weight and provided better grain yield of mungbean (Tamang *et al.*, 2015). The highest grain yield was recorded in two hand hoeings at 25 and 40 DAS followed by pendimethalin 0.75 kg/ha (Kaur *et al.*, 2009). Two HW at 4 weeks after sowing (WAS) and 6 WAS provided the highest grain yield of mungbean (Singh and Singh, 2020). Two hand weedings at 25 and 40 DAS recorded the highest nitrogen and phosphorus uptake by the mungbean crop (Kaur *et al.*, 2010). Two hand weedings at 25 and 40 DAS recorded the highest grain yield of urdbean by effectively controlling the weeds and reducing crop-weed competition (Singh, 2011). One hand weeding 25 DAS also produced significantly higher grain yield of urdbean than weedy check (Bhandari *et al.*, 2004).

3.3.2 Chemical method

Herbicides are chemicals used to kill or inhibit the growth of weeds without affecting crop plants. Non-availability of labour and involvement of high cost in manual removal of weeds by hand weeding are the major factors responsible for the use of herbicides. Therefore, in agriculture due to high yield losses by weeds, the use of herbicides is increasing. Chemical control is the easiest and cheapest method of weed management and provides weed control up to 30-35 days from emergence. Herbicides should be selected based on weed flora of the field. Herbicides have shown promising results in controlling weeds and improving grain yield of summer pulses (Singh, 2011; Singh and Singh, 2020). Application of herbicides improved the grain yield in mungbean and urdbean to the tune of 27.1-35.2% (Kundu *et al.*, 2009; Sahu *et al.*, 2019) and 63.2% (Singh, 2011), respectively over weedy check. Application of pre-mix pendimethalin 30 EC+ imazethapyr 2 EC @1.00 kg a.i./ha was found most effective in reducing population and dry mass of weeds and producing the highest grain yield of mungbean at Nadia, West Bengal (Tamang *et al.*, 2015). Similarly, at Ludhiana, Punjab also application of pendimethalin @ 0.75 kg/ha was found to be effective in controlling weeds and increasing the grain yield of mungbean over weedy check (Ram *et al.*, 2016). Application of imazethapyr 100 g/ha and imazethapyr 80 g/ha effectively controlled weeds and also improved the grain yield of mungbean which was on par with the grain yield of weed free treatment (Kumar *et al.*, 2016). However, application of fenoxaprop-p-ethyl @ 50 g and 100 g/ha was found less effective for controlling weeds (Tamang *et al.*, 2015). Further, some herbicides control weeds but also show phytotoxic effects on crop. Application of chlorimuron @ 9 and 15 g/ha had phytotoxic effect on the mungbean crop (Kaur *et al.*, 2009).

Application of pendimethalin 0.75 kg/ha (PE), pendimethalin 0.45 kg/ha (PE) + hand weeding (HW) 25 days after sowing (DAS), fluchloralin 0.675 kg/ha (pre-plant) and two HW 25 & 40 DAS recorded lower weed dry matter and higher grain yield and net returns of urdbean than weedy check (Singh, 2011). Similarly, application of pendimethalin 1.0-2.0 kg/ha, pendimethalin 1 kg/ha + HW 25 DAS and fluchloralin 0.5-1.5 kg/ha improved grain yield of urdbean (Bhandari *et al.*, 2004). Application of pendimethalin (1.25 kg/ha) as pre-emergence and fluazifop-p-butyl (0.375 kg/ha) as post-emergence treatment under sequential application was found very effective against *Trianthema monogyna* and *Sorghum halepense,* respectively and provided similar grain yield of urdbean to that obtained under weed-free (Kumar and Tiwari, 2004a). Some herbicides have inhibitory effect on *Rhizobium* and nodulation. Application of metolachlor, pretilachlor, imazethapyr (pre-plant incorporation) and fenoxaprop resulted in reduced number and dry weight of nodules and also significantly decreased the bacterial count compared to control. However, application of pendimethalin, imazethapyr (post-emergence), quizalofop and fluchloralin did not affect the nodulation and *Rhizobium* count in urdbean (Mishra and Bhanu, 2006).

3.3.3 Integrated weed management

Integrated weed management is the integration of different methods of weed management including cultural, mechanical and chemical. Herbicides are able to control weeds up to certain time but flushes of weeds in the further growing stage of crops pose a great challenge for the weed management. Moreover, excessive use of herbicides has resulted in serious environmental and ecological issues. Further, high cost of herbicides, their timely unavailability and lack of technical know-how also make weed control difficult. So, there is a need to integrate different cultural, mechanical and chemical methods of weed management for effective control of weeds. Integration of hand weeding with application of pre-emergence herbicide helps to control the weeds and reduces the crop-weed competition and improves the grain yield (Singh and Singh, 2020). Integrated weed management approach improved the grain yield in mungbean and urdbean to the tune of 48.1% (Sahu *et al.*, 2019) and 67.4% (Singh, 2011), respectively over weedy check. Since application of a single herbicide may not be effective in providing broad spectrum weed control, therefore, application of pre- and post-emergence herbicides in sequence or integration with manual weeding may be more beneficial. Application of quizalofop-p-ethyl @ 50 g/ha at 21 DAE (days after emergence) + hand weeding at 28 DAE recorded the highest yield attributes, grain yield and benefit:cost ratio in mungbean compared with application of herbicide alone (Kundu *et al.*, 2009). Application of pendimethalin 1 kg a.i./ha as pre-emergence followed by hand weeding at 20 DAS significantly reduced weed density and biomass at 20 and 40 DAS than pendimethalin 1 kg/ha alone and weedy check in mungbean (Sahu *et al.,* 2019). Moreover, application of pendimethalin (1 kg/ha) 2 DAS + one hand weeding at 20 DAS recorded significantly higher growth and yield attributes by effectively controlling weeds and provided higher grain yield, maximum net returns and B:C ratio and was found at par with two hand weeding at 20 and 40 DAS in mungbean (Sahu *et al.*, 2019). Application of pendimethalin 30 EC at 0.45 kg/ha (PE) + HW at 4 WAS, pendimethalin 30 EC at 0.75 kg/ha (PE), pre-mix pendimethalin 30 EC + imazethapyr 2 SL at 0.45 kg/ha (PE) + HW at 4 WAS and imazethapyr 10 SL at 75 g/ha at 15 DAS can act as alternative to two HW where labour is costly or not available at appropriate time for manual weeding in mungbean

(Singh and Singh, 2020). Two HW at 25 and 40 DAS recorded the highest weed control efficiency and grain yield of urdbean, which was followed by integration of pendimethalin 0.45 kg/ha + HW 25 DAS. However, integration of pendimethalin 0.45 kg/ha with HW 25 DAS recorded the highest net returns (Singh, 2011). Similarly, Bhandari *et al.* (2004) also reported that integration of pendimethalin 1 kg/ha and fluchloralin at 0.5 kg/ha with HW 25 DAS recorded significantly higher grain yield of urdbean than weedy check and at par with one HW at 25 DAS.

4. CONCLUSION

Nutrients are very important for the initial growth of the plants. Macro and micro nutrients are required for the fulfillment of the crop requirements. Balanced application of nutrients through organic and inorganic sources helps to enhance the productivity of pulses, nutrient uptake and improve the soil properties. Nutrient and weed management are the important strategies to improve the pulses productivity. Weeds are the serious threat to agricultural productivity causing about 34% yield reduction. Weeds are the serious pest in summer pulses. Weeds can be controlled by mechanical, chemical or integrated method. Depending upon the weed flora and intensity, different methods of weed control can be selected. Pre-emergence herbicide pendimethalin and post-emergence herbicides imazethapyr, fluazifop-p-butyl and quizalofop-p-ethyl provide effective control of weeds and reduce the yield losses. Among different weed control methods, integrated weed management is the best approach for effective weed management in summer pulses in IGP.

REFERENCES

Amruta, N., Maruthi, J.B., Sarika, G. and Deepika, C. (2015) Effect of integrated nutrient management and spacing on growth and yield parameters of black gram cv. Lbg-625 (rashmi). *The Bioscan* 10, 193-198.

Asaduzzaman, M., Chowdhury, S. and Ali, M.A. (2010) Phosphorus and weeding on growth and yield of mungbean (*Vigna radiata* L.). *International Journal of Bio-resource Management* 1, 54-58.

Bhandari, V., Singh, B., Randhawa, J.S. and Singh, J. (2004) Relative efficacy and economics of integrated weed management in blackgram under semi-humid climate of Punjab. *Indian Journal of Weed Science* 36, 276-277.

Bhat, S.A., Thenua, O.V.S., Shivakumar, B.G. and Malik, J.K. (2005) Performance of summer green gram (*Vigna radiata* L.) as influenced by biofertilizer and phosphorus nutrition. *Haryana Journal of Agronomy* 21, 203-205.

Bilkis, S., Islam, M.R,, Jahiruddin, M., Rahman, M.M. and Hoque, T.S. (2018) Residual effects of different manures and fertilizers applied to preceding potato crop on succeeding mung bean (*Vigna radiate* L.) crop in potato-mung bean-rice cropping pattern. *SAARC Journal of Agriculture* 16, 167-179.

Choudhary, P., Ghosh, G., Neha, and Kumari, S. (2017) Effect on yield and benefit cost ratio of greengram at different phosphorus levels and frequency of boron levels. *International Journal of Current Microbiology and Applied Science* 6, 1095-1103.

Choudhary, V.K,, Kumar, P.S. and Bhagawati, R. (2012) Integrated weed management in blackgram (*Vigna mungo*) under midhills of Arunachal Pradesh. *Indian Journal of Agronomy* 57, 382-385.

Dharwe, D.S., Dixit, H.C., Dotaniya, C.K., Khandagle, A., Mohbe, S. and Doutaniya, R.K. (2019) Effect of phosphorus and sulphur on the yield & nutrient content of green gram. *International Journal of Chemical Studies* 7, 01-05.

Dungarwal, H.S., Chaplot, P.C. and Nagda, B.L. (2003) Chemical weed control in mungbean (*Phaseolus radiatus* L.). *Indian Journal of Weed Science* 35, 283-284.

Ghosh, P.K., Venkatesh, M.S., Hazra, K.K. and Kumar, N. (2012) Long-term effect of pulses and nutrient management on soil organic carbon dynamics and sustainability on an Inceptisol of Indo-Gangetic Plains of India. *Experimental Agriculture* 48, 473-487.

Hayat, R., Ali, S., Siddique, M.T. and Chatha, T.H. (2008) Biological nitrogen fixation of summer legumes and their residual effects on subsequent rainfed wheat yield. *Pakistan Journal of Botany* 40, 711-722.

Hossen, M.M., Hussain, A.S.M.I., Abdullah-Al-Zabir, Biswas, M.J.H. and Islam, M.R. (2015) Effect of nitrogenous fertilizer on yield of mungbean [*Vigna radiata* (L.) Wilczek] in Patuakhali district of Bangladesh. *Asian Journal of Medical and Biological Research* 1, 508-517.

Hussain, F., Buriro, M., Nizamani, M.R., Ahmed, S., Rehman, S., Ahmed, N. and Huma, Z. (2016) Growth and yield response of mungbean to different levels of potassium. *International Journal of Agricultural & Environmental Research* 2, 67-76.

Hussain, Z., Khan, N., Ullah, S., Liaqat, A., Nawaz, F., Khalil, A.U.R., Shah, J.A., Junaid, M. and Ali, M. (2017) Response of mungbean to various levels of biochar, farmyard manure and nitrogen. *World Journal of Agricultural Sciences* 13, 26-33.

Jat, S.L., Prasad, K. and Parihar, C.M. (2012) Effect of organic manuring on productivity and economics of summer mungbean (*Vigna radiata* var. *radiata*). *Annals of Agricultural Research New Series* 33, 17-20.

Kaur, G., Brar, H.S. and Singh, G. (2009) Effect of weed management on weeds, growth and yield of summer mungbean [*Vigna radiata* (L.) Wilczek]. *Indian Journal of Weed Science* 41, 228-231.

Kaur, G., Brar, H.S. and Singh, G. (2010) Effect of weed management on weeds, nutrient uptake, nodulation, growth and yield of summer mungbean (*Vigna radiata*). *Indian Journal of Weed Science* 42, 114-119.

Kaur, J. and Sharma, P. (2016) Response of summer mungbean (*Vigna radiata* L.) to *Rhizobium* and PGPR inoculation under different planting methods. *Annals of Agricultural Research* 37, 87-90.

Khan, K. and Prakash, V. (2014) Effect of rhizobial inoculation on growth, yield, nutrient uptake and economics of summer urdbean [*Vigna mungo* (L.) Heppe] in relation to zinc and molybdenum. *International Journal of Advanced Research in Chemistry and Chemical Engineering* 1, 1-10.

Kumar, A. and Tewari, A.N. (2004a) Efficacy of pre- and post-emergence herbicides in summer blackgram *(Vigna mungo* L.). *Indian Journal of Weed Science* 36, 73-75.

Kumar, A. and Tewari, A.N. (2004b) Crop weed competition studies on summer sown black gram (*Vigna mungo* L.). *Indian Journal of Weed Science* 36, 76-78.

Kumar, N., Hazra, K.K. and Nadarajan, N. (2016) Efficacy of post-emergence application of imazethapyr in summer mungbean (*Vigna radiata* L.). *Legume Research* 39, 96-100.

Kumar, P., Kumar, P., Singh, T., Singh, A.K. and Yadav, R.I. (2014) Effect of different potassium levels on mungbean under custard apple based agri-horti system. *African Journal of Agricultural Research* 9, 728-734.

Kumar, R. and Kumawat, N. (2014) Effect of sowing dates, seed rates and integrated nutrition on productivity, profitability and nutrient uptake of summer mungbean in Eastern Himalaya. *Archives of Agronomy and Soil Science* 60, 1207-1227.

Kumar, S., Jakhar, D.S. and Singh, R. (2018a) Growth and yield response of mung bean (*Vigna radiata* L.) in different levels of potassium. *Acta Scientific Agriculture* 2, 23-25.

Kumar, V., Jat, H.S., Sharma, P.C., Balwinder-Singh, Gathala, M.K., Malik, R.K., Kamboj, B.R., Yadav, A.K., Ladha, J.K., Raman, A., Sharma, D.K. and McDonald, A. (2018b) Can productivity and profitability be enhanced in intensively managed cereal systems while reducing the environmental footprint of production? Assessing sustainable intensification options in the breadbasket of India. *Agriculture, Ecosystem and Environment* 252, 132-147.

Kundu, R., Bera, P.S. and Brahnachari. (2009) Effect of different weed management practices in summer mungbean [*Vigna radiata* L.] under new alluvial zone of West Bengal. *Journal of Crop and Weed* 5, 117-121.

Ladha, J.K., Dawe, D., Pathak, H., Padre, A.T., Yadav, R.L., Bijay, S., Singh, Y., Singh, Y., Singh, P., Kundu, A.L., Sakal, R., Ram, N., Regmi, A.P., Gami, S.K., Bhandari, A.L., Amin, R., Yadav, C.R., Bhattarai, E.M., Das, S., Aggarwal, H.P., Gupta, R.K. and Hobbs, P.R. (2003) How extensive are yield declines in long-term rice–wheat experiments in Asia? *Field Crops Research* 81,159-180.

Mandal, S., Biswal, K.C. and Jana, P.K. (2005) Yield, economics, nutrient uptake and consumptive use of water by summer greengram (*Vigna radiata* L.) as influenced by irrigation and phosphorus application. *Legume Research* 28, 131-133.

Manoj, Singh, R.K., Singh, A.N., Ram, H. and Prasad, S.R. (2014) Growth, yield attributes and quality of summer greengram (*Vigna radiata* L.) as influenced by nitrogen and irrigation levels. *Annals of Agricultural Research New Series* 35, 47-53.

Mazed, H.E.M.K., Yeasmin, M., Moonmoon, J.F., Moniruzzaman, M. and Tarque, M.H. (2016) The concentrations of N, P, K and S in mungbean stover and seed as influenced by potassium and sulphur application. *Bulletin of the Institute of Tropical Agriculture Kyushu University* 39, 95-101.

Mishra, J.S. and Bhanu, C. (2006) Effect of herbicides on weeds, nodulation and growth of *Rhizobium* in summer black gram (*Vigna mungo*). *Indian Journal of Weed Science* 38, 150-153.

Nath, T., Kumar, A., Raha, P. and Singh, R.K. (2010) Nutrient uptake by summer green gram (*Vigna radiata* L. Wilczek) as influenced by different doses and sources of sulphur in alluvial soils of Indo-Gangetic Plain. *International Journal of Tropical Agriculture* 28, 303-306.

Oerke, E.C. (2006) Crop losses to pests. *Journal of Agricultural Science* 144, 31-43.

Raj, A.B. and Raj, S.K. (2019) Zinc and boron nutrition in pulses: A review. *Journal of Applied and Natural Science* 11, 673- 679.

Ram, H., Singh, G. and Aggarwal, N. (2016) Effect of irrigation, straw mulching and weed control on growth, water use efficiency and productivity of summer mungbean. *Legume Research* 39, 284-288.

Rani, M., Prakash, V. and Khan, K. (2016) Response of mungbean [*Vigna radiata* (L.) Wilczek] to phosphorus, sulphur and PSB during summer season. *Agricultural Science Digest* 36, 146-148.

Roy, R.N., Finck, A., Blair, G.J. and Tandon, H.L.S. (2006) Plant Nutrition for Food Security. A guide for integrated nutrient management. FAO Fertilizer and Plant Nutrition Bulletin **16**. Food and Agriculture Organization of the United Nations, Rome, Itlay. Pp 368.

Sahu, R., Sharda, K. and Mandal, S.K. (2019) Sowing date and weed management effects on weeds, nutrient uptake and productivity of summer greengram. *Indian Journal of Weed Science* 51, 302-305.

Saini, A.K. and Singh, R. (2017) Effect of sulphur and iron fertilization on growth and yield of greengram [*Vigna radiata* L.]. *International Journal of Current Microbiology and Applied Sciences* 6, 1922-1929.

Sardana, V., Mahajan, M., Jbran, K. and Chauhan, B.S. (2017) Role of competition in managing weeds: An introduction to the special issue. *Crop Protection* 95, 1-7.

Sharma, A., Patni, B., Shankhdhar, D. and Shankhdhar, S.C. (2013) Zinc–An indispensable micronutrient. *Physiology and Molecular Biology of Plants* 19, 11-20.

Shuaib, O.S.B. (2001) Critical period for weed competition in green gram. *Journal of Natural and Applied Science* 5, 11-18.

Shukla, L. and Tyagi, S.P. (2009) Effect of integrated application of organic manures on soil parameters and growth of mungbean (*Vigna radiata*). *Indian Journal of Agricultural Sciences* 79, 174-177.

Singh, G. and Sekhon, H.S. (2002) Relative contribution of different inputs in mungbean [*Vigna radiata* (L.) Wilczek] in summer and *kharif* seasons. *Environment & Ecology* 20, 757-761.

Singh, G. and Sekhon, H.S. (2008a) Effect of macro and micronutrients on the growth and yield of summer mungbean [*Vigna radiata* (L.) Wilczek]. *Journal of Plant Science Research* 24, 61-63.

Singh, G. and Sekhon, H.S. (2008b) Effect of various inputs on the growth and yield of summer greengram (*Vigna radiata*). *Indian Journal of Agricultural Sciences* 78, 87-89.

Singh, G., Ram, H., Sekhon, H.S., Aggarwal, N., Kumar, M., Kaur, P., Kaur, J. and Sharma, P. (2011) Effect of nitrogen and phosphorus application on productivity of summer mungbean sown after wheat. *Journal of Food Legumes* 24, 327-329.

Singh, G., Sekhon, H.S., Ram, H. and Sharma, P. (2008) Effect of fertilizer application on nodulation, growth and yield of summer mungbean [*Vigna radiata* (L.) Wilczek]. *Indian Journal of Ecology* 35, 28-30.

Singh, G. (2011) Weed management in summer and *kharif* season blackgram [*Vigna mungo* (L.) Hepper]. *Indian Journal of Weed Science* 43, 77-80.

Singh, M., Deokaran, Mishra, J.S. and Bhatt, B.P. (2017) Effect of integrated nutrient management on production potential and quality of summer mungbean (*Vigna radiata* L.). *Journal of Krishi Vigyan* 5, 39-45.

Singh, R. and Singh, G. (2017) Economic analysis of application of weed management practices in *kharif* and summer mungbean [*Vigna radiata* (L.) Wilczek). *International Journal of Current Microbiology and Applied Sciences* 6, 3182-3190.

Singh, R. and Singh, G. (2020) Influence of herbicides on symbiotic parameters, growth, yield and nutrient uptake in mungbean [*Vigna radiata* (L.) Wilczek]. *Archives of Agronomy and Soil Science*. 67, 410-425.

Singh, V., Sharma, S.K., Thakral, S.K. and Sharma, M.K. (2019) Effect of phosphorus on the performance of greengram (*Vigna radiata* L) varieties during summer. *Legume Research* 42, 247-249.

Sultana, S., Ullaah, M.J., Karim, M.F. and Asaduzzaman, M. (2009) Response of mungbean to integrated nitrogen and weed management. *American-Eurasian Journal of Agronomy* 2, 104-108.

Tamang, D., Nath, R. and Sengupta, K. (2015) Effect of herbicide application on weed management in green gram [*Vigna radiata* (L.) Wilczek]. *Advances in Crop Science and Technology* 3, 163.

Taneja, G., Pal, B.D., Joshi, P.K., Aggarwal, P.K. and Tyagi, N.K. (2014) Farmers preferences for climate-smart agriculture: An assessment in the Indo-Gangetic Plain. International Food Policy Research Institute. Pp 2.

CHAPTER 11

Precision water management for higher crop and water productivity in pulse crops

C.S. Praharaj*, N. Kumar, C.P. Nath, K.K. Hazra and Prasoon Verma
ICAR-Indian Institute of Pulses Research, Kanpur- 208 020, Uttar Pradesh
*Corresponding author email: cspraharaj@hotmail.com

Abstract

Technological backup complemented with precision input inclusive water management strategies for proven farm level impact in India has resulted in substantial increase in productivity of targeted field crops. Several key technological innovations enabling precision water management such as precision land leveling, no-till systems, FIRB planting systems, crop diversification and residue management have shown tremendous potential for higher water productivity and its use efficiency needed for sustainability. For example, precision technologies such as micro-irrigation are used for efficient management of both water and nutrient precisely near the root zone of crop plant with proven advantages of enhanced conveyance, water productivity and its use efficiency. Moreover, economizing of water through laser leveling and sprinkler as a water saving measure under dry and hot summer could reduce irrigation frequency following growing of a catch crop through summer pulses. Similarly, a typical Furrow Irrigated Raised Bed (FIRB) planting system enhances crop and water productivity. Proven agronomic advantages of raised beds include improved soil structure due to controlled trafficking and reduced water logging and timeliness in mechanical operations. In the same way, an altered land configuration such as raised bed system in chickpea could out-yield over flat planting significantly with enhanced water use efficiency. Therefore, suitable strategies will be highly site specific and offers an alternative for a quantum jump in outputs in pulse crops on expected lines for a sustainable resource management. In this chapter, besides water requirement of crops, scheduling of irrigation and other water management practices through precision technologies in aid of scaling water productivity have also been discussed.

Keywords: Conservation agriculture, Precision water management, Resource conservation technologies, Technological interventions, Water productivity

1. INTRODUCTION

In India efforts to adapt and promote precision technologies including those related to resource conservation (RCT) for accelerating resource efficiency (RUE) /input use efficiency (IUE) have been underway for nearly two decades but it is only in the past decade that these technologies are finding rapid acceptance by the farmers although these are more or less confined to irrigated agro-ecosystems (Kumar *et al.,* 2016; Kumar *et al.,* 2020). Yet, it is becoming popular in water deficit conditions that include both rainfed and dryland conditions. Water being the critical input for productivity enhancement, there is a need for its optimum and judicious use (through complementary/supplementary irrigation) for realizing higher input use efficiency through various technological options available (Singh *et al.,* 1993; Praharaj *et al.*, 2018). Similar is the case for nutrient and its use efficiencies. These should be in synchrony with the basic principles of resource conservation i.e., crop rotation, tillage and residue retention (Praharaj *et al.*, 2011). In addition two other principles viz., efficient weed control and improved farm mechanization play their role tremendously in a prominent way (Sangar *et al.*, 2004).

In this chapter, an attempt is made for use of precision water management for higher crop and water productivity through technological interventions in pulse crops. Moreover, there is also a need to discuss the novel strategies for an effective input (water or fertilizer or others) management mediated through RCT. An implication of this is to bring together all the stake holders to share information/experiences and to encourage interaction for future research and development efforts in fulfilling our Sustainable Developmental Goals (SDG beyond 2015 uptil 2030) for realizing production sustainability through conservation agriculture.

Pulse crops are mostly grown under rainfed condition all over India during both rainy months (pigeonpea, mungbean, urdbean and cowpea) and the winter (chickpea, lentil, fieldpea and rajmash). Among the pulses grown during rainy months, pigeonpea (*Cajanus cajan* L. Millsp) is primarily grown as a rainfed crop under diverse cropping systems including inter/mixed cropping followed by mungbean, urdbean, cowpea and cluster bean (Singh *et al.*, 2011; Praharaj *et al.*, 2019, 2020; Praharaj and Singh, 2019). The crop productivity does also vary with the length of growing season and its life cycle (duration of crop). However, the factors largely responsible for its average low productivity in pulses (<1 t/ha except chickpea grown in winter season) in Indian subcontinent is mainly attributed to the abiotic stresses related to microclimate, such as moisture (that includes climate change)and nutrient availability (Basu *et al.*, 2016; Mishra *et al.*, 2012a,b; Kumar *et al.*, 2015).

India is the world's largest producer of pulses with an average production of around 24 Mt during 2016-21. In India, over a dozen of pulse crops are grown viz., chickpea, pigeonpea, lentil, mungbean, urdbean, lathyrus, fieldpea and rajmash (Praharaj *et al.*, 2016). The productivity of these pulses however, continues to remain low as these are generally grown (as a rainfed crop) under poor management condition including prevalent biotic and abiotic stresses. Moreover, both hungry and thirsty soils, unfavourable weather, low availability of quality seeds, socio-economic factors, poor post-harvest handling/ storage and inadequate market support are the major constraints in realizing potential of productivity gains in these pulses (Palanisamy and Palanisamy, 2000). In spite of these factors, pulse crops have witnessed several technological breakthroughs that have helped not only its spread in new niches but also made impressive productive gains. A remarkable gain in production and productivity have been realized following introduction of new varieties, improved precision agro-technologies, and their adoption.

Pulses are also the important vegetable protein sources of Indian food as per FAO, every person requires 50 g of pulses daily. Both *Kharif* and *Rabi* (and to a minor extend zaid/spring grown) pulses play a major role in Indian food grain production. The split grains of these pulses are called *dal* and are excellent source of high quality protein, essential amino and fatty acids, fibres, minerals and vitamins. These crops have an inherent role in improving soil fertility through biological nitrogen fixation (BNF) or symbiotic N Fixation (SNF) by its root nodules (Praharaj *et al.* 2001; Praharaj and Dhingra, 2003) thereby enhancing soil nitrogen status, long-term soil fertility and sustainability of the cropping systems (Borase *et al.*, 2020a,b; Hazra *et al.*, 2019). Thus, a majority of N need of these pulses is met from symbiotic nitrogen fixation from air and the rest is left behind in the form of residual nitrogen and organic matter for the use of subsequent crops in rotation (Ghosh *et al.*, 2020). In addition, the input needs of these pulses are also meager and that in respect of water is about one-fifth of the requirement of cereals (Table 1). Although these are mostly grown as rainfed crops all over India (85%), yet these pulses are immensely valued as these are having tremendous importance in nutritional security, soil amelioration and sustainable crop production (Grace *et al.*, 2002; Hobbs and Gupta, 2003; Nath *et al.*, 2019; Pal *et al.*, 2002; Jat *et al.*, 2005b; Praharaj *et al.*, 2001).

Excess soil moisture or water-logging during monsoon season creates unfavourable conditions for crop growth including reduced aeration, hampered nodulation, reduced nutrient uptake, and favourable environment for blight and seedling rot resulting in reduced crop stand and low yield. Thus, the effect of suitable or appropriate precision technologies (APT) involving input and water management play crucial role in scaleing farm productivity and profitability. To aid in scaling efficiency in APT, suitable land configurations such as ridge and raised planting or raised beds or broad bed furrows (BBF) has a role in maintenance of optimum plant population and crop productivity vis-à-vis flat planting/broadcasting. On the other hand, moisture stress in the post-monsoon period adversely affects the development of reproductive organs leading to depressed yields. Thus, soil moisture related limitation is by far prevailed the major constraint that put impediments to higher productivity realization in pulses in Indian Subtropics. Similarly, in the absence of moisture, availability of nutrient is another constraint limiting productivity of these crops.

Table 1. Water requirements of major food crops

Crops	Duration (days)	Water requirements (cm)
Sugarcane	300	225-250
Rice	100	95-100
Cotton	165	60-75
Groundnut	105	60-65
Ragi	105	45-50
Maize	100	40-45
Pulses	70	20-25
Pulses(long duration)	150-250	30-50

Therefore, crops require water in a particular quantity for its optimum growth. Excessive or deficit amount of water could affect crop growth and reduce the yields. The factors influencing the rate of water use by plants include the type of the crop, stage of growth and climatic parameters like temperature, wind velocity, humidity etc. Thus, knowledge of the water requirement of different crops is needed for scheduling of precision irrigation, in planning the farm irrigation systems and in the design of irrigation projects. Here in the subsequent sections, we will discuss about precision water management in pulses as a case study for higher crop and water productivity.

2. CROP WATER REQUIREMENT

Crop water requirement is the water needed for raising a crop which includes consumptive use of the plant and other unavoidable losses and special operations. Consumptive use is the quantity of water lost in evaporation, transpiration and that used by the crop used for metabolic activities. As the water used for metabolic activities is very negligible in comparison to the evapotranspiration, consumptive use is considered almost same as evapotranspiration. The water use by the plants is primarily governed by the climatological parameters including the energy available at the land surface. The evapotranspiration process consists of conversion of water to vapour from liquid phase.

2.1 Climatological approach

Some of the climatological approaches for measurement of evapotranspiration are Thornthwaite method, Blaney-Criddle method, Radiation method, Christiansen Method, Penman Method, Modified Penman method and Penman-Monteith method. Some of the methods are described below. The Penman-Monteith method is the most standard and accurate method for estimation of evapotranspiration.

2.1.1 Thornthwaite method

Using this method, potential evapotranspiration is obtained using the following formula:

$$PET = 16.0\ (10T/I)^{a}$$

Where, T = Mean monthly temperature in °C,

I = 'Heat Index' for the 12 months in a year = Σi,

$i = (T/5)^{1.514}$ for each month in the year, and

$a = 6.75 \times 10^{-7} I^3 - 7.71 \times 10^{-5} I^2 + 1.792 \times 10^{-2} I + 0.49239$

The potential evapotranspiration calculated with the above formula is corrected for the duration of sunlight by multiplying with the factors for the month and latitude.

2.1.2 Blaney-Criddle Method

This method uses the mean temperature and the monthly percentage of day time hours of the year. It is expressed mathematically as:

$$\mathbf{U = K\Sigma pt = KF}$$

Where, U = Consumptive use of crop, inches for a given time period,

F = Sum of the consumptive use factors for the period = $(t \times p)/100$

K = Empirical coefficient

t = mean temperature °F, and

p = percentage of day-time hours of the year, occurring during the period

The Blaney-Criddle formula was developed to fit arid conditions and will give satisfactory estimates of seasonal water requirement under these conditions.

2.1.3 Penman-Monteith Method

The FAO Penman-Monteith equation is expressed by the following relationship

$$ET_0 = \frac{0.408\Delta(R_n - G) + \gamma \dfrac{900}{T+273} u_2 (e_s - e_a)}{\Delta + \gamma\,(1 + 0.34u_2)}$$

Where,

ET_0 = Reference evapotranspiration (mm/day)
R_n = Net radiation at the crop surface (MJ. m^2/day)
G = Soil heat flux density (MJ. m^2/day)
T = Air temperature at 2 m height (m/s)
U_2 = Wind speed at 2 m height (m/s)
e_s = Saturation vapour pressure (kPa)
e_a = Actual vapour pressure (kPa)
$e_s - e_a$ = Saturation vapour pressure deficit (kPa)
δ = Slope vapour pressure (kPa/^{0}C)
γ = psychrometric constant (kPa/^{0}C)

The FAO Penman- Monteith equation determines the evapotranspiration from the hypothetical grass reference surface and provides a standard to which evapotranspiration in different periods of the year or in other regions can be compared and to which the evapotranspiration from other crops can be related.

2.2 Pan evaporation

Pan evaporimeters provide a measurement of the integrated effect of radiation, wind, temperature and humidity on the evaporation from an open water surface. Although the pan responds in a similar fashion to the same climatic factors affecting crop transpiration, several factors produce significant differences in loss of water from a water surface and from a cropped surface. Therefore, reflection of solar radiation from water in the shallow pan could be different from the grass reference surface. Storage of heat within the pan could be appreciable and might cause significant evaporation during night time while most crops transpire only during the day time. There are also differences in turbulence, temperature and humidity of the air immediately above the respective surfaces. Heat transfer through the sides of the pan occurs and affects the energy balance. The pan evaporation is related to the reference evapotranspiration by an empirically derived pan coefficient. Pan coefficient values for different conditions, therefore, is selected from standard tables. As a thumb rule, an average value of 0.7 is considered as pan coefficient.

$$ET_0 = K_p \times E_{pan}$$

Where,

ET_0 = reference evapotranspiration (mm/day)
K_p = pan coefficient

E_{pan} = pan evaporation (mm/day)

2.3 Crop coefficient

In order to get the evapotranspiration values for a particular crop, ET_0 is to be multiplied by respective crop coefficients

$$ET_{crop} = K_c \times ET_0$$

Where,

ET_{crop} = crop evapotranspiration (mm/day)

K_c = crop coefficient

ET_0 = reference crop evapotranspiration (mm/day)

Since crop coefficients are affected by the crop characteristics, time of planting or sowing stage of crop development, it affects ET. For determining the crop coefficients, the crop development (stages) is considered in four stages, i.e., initial stage, crop development stage, mid-season stage and late season stage. Crop coefficient values at different stages for different crops are selected from standard table meant for the purpose.

3. IRRIGATION SCHEDULING

Irrigation scheduling is the process of determining when to irrigate and how much water to apply per irrigation. Proper scheduling is essential for the efficient use of water and other production inputs. The benefits of proper irrigation scheduling include improved crop yield, water conservation and higher economic gains.

3.1 Method based on soil indicators

In this method, soil moisture content is monitored and the field is irrigated when the predetermined deficit is reached. The intervals for irrigating the crop are to be fixed depending on the degree of depletion permissible for that crop. Soil based irrigation scheduling involves determining the current moisture content of the soil, comparing it to a predetermined minimum moisture content and irrigating to bring the moisture content upto field capacity. Soil indicators of when to irrigate also provide data for estimating the amount of water to be applied for irrigation. The soil based indicators can be appearance, gravimetric sampling, electrical resistance, soil matric potential or neutron scattering.

3.2 Methods based on plant factors

In this method, measures of the plant water stress can be monitored which in turn should indicate the need for irrigation. The plant water stress could be used as a measure beyond which the growth and yield of the crop is reduced significantly. The different plant based indicators are appearance, leaf temperature, leaf water potential and stomatal resistance.

4. MEASUREMENT OF IRRIGATION WATER

The different methods available for measuring water in open channel may be grouped as (1) velocity-area methods, and (2) direct-discharge methods.

4.1 Velocity-area method

In these methods, the velocity of the flow in the channel is measured by some means and the discharge is calculated from the velocity and the area of cross-section. The common methods for measuring velocity are float method and current meter method. In the float method, an estimate of the velocity of flow is made by determining the velocity of an object floating with the current. The time required to traverse a known distance by a floating object is measured and the velocity is calculated. Mean velocity in the whole of the cross-section is obtained by applying a coefficient 0.80 to the surface velocity. The area of cross-section of the channel is multiplied by the average velocity to get the rate of flow.

Current meter consists of a wheel having several cups attached and suspended by means of a cable or mounted on straight rod. The wheel in the current meter is rotated by the action of flowing water. The rate at which the wheel revolves varies with the velocity of water. From the rotating speed of the wheel, the velocity of flow is measured. A single reading taken at 0.6 depth of the channel represents the mean velocity. Knowing the average velocity and area of a particular section, the rate of flow is calculated.

4.2 Direct discharge method

In these methods, velocity measurement is not involved, but rates of flow are measured directly by using certain devices like weir, notch, orifices and flumes. The weir is a rectangular opening in an open channel through which the water flows. The weir can be made of wooden planks, sheet metal or concrete and the opening cut on the top edge. Weirs can be divided into two broad classes, sharp crested weir and broad crested weir. A notch is a 90° triangular weir formed by two sides sloping outward from vertical at 45° angle. In case of rectangular weir, the discharge is given by the Formula

$$Q = 0.0184\ LH^{3/2}$$

Where, Q is discharge in l/s, L is length of crest in cm, and H is head over the crest in cm.

In case of triangular notch, the discharge is given by the formula

$$Q = 0.0138\ H^{5/2}$$

An orifice is an opening with closed perimeter and of a regular shape through which water flows. Orifice must have sharp edges or else it is treated as tube. The stream of water coming out of the orifice is known as jet. Orifices may be circular, square, rectangular or of any other regular shape. Circular and rectangular orifices are common for the measurement of water on the farm. The equation of discharge through a sharp edge submerged orifice is given by:

$$Q = \text{Ca Sqrt(2gH)}$$

Where, Q = discharge in l/s, a = area of the orifice opening in sq. cm, g = acceleration due to gravity (cm/s^2), H = head of water causing the flow in cm, and C= coefficient (taken as 0.62 for sharp edged orifices).

Flumes are specially shaped and constructed channel sections used to measure the flow of water. The principle of flumes is based on the concept of specific energy and critical flow in open channels. By measurement of water level in the flumes, the discharge is measured using a relation between the head and the discharge. The different types of commonly used flumes are Parshall flume, trapezoidal flume, H-flume, cutthroat flume and RBC flume.

5. CLIMATE SMART WATER MANAGEMENT PRACTICES IN PULSES

Improved agro-technologies on water use have been a boon to profitable pulses cultivation. These include precision water management strategies. For optimum water management in pulses, normally 1-2 irrigation at critical stages such as branching and/or pod development prove highly productive (Table 2) in most of winter pulse crops on light textured soils in comparison to other food crops.

Table 2. Critical stages of irrigation in pulses

Crop	Critical stages
Chickpea and lentil	Branching and pod development
Dwarf fieldpea	Branching, flowering and pod development
Mungbean and Urdbean (Summer)	Growth, flowering and pod development
Mungbean and Urdbean (Rainy season)	Flowering and pod development
Pigeonpea	Flowering and pod development
Rajmash	Growth, flowering and pod development

Water being the critical input for productivity enhancement, there is a need for its optimum and judicious use (through supplementary irrigation) for realizing higher input use efficiency through various technological options available. These should be in synchrony with the above basic principles of resource conservation.

Many of our technology adoption were largely influenced by externalities. To cite an example, say in drip-fertigation, serious problem associated with the system is salt encrustation and clogging of lateral pipes in case of salt water (Singh *et al.*, 2015). While ranking the reasons for non-adoption of drip irrigation by Garrett's ranking technique, salt encrustation and clogging of conveyance pipes ranked first, followed by high initial cost, delay in incentives amount disbursement, and finally undulated terrain nature. To meet the high initial cost and to popularize this water saving method, the government has extended incentives for varying categories of farmers at present up to 50 per cent of the drip irrigation system cost (Sankaranaryan *et al.*, 2007, 2008, 2010, 2011).

6. UP-SCALING WATER PRODUCTIVITY IN PULSES

There is a need for evaluating existing technologies for developing the efficient water management strategies for their farm level impact in India. Technologies such as precision land levelling, no-till systems, furrow irrigated raised bed (FIRB) planting systems, crop diversification and its residue management have shown tremendous potential for efficient water use and its use efficiency (WUE) for sustainable farming systems (Praharaj *et al.*, 2016, Singh *et al.*, 2016). Unevenness of the soil surface influences the farming operations, drudgery involved, energy use, aeration, crop stand and productivity mainly through nutrient-water interactions. The general practices of land levelling used by the farmers in India is either through use of plankers drawn by draft animals and tractors or by iron scrappers/levelling boards drawn by 4-wheel tractors (as in Indo-Gangatic Plains of India known as IGP) are not so perfect (less input use efficiencies and low yield at the cost of more water).

Here **laser land levelling** is useful especially in intensively cultivated irrigated farming through achieving a better crop stand while saving irrigation water with improved input use efficiencies (Jat *et al.*, 2004, 2005a). As a result, zero-till seed drill performed better on a well levelled field compared to unlevelled or fairly levelled field due to better seed placement, germination and uniform distribution of irrigation water and plant nutrients (Kumar *et al.*, 2016, 2019a; Kumar *et al.*, 2020). Zero tillage allows timely sowing of wheat, enables uniform drilling of seed, improves fertilizers use efficiency, saves water and increases yield up to 20 percent. Similarly, the importance of no till system in India is quite evident in terms of greenhouse gas emission and carbon sequestration (Venkatesh *et al.*, 2013) as for each litre of diesel fuel consumed, 2.6 kg of CO_2 is released to the atmosphere. Assuming that 150 litres of fuel is used per hectare per annum for use of tractor and irrigation in conventional system, it would amount to nearly 400 kg CO_2 being emitted per annum per hectare. Thus, the role of no tillage/conservation agriculture in economic growth can't be undermined (Kumar *et al.*, 2016, 2019; Kumar *et al.*, 2020).

In **FIRB planting systems**, the crop is sown on ridges or beds of 15-20 cm height and 40-70 cm width depending on the crops to enhance crop productivity and save the irrigation water. Potential agronomic advantages of beds include improved soil structure due to reduced compaction through controlled trafficking, and reduced water logging and timelier machinery operations due to better surface drainage. Typical irrigation savings range from 18% to 30-50%. Trials by farmer/researcher in IGP suggest irrigation water savings of 12 to 60% was accrued for direct seeded (DSRB) and transplanted (TRB) rice on beds, with similar or lower yields for TRB compared with puddled flooded transplanted (PTR) rice. Similarly, raised bed planting out-yielded flat planting by 18.8% and also enhanced both water use and WUE in chickpea (Kumar *et al*,. 2015; Mishra *et al.*, 2012a,b).

In ***micro-irrigation techniques***, precision technologies are used for efficient management of both water and nutrient precisely near the root zone of crop plant with proven advantages of enhanced conveyance and water use efficiency. In the era of supplementary irrigation, there is a greater need to apply both fertilizer and water through drip especially at very critical stages to improve input productivity of crop, water and nutrient. Study also suggests that a single irrigation (20 mm in 5 splits) by drip-fertigation with half of N+K fertilizers at branching produced significantly higher (20%) seed yields and economic return over rainfed pigeonpea (Praharaj *et al.*, 2017; Singh *et al.* 2015). In chickpea, pre-plant irrigation + one irrigation at pre-pod development stage increased seed yield by 77% over no irrigation. Similarly, a supplementary life irrigation could do wonder under moisture deficit rice fallow condition (Singh *et al.*, 2017, 2018; Singh and Praharaj, 2019).

Out of several technological innovations, **life saving and supplementary irrigation** plays a very crucial role on growth, development and yield formation in pulses. This irrigation(s) when supported with appropriate field condition and improved agronomy, it could lead to yield optimization. On sowing windows, field experiments at ICAR-IIPR under North East Plain Zones showed that when mungbean was planted during last week of March (popularly called spring mungbean, sown after potato/garlic or winter vegetables) it required only two irrigations (due to higher residual soil moisture) in comparison to 3-4 irrigations (due to low residual soil moisture) for late planted crop (summer mungbean after wheat/ seasonal vegetables).

Further study conducted under a **micro-irrigation management in summer mungbean** showed that a significant improvement in seed yield (31%) with water saving (11% less water use and 43.2% enhanced WUE) were recorded in summer mungbean with precision tillage carried out by laser leveler. Sprinkler irrigation was advantageous for enhancing the irrigation efficiency even for two months duration of mungbean crop (with 20% less water use and 24% higher WUE) over flood or normal irrigation given at pod development and seed setting. It was attributed to consistent supply of water maintaining rhizosperic soil moisture content and normal plant water balance.

Sprinkler irrigation could play a safe proposition for precision/regulated irrigation scheduling in respect of its frequency/time/quantum. The beneficial effect of blanket flood irrigation was not pertinent under field condition in terms of plant stand, biomass and grain yield which was more likely in absence of a laser leveler. Owing to irregular in situ depressions/ponding zones developed in field especially when it was not accompanied by a laser leveler, this resulted in water stress condition due to blanket irrigation in hot summer months (Jat *et al.*, 2004, 2005a). Large plots demonstrations laidout to study the effect of overhead sprinkler irrigation + improved agro-techniques (paired row, narrow row spacing with sprinkler irrigation) convincingly showed the beneficial role of sprinkler irrigations in the late afternoon/evening hours in summer mungbean (Praharaj *et al.*, 2017, Kumar *et al.*, 2018, 2019; Praharaj *et al.*, 2015). Although there was similar yield under sprinkler vis-à-vis flood irrigation at critical stages (two irrigations given at branch and pod development by both methods), yet there is significant water economy through micro-irrigation. In fact, sprinkler irrigation consumed 27% less consumptive water use and enhanced WUE by 67.1%, WP by 67.3%, net return by INR 9,083 and BCR by 0.13 over flood irrigation applied by farmers at 30 cm row spacing. In addition, farmers' practice of planting at uniform 30 cm row spacing reduced seed yield to the extent of 16-20% over 22.5 cm rows spacing. Although varieties differ in their performance in yield, yet 22.5 × 10 cm was found to be optimum and economically superior (as with low seed rate) under existing condition irrespective of varieties and sowing dates.

In another trial on chickpea 'JG 16', significantly higher grain (16.1%) and biomass yield (9%), harvest index (5.7%), net return (22.4%), BCR (22.8%) and productivity per day (16.4%) were recorded in sprinkler irrigation given at branch and pod development over that in branching stage only (one sprinkler irrigation is applied discharging a total of 3-4 cm irrigation water in 3 alternate days thereby covering 6 days of plant growth). Similar significant increase in water saving (29.4%), WUE (30.7%) and WP (20.8%) with sprinkler at branch and pod development over those in flood irrigation (at both these stages) was observed to realize the same yield levels (2.65 t/ha). The advantages of micro-irrigation are many which includes 1) Uniform germination and optimum stand, 2) Reduced water use up to 55% (may be maximum), 3) Elimination of wide fluctuation of water, 4) Control of weeds and reduced weeding cost, 5) Increase in efficiency of fertilizers, Early and uniform maturity, 6) For early planting - prerequisite for IPM, 7) Allows summer crop (in pest free environment), opportunity for high value crops, maintenance of soil health, 8) Increased/ doubled yield. In case of semi-arid, arid and saline soil-water condition, drip-irrigation has also been a boon to agriculture.

The study also suggested the pertinent role of appropriate rainfall forecast and the quantum of precipitation received for appropriate irrigation scheduling decision(s) in chickpea. While studying the efficient utilization of water and nutrients through drip-irrigation and pigeonpea based intercropping, it showed that mean seed yields to the tune of 0.43 and 2.07 t/ha were realized with urdbean and sorghum intercropping (50% area basis), respectively in addition to normal seed yield of pigeonpea (Praharaj and Blaise, 2016). Based on biometrics and other attributes, it showed that partial replacement of gaps in situ seeded crop to the extent of 10% was feasible by transplanting seedling and was most economical in comparison to sole transplanting (Praharaj *et al.*, 2015a). In the above drip-fertigation schedule, the study conclusively confirmed the utility of land configuration (Raised bed of 120-60 cm to accommodate a paired row of pigeonpea along the furrows and two rows of intercrop in between two rows of pigeonpea) involving double crops wherein one was harvested within 3 months (but before the other crop covering the ground) and the other at full maturity (260 days). It indicated that drip-fertigation in pigeonpea + urdbean produced significantly higher pigeonpea seed yields by an average 14% over the sole crop. Similar higher values on WUE and WP with low water use were obtained in case of the above treatment. However, pigeonpea equivalent yield (3,303 kg/ha) and net return were highest with sorghum based intercropping system with drip-fertigated plots (onpar with urdbean). Therefore, both urdbean and sorghum (as per choice of farmer's need or market demand in respect of cereal *versus* pulses) are equally profitable when intercropped in pigeonpea applied with drip fertigation at 0.4 IW/CPE ratio in a long duration pigeonpea (if rainfall occurs, fertigation only for N and K-supply at scheduled irrigation). Varied irrigations (a minimum of 2, 3 and 4 irrigations, respectively depending on rainfall) frequencies could not influence productivity levels in the existing agro-climatic situation. Hence, considering the amount of rainfall and evaporation, IW/CPE ratio of 0.4 was adequate for long duration pigeonpea (Ahlawat *et al.*, 2005). A typical experiment conducted at ICAR-IIPR, Kanpur indicated profitability with drip fertigation in long duration pigeonpea (Table 5, Fig 2).

Table 5. Effect of drip-fertigation on economics, efficiencies and soil organic carbon

Drip-fertigation~	**Seedyield (kg/ha)**	**Net return (₹ 000/ha)**	**WUE (kg/ha-cm)**	**Agronomic efficiency (kg grain/kg NPK)**	**SOC (%)**	
					0-15 cm	**15-30 cm**
Rainfed	2858	66.40	58.2	10.6	0.27	0.18
$Drip_{Br}$	3419	74.91	66.9	16.9	0.31	0.23
$Drip_{pod}$	3092	64.36	60.1	13.2	0.28	0.19
$Drip_{Br+pod}$	3468	76.05	65.1	17.4	0.32	0.25
$Irrigation_{Br+pod}$	3262	74.49	60.2	15.0	0.29	0.22
C.D. (0.05)	225	7.01	4.4	2.6	0.21*	0.17*

+pooled data of 2 years, ~Treatmentsat branch (Br) or pod development (pod), WUE water use efficiency, SOC soil organic carbon, * initial status of soil at the start of the trial, 1$= INR 56.59

Therefore, diversification and intensification of rice-wheat cropping system in northern India (Grace *et al.*, 2002; Hobbs and Gupta, 2003; Nath *et al.*, 2019; Pal *et al.*, 2002) through mungbean is possible with development of infrastructure facility such as irrigation water availability (Balasubramanian *et al.*, 2003). Over several trials conducted on-farm situations, it has been amply demonstrated that such possibilities do exist and wherever feasible/economically viable, low input requiring pulses could be popularized as a soil building crop. In the existing studies made at on-farm (Fatehpur and Kanpur Dehat of Uttar Pradesh), farmers sowed short duration mungbean variety 'Samrat' just after harvest of winter wheat with low inputs with only 2-3 irrigations as per need. There are two situations where the crop is either planted at 30 cm row spacing in line or broadcasted in the entire field after plough followed by a plank (Fig 1, 2). Comparison made for both these situation showed the most yield reduction in the later due to inadequate plant stand/ improper maintenance of plant population and little/inadequate plant protection. The seed yield of summer mungbean realized was up to 750 kg/ha for a period of 60-65 days without any second picking (due to synchronous maturity as an additional attribute of the plant types). However, higher gross return to the extent of INR 33,000 within a short period of 2 months motivated farmers to take up spring/summer mungbean cultivation especially where supplementary irrigation can be managed. Farmers also realized higher rice yield due to improved soil fertility (as mungbean being buried over in the field). As a result of better return, the farmers have started cultivating summer mungbean after wheat/garlic or even after potato. As the water requirement of the crop is less in comparison to other cereals and oilseeds, this can be profitably grown and adopted under water scarcity areas and rainfed/dryland areas (through supplementary irrigation with water harvested by farm pond, micro-water storage tanks).

Fig 1. IIPR No Till drills (with labour requirements of around 40 man-h/ha, (a) left (b) right Field capacity 20 h/ha, low cost of <1,000 INR/ha and low energy of operation of <80MJ/ha)

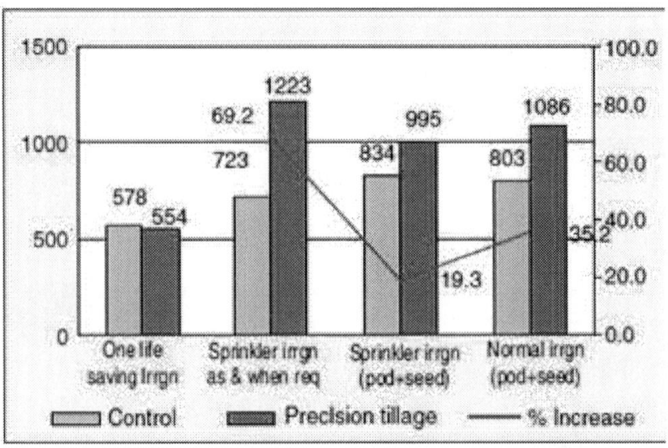

Fig 2. Interacting influence of tillage and irrigation on mungbean yield (kg/ha)

7. CONCLUSION

The surface irrigation techniques are most common practice for pulse crops but depleting water table and frequent occurrence of drought in most part of the country is most challenging in current scenario which needs retrospection and inclusion of alternatives. Therefore, adoption of micro-irrigation techniques and judicious use of water at critical growth stage of pulses in drought prone areas would help to mitigate water scarcity and also save the resources for future generations. Therefore, based on water requirement of crops, scheduling of irrigation and other water management practices through precision technologies could add in scaling of crop and water productivity and sustainability of pulse crops in diverse agro-ecosystems.

REFERENCES

Ahlawat, I.P.S., Gangaiah, B. and Singh, I.P. (2005) Pigeonpea (*Cajanus cajan*) research in India-an overview. *Indian Journal of Agricultural Sciences* 75(6), 309-20.

Balasubramanian, V., Ladha, J.K., Gupta, R.K., Naresh, R.K., Mahela, R.S., Singh, B. and Singh, Y. (2003) Technology options for rice in rice-wheat system in south Asia. In: JK Ladha *et al.* (Eds), Improving the productivity and sustainability of rice-wheat systems: Issues and impact. ASA Spec. Pub. 65ASA, CSSA, and SSSA, Madison, WI. pp 115-118.

Basu, P.S., Singh, U., Kumar, A., Praharaj, C.S. and Shivran, R.K. (2016) Climate change and its mitigation strategies in pulses production. *Indian Journal of Agronomy* 61(4th IAC Special issue), S71-S82.

Borase, D.N., Nath, C.P., Hazra, K.K., Sentilkumar, M., Singh, S.S., Praharaj, C.S., Singh, U. and Kumar, N. (2020a) Long-term impact of diversified crop rotations and nutrient management practices on soil microbial functions and soil enzymes activity. *Ecological Indicators*114, 1-11. https://doi.org/10.1016/j.ecolind.2020.106322

Borase, D.N., Sentilkumar, M., Nath, C.P., Hazra, K.K., Singh, S.S., Kumar, N., Singh, U. and Praharaj, C.S. (2020b) Long-term impact of grain legumes and nutrient management practices on soil microbial activity and biochemical properties. *Archives of Agronomy and Soil Science*. DOI: 10.1080/03650340.2020.1819532

Ghosh, P.K., Hazra, K.K., Venkatesh, M.S., Praharaj, C.S., Kumar, N., Nath, C.P., Singh, U. and Singh, S.S. (2020) Grain legume inclusion in cereal-cereal rotation increased base crop productivity in the long run. *Experimental Agriculture* 56(1), 142-158.

Grace, P.R., Jain, M.C. and Harrington, L.W. (2002) Environmental concerns in rice-wheat system. In: Proc. International Workshop on Developing Action Programme for Farm level Impact in Rice-Wheat system of the Indo-Gangetic Plains, 25-27 Sept. 2000, New Delhi, India. RWC Consortium paper series 14, New Delhi, India. pp 99-111.

Hazra, K.K., Nath, C.P., Singh, U., Praharaj, C.S., Kumar, N., Singh, S.S. and Singh, N.P. (2019) Diversification of maize - wheat cropping system with legumes and integrated nutrient management increases soil aggregation and carbon sequestration. *Geoderma* 353, 308-19.

Hobbs, P.R. and Gupta, R.K. (2003) Resource Conserving Technologies for Wheat in Rice-Wheat Systems. In: JK Ladha, J Hill, RK Gupta, J Duxbury and RJ Buresh

(Eds), Improving the productivity and sustainability of rice-wheat systems: issues and impact. ASA, Spec. Publ. 65, chapter 7, ASA Madison, WI. USA. pp: 149-171.

Jat, M.L., Pal, S.S., SubbaRao, A.V.M., Sirohi, K., Sharma, S.K. and Gupta, R.K. (2004) Laser land leveling- the precursor technology for resource conservation in irrigated eco-system of India. In: Proc. National Conf. Conservation Agriculture: Conserving Resources-Enhancing Productivity, September 22-23 2004, NASC Complex, Pusa, New Delhi. pp 9-10.

Jat, M.L., Sharma, S.K., Gupta, R.K., Sirohi, K. and Chandana, P. (2005a) Laser land leveling: the precursor technology for resource conservation in irrigated eco-system of India. In: IP Abrol, Raj K Gupta & RK Malik (Eds), Conservation Agriculture-status and prospects, CASA, New Delhi. pp 145-154.

Jat, M.L., Shrivastava, A., Sharma, S.K., Gupta, R.K., Zaidi, P.H., Rai, H.K. and Srinivasan, G. (2005b) Evaluation of Maize-Wheat Cropping System under Double-No-Till Practice in Indo-Gangetic Basin of India. In: 9th Asian Maize Research Workshop, September, 4-10, 2005, Beijing, China.

Kumar, N., Hazra, K.K., Nath, C.P., Praharaj, C.S., Singh, U. and Singh, S.S. (2016) Pulses in irrigated eco-system: Problems and prospects. *Indian Journal of Agronomy* 61(4th IAC Special issue), S262-S268.

Kumar, N., Nath, C.P., Hazra, K.K., Das, K., Venkatesh, M.S., Singh, M.K., Singh, S.S., Praharaj, C.S. and Singh, N.P. (2019) Impact of zero-till residue management and crop diversification with legumes on soil aggregation and carbon sequestration. *Soil & Tillage Research* 189, 158-167.

Kumar, N., Singh, M.K., Praharaj, C.S., Singh, U. and Singh, S.S. (2015). Performance of chickpea under different planting method, seed rate and irrigation level in Indo-Gangetic Plains of India. *Journal of Food Legumes* 28(1), 40-44.

Kumar, N., Singh, S.S., Ghosh, P.K., Hazra, K.K., Venkatesh, M.S., Praharaj, C.S., Singh, M.K., SenthilKumar, M., Basu, P.S., Yadav, A., Yadav, S.L., Singh, S. and Singh, N.P. (2020) Improving chickpea productivity in rice-fallow of Indo-Gangetic Plain with soil moisture conservation and cultivar selection. *Journal of Food Legumes* 33(1), 28-35.

Kumar, R., Bhat, S., Tripathi, C.M., Katiyar, P.K., Praharaj, C.S. and Singh, N.P. (2018) Technological Impact on production and income of pulses growers under farmer FIRST project in Fatehpur district of Uttar Pradesh- A case study. *Journal of Food Legumes* 31(3), 174-177.

Kumar, R., Prasad, N., Gautam, V.K., Tripathi, C.M., Singh, R., Kumar, R. and Praharaj, C.S. (2019a) Pulse based bio-village sustainable models through participatory demonstrations For Livelihood Security. *Journal of Food Legumes* 32(1), 45-48.

Mishra, J.P., Praharaj, C.S. and Singh, K.K. (2012a) Enhancing water use efficiency and production potential of chickpea and fieldpea through seed bed configurations and irrigation regimes in North Indian Plains. *Journal of Food Legumes* 25, 310-313.

Mishra, J.P., Praharaj, C.S., Singh, K.K. and Kumar, N. (2012b) Impact of conservation practices on crop water use and productivity in chickpea under middle Indo-Gangetic plains. *Journal of Food Legumes* 25, 41-44.

Nath, C.P., Hazra, K.K., Kumar, N., Praharaj, C.S., Singh, S.S., Singh, U. and Singh, N.P. (2019) Including grain legume in rice-wheat cropping system improves soil organic carbon pools over time. *Ecological Engineering* 129, 144-153.

Pal, S.S., Jat, M.L., Sharma, S.K. and Yadav, R.L. (2002) Managing crop residues in rice-wheat system. *PDCSR Technical Bulletin* 2002-1, PDCSR, Modipuram, India.40 pp.

Palanisamy, K. and Palanisamy, V. (2000) Socio-economic aspect of drip irrigation. Training manual published by water technology centre, Tamil Nadu Agricultural University, Coimbatore.

Praharaj, C.S. andDhingra, K.K. (2003) Productivity and profitability of soybean (*Glycine max* L. Merrill) as influenced by *Bradyrhizobium* inoculation, nitrogen and potassium levels. *Journal of Research (BAU)* 15(1), 89-93.

Praharaj, C.S. and Blaise, D. (2016). Intercropping: An approach for area expansion of pulses. *Indian Journal of Agronomy* (4th IAC Special issue) 61, S113-S121.

Praharaj, C.S. and Dhingra, K.K. (2001) Growth, productivity and BNF in soybean (*Glycine max* L. Merr.) under *Bradyrhizobium* inoculation, pendimethalin and nitrogen schedules and their residual effect on succeeding wheat (*Triticum aestivum* L.) crop. *Indian Journal of Agronomy* 46 (4), 635-642.

Praharaj, C.S. and Singh, N.P. (2019) Raising productivity of pulses in diverse agro-ecologies of North East Hill region of India - A case study. *Journal of Food Legumes* 32(2), 90-96.

Praharaj, C.S., Jat, R.L., Singh, S.S. and Singh, N.P. (2020). Enhancing farm income and system productivity in soybean-lentil through land configuration, conservation tillage, seed priming and mulching under rainfed Central India. *Journal of Food Legumes* 33(1), 41-47.

Praharaj, C.S., Jat, R.L., Singh, U., Singh, S.S., Singh, R.P., Elanchezhian, R. and Singh, N.P. (2019) Scaling productivity and farm income through soybean based inter- & sequential cropping under rainfed Central India with improved agro-technologies. *Journal of Food Legumes* 32(4), 242-49.

Praharaj, C.S., Kumar, D., Sharma, R.C. and Khurana, S.M.P. (2001) Potato-wheat-Paddy, a new emerging alternative crop rotation for Indo-Gangetic Plains of Bihar. *Journal Indian Potato Association* 28(1), 44-45.

Praharaj, C.S., Kumar, N., Singh, U., Singh, S.S. and Singh, J. (2015a) Transplanting in pigeonpea- A contingency measure for realizing higher productivity in Eastern Plains. *Journal of Food Legumes* 28(1), 34-39.

Praharaj, C.S., Kumar, R., Akram, M., Jha, U.C., Singh, U., Kumar, N., Singh, S.S. and Singh, S.K. (2015) Dissemination of pulses production technologies for enhancing profitability of farmers in Uttar Pradesh. *Journal of Food Legumes* 28(2), 59-63.

Praharaj, C.S., Mishra, J.P., Kumar, N., Singh, K.K. and Ghosh, P.K. (2011) Improving crop productivity and water use efficiency in chickpea genotypes through in situ water conservation practices in EGPZ. In: Proc. X Agric. Sci. Congress on Soil-Plant-Animal Health: safety and Security NBFGR, Lucknow, U.P. India, February 10-12, 2011. pp 410-411.

Praharaj, C.S., Singh, U., Singh, S.S. and Kumar, N. (2017) Micro-irrigation in rainfed pigeonpea-Upscaling productivity under Eastern Gangetic Plains with suitable land configuration, population management and supplementary fertigation at critical stages. *Current Science* 112(1) , 95-107.

Praharaj, C.S., Singh, U., Singh, S.S. and Kumar, N. (2018) Tactical water management in field crops: the key to resource conservation. *Current Science* 115(7), 1262-1269.

Praharaj, C.S., Singh, U., Singh, S.S., Singh, N.P. and Shivay, Y.S. (2016) Supplementary and life-saving irrigation for enhancing pulses production, productivity and water use efficiency in India. *Indian Journal of Agronomy* 61(4th IAC Special issue), S249-S261.

Sangar, S., Abrol, I.P. and Gupta, R.K. (2004) Conservation Agriculture: Conserving Resources- Enhancing Productivity, Concept paper, September 22-23, 2004, Centre for Advancement of Sustainable Agriculture, NASC Complex, DPS Marg, Pusa Campus, New Delhi 110 012.

Sankaranarayanan, K., Nalayini, P., Praharaj, C.S., Sathiskumar, N. and Gopalakrishnan, N. (2008) Increasing irrigation efficiency through water saving devices. In: Training Manual on National Level Training Programme on Farm mechanization in cotton, 18-19 Dec, 2008, DEE, Coimbatore (T.N.), India.

Sankaranarayanan, K., Praharaj, C.S. and Gopalakrishnan, N. (2007) Precision water and nutrient management in ELS cotton. *Cotton Research Journal* 32(3), 143-152.

Sankaranarayanan, K., Praharaj, C.S., Nalayini, P. and Gopalakrishnan, N. (2011) Legume as companion crop for cotton. *Journal cotton Research and Development* 24(1), 115-126.

Sankaranarayanan, K., Praharaj, C.S., Nalayini, P., Bandyopadhyay, K.K. and Gopalakrishnan, N. (2010) Low cost drip as a precision irrigation tool in Bt cotton (*Gossypium hirsutum*) cultivation. *Indian Journal of Agronomy* 55 (4), 312-318.

Singh, K.K., Singh, S.K., Singh, B., Naimuddin, Ghosh, P.K., Kumar, N., Venkatesh, M.S., Praharaj, C.S. and Hazra, K.K. (2011) Effect of crop residue and NPKS on crop productivity and soil fertility in rice-lentil cropping system. In: X Agric. Science Congress on "Soil-Plant-Animal Health: safety and Security, NBFGR, Lucknow, U.P.India, Feb., 10-12, 2011. pp 48-49.

Singh, N.P., Praharaj, C.S. and Sandhu, J.S. (2016) Utilizing untapped potential of rice fallow of East and North-east India through pulse production. *Indian Journal of Genetics and Plant Breeding* 76(4), 388-98.

Singh, R., Praharaj, C.S. and Mahey, R.K. (1993) Effect of irrigation and nitrogen on yield and yield contributing characters of upland cotton (*Gossypium hirsutum* L.). *Indian Journal of Agronomy* 38(4), 609-12.

Singh, R.N., Praharaj, C.S., Kumar, R., Singh, S.S., Kumar, N. and Singh, U. (2017) Influence of rice habit groups and moisture conservation practices on soil physical and microbial properties in rice + lathyrus relay cropping system under rice fallows in Eastern Plateau of India. *Indian Journal of Agricultural Science* 87(12), 1633-39.

Singh, R.N., Praharaj, C.S., Kumar, R., Singh, S.S., Kumar, N. and Singh, U. (2018) Strengthening soil health under rice fallow in Eastern Plateau of India with dwarf rice and moisture conservation practices. *Indian Journal of Agricultural Sciences* 88(12), 1869-78.

Singh, S.K. and Praharaj, C.S. (2019) Pulses for nutritional security and ecological sustainability. *Indian Journal of Extension Education* 55(2), 86-89.

Singh, U., Kumar, N., Praharaj, C.S., Singh, S.S. and Kumar, L. (2015) Ferti-fortification: an easy approach for nutritional enrichment of chickpea. *The Ecoscan* 9(3&4), 731-736.

Venkatesh, M.S., Hazra, K.K., Ghosh, P.K., Praharaj, C.S. and Kumar, N. (2013) Long-term effect of pulses and nutrient management on soil carbon sequestration in Indo-Gangetic plains of India. *Canadian Journal of Soil Science* 93, 127–136.

CHAPTER 12

Biofertilizers for sustainable pulse production in India

Krishnashis Das*, Narendra Kumar, M. Senthilkumar

ICAR-Indian Institute of Pulses Research, Kanpur-208 024, Uttar Pradesh

*Corresponding author email: krishnashis38@gmail.com

Abstract

Since green revolution, application of chemical fertilizers has been the main strategy for achieving higher crop productivity in India. But continuous and indiscriminate use of chemical fertilizers is hazardous to human health and environment. Pulses, a major source of protein, vitamin and minerals play important role in providing nutritional security worldwide. Although India is the largest producer of pulses in the world, the crop productivity is quite low. Plant growth promoting rhizobacteria (PGPR) are a group of microorganisms which live in close association with plants and play significant role in improving nutrient use efficiency of applied fertilizers and nutrient uptake. PGPR biofertilizers are also known for enhancing tolerance of plants towards various biotic and abiotic stresses. Harnessing the beneficial effects of plant growth promoting microbes can be the potential solution towards improving crop productivity and soil health in a sustainable manner. Therefore, this book chapter highlights the types of microbes being used as biofertilizer in pulses and their role in sustainable pulse production in India.

Keywords: Abiotic stress, Arbuscular mycorrhizal fungi, Nitrogen fixation, Phosphate-solubilizing microorganisms, Plant growth promoting rhizobacteria (PGPR)

1. INTRODUCTION

Pulses are major source of protein, dietary fibres, vitamins and minerals. They are an essential ingredient in predominantly vegetarian diets of Indian people. They contain 18 to 30% protein (depending on the crop species), which is almost twice the protein content in wheat and thrice that of rice (Shukla *et al.*, 2013). Pulses are major source of vitamins like riboflavin, thiamine, niacin and iron. They are also good source of essential amino acids like lysine, which complements the deficiency of such amino acids in most of the cereals in vegetarian diet. The pulse crops find important place in the farming systems adopted by small and marginal farmers in a large number of developing countries as it restores the soil fertility by fixing atmospheric nitrogen. Pulses can be grown on a wide range of soil and agro-climatic conditions and play important role in crop rotation, mixed and intercropping systems and contribute towards sustainability of the farming system. India is the largest producer as well as consumer of pulses in the world. During 2017-18, pulses were cultivated over 29.81 M ha of area and recorded the highest ever production of 25.42 Mt (DES, 2020). Yet the country has to import around 2-3 Mt of pulses every year to meet the domestic demand. It is projected that the domestic requirement of pulses would be around 39.0 Mt by the year 2050 which will require pulses production to grow at an annual rate of 2.2%. In India pulses are mostly grown in marginal lands with low inputs. Coupled with increasing biotic and abiotic stress, climate change and deteriorating soil health, increasing productivity of pulses seems to be a major challenge ahead.

In this situation, microorganisms have emerged as the potential solution towards increasing crop productivity in an eco-friendly and sustainable manner. Plant growth promoting rhizobacteria (PGPR) were first defined by Kloepper and Schroth (1978) to describe rhizospheric microorganisms which colonize plant roots and enhance plant growth. Microbial biofertilizer is 'a substance which contains living microorganisms, when applied to seed, plant surfaces, or soil, colonizes the rhizosphere or the interior of the plant and promotes growth by increasing the supply or availability of primary nutrients to the host plant' (Vessey, 2003). The practice of 'naturally inoculated' soil with legume seeds in the 1800s and the subsequent grant of first patent, "Nitragin," (Nobbe and Hiltner, 1896) led to the development of technologies worldwide for legume inoculation with *Rhizobium* sp. It is well known that microbes are the major driving force behind the nutrient cycle in soil and can enhance nutrient availability to plants through multifarious ways like atmospheric nitrogen fixation, phosphorous solubilization or decomposition of organic matters: They also help in enhancing plant growth and yield through production of various plant growth promoting substances like phytohormones, siderophores and protect plants from soil borne pathogens by producing antimicrobial compounds (Bhattacharyya and Jha, 2012; Wani *et al.*, 2013; Malusá and Vassilev, 2014).

2. BIOFERTILIZERS FOR SUSTAINABLE AGRICULTURE

The worldwide human population is increasing at an alarming rate and it poses direct threat to food security as the agricultural land is limited and getting reduced day-by-day. Earlier during green revolution, increase in crop productivity was achieved through application of chemical fertilizers. But indiscriminate use of chemical fertilizers has shown negative impact on crop productivity, soil health which led to environmental pollution (Savci, 2012). Too much dependency on chemical fertilizers for future agricultural needs are likely to result in further loss in soil fertility and negative impact on beneficial soil microbiota (Cristina *et al.*, 2013; Khare and Arora, 2015). In last few decades, microbial biofertilizer technology has come up as a low cost, eco-friendly alternative, which can improve crop productivity and soil health in a sustainable manner (Mahdi *et al.*, 2010). It was reported that the use of biofertilizers elevate crop yield around 10–40% in addition to increasing contents of proteins, essential amino acids, vitamins, and nitrogen fixation (Bhardwaj *et al.*, 2014). Bacterial biofertilizers can improve plant growth through several different mechanisms: (i) mobilization of soil nutrients (macro as well as micro-nutrients), making them available for the plant to be used, (ii) synthesis of phytohormones, and growth regulators, (iii) abiotic stress management, or (iv) protection against plant pathogens (Zhang *et al.*, 2014; Walpola and Yoon, 2013; Glick, 2014; Bhowmik and Das, 2018). Several plant growth-promoting rhizobacteria (PGPR) are being used worldwide as biofertilizers for improving crop yield and productivity.

3. IMPORTANCE OF BIOFERTILIZERS IN PULSE PRODUCTION

Microbial communities residing in the rhizosphere region of plants play significant role in healthy growth and development of plants. Plant-microbe interaction as well as the interactions among the microbial community is the main driving force behind organic matter decomposition and nutrient cycling in soil which further facilitates nutrient availability to plants (Berg *et al.*, 2013). Thus utilization of beneficial microbes as biofertilizers has become a subject of importance in sustainable agriculture and biosafety programs worldwide. Microorganisms used as biofertilizers in pulse production can be categorized as nitrogen fixers, phosphorous solubilizers and other plant growth promoting rhizobacteria.

3.1 Biofertilizers for enhancing nitrogen fixation

Nitrogen, a major essential nutrient is required by plants in large quantities and its availability in soil most frequently limits the crop growth and productivity. Although atmospheric nitrogen gas (N_2) constitutes 78% of the air, it cannot be directly utilized by the plants for their nutrition. Diazotrophs represents a large group of prokaryotes which can reduce atmospheric N_2 to ammonium, a process known as biological nitrogen fixation (BNF). Rhizobia, a group of diazotrophic organisms which establish symbiotic associations with plants of the family *Leguminosae* play a significant role in the sustenance of soil fertility (Vance, 2001; Herridge *et al.*, 2008). The symbiotic association between legumes and rhizobia may contribute up to 13-360 kg N/ha (Bohlool *et al.*, 1992). Beside food legumes, forage legumes and tree legumes also play a vital role in total nitrogen fixation globally (Baddeley *et al.*, 2013). However, the efficiency of biological nitrogen fixation may vary in different legumes and is also dependent upon the various biotic and abiotic factors like host species, rhizobial efficiency and soil physico-chemical properties (Gopalakrishnan *et al.*, 2015).

3.1.1 Symbiotic nitrogen fixation in pulses

Pulse crops are well known for their symbiosis with several *Rhizobium* species which fix atmospheric N_2 by forming root nodules (Bhardwaj *et al.*, 2014). Legume-*Rhizobium* interaction is highly crop specific and has been classified into different 'cross inoculation groups' for example, *Rhizobium leguminosarum* for lentil and pea, *Mesorhizobium ciceri* for chickpea, *Rhizobium phaseoli* for temperate beans, *Rhizobium meliloti* for leucerne, *Rhizobium trifolii* for berseem, *Bradyrhizobium* for soybean etc. Therefore, use of right inoculant for the right legume is very important for obtaining adequate benefit from the use of *Rhizobium* biofertilizers. Successful symbiosis depends on interaction of signaling molecules from plant and *Rhizobium*. Within the nodule tissue, atmospheric nitrogen fixation is carried out by the enzyme nitrogenase and the fixed nitrogen is transferred to plant. Amount of nitrogen fixation by different legume-*Rhizobium* system varies significantly. Estimates of nitrogen fixation in different Indian pulse crops are presented in Table 1.

Table 1. Estimates of nitrogen fixation in different Indian pulses

Crop	N_2 fixed (kg/ha/yr)
Chickpea	26-63
Pigeonpea	68-200
Lentil	35-100
Mungbean	50-55
Cluster bean	37-196
Cowpea	53-85
Pea	46

Source: Brahmaprakash and Sahu (2012)

Rhizobium inoculation increases the crop yield in the range 10–35% (Motsara *et al.*, 1995). However, regional variation in responses to *Rhizobium* inoculation in field was noticed. Lack of efficient rhizobia, competition of inefficient native strains to efficient inoculants strains in soil, quality of inoculant and agro-climatic conditions are some of the factors responsible for variable response.

3.1.2 Non-symbiotic nitrogen fixation

Most important bacteria in this group are *Azotobacter, Derxia* and *Beijerinkia*. Among this *Azotobacter* has been the most exploited microbe as biofertilizer in pulses. It is a non-symbiotic free living aerobic bacteria possessing highest respiratory rate and can fix N up to 25 kg/ha under optimum conditions. *Azotobacter* is also known to produce plant growth hormones like indole acetic acid (IAA), gibberellic acid and exhibit antifungal activity (Mazid *et al.*, 2011). Apart from pulses *Azotobacter* biofertilizer is being used for increasing yield in many cereals such as maize, pearl millet, wheat and sorghum in allover India.

3.2 Phosphate-solubilizing microorganisms

Phosphorus is an essential element for plant development and growth making up about 0.2% of plant dry weight. Plants acquire phosphorous from soil solution as phosphate anions, however, major portion of phosphorous applied through chemical phosphatic fertilizers are fixed in soil through precipitation with cations such as Ca^{2+}, Mg^{2+}, Fe^{3+} and Al^{3+} depending on the particular properties of a soil (Richardson, 2001). It is estimated that 75% of P of superphosphate applied gets fixed, and only 25% is available for plant growth in tropical soil. There are some bacteria and fungi which can solubilize unavailable form of P to available form by the virtue of secretion of certain organic acids (lactic acid, succinic acid, acetic acid, fumaric acid) and are labeled as phosphate-solubilizing microorganisms (PSM) (Khan *et al.*, 2009). Soil microorganisms possessing phytase activity can contribute to plant-phosphorus nutrition through phytate mineralization (Idriss *et al.*, 2002). Inoculation of crops can solubilize applied phosphate varying from 40 to 50 kg P_2O_5/ha and increase crop yield by 10–20% (Khan *et al.*, 2009, Sharma *et al.*, 2013).

Biological nitrogen fixation has synergistic relationship with availability of phosphorous. Hence, co-inoculation of nitrogen (N) fixers and PSMs benefits the plant better. The dual inoculation of phosphobacterium (*Bacillus megaterium* var. *phosphaticum*) and *Rhizobium* significantly increased the plant height, nodule number, and nodule weight of black gram under field condition (Balachandran and Nagarajan, 2002). It has been reported that PSB can improve the competitive ability and symbiotic effectiveness of inoculated *Rhizobium* sp. in lentil (Kumar and Chandra, 2008) and leghemoglobin content in chickpea nodules (Tagore *et al.*, 2013) under field conditions.

3.3 Arbuscular mycorrhizal fungi as biofertilizer

Arbuscular mycorrhizal fungi (AMF) popularly known as VAM is a group of fungi that colonize roots of several crop plants. It drastically increases the absorption surface area of roots and improves water uptake and phosphorous acquisition through absorption and translocation of soil solution phosphorous by their high-affinity P-uptake mechanisms (Aggarwal *et al.*, 2011). Beside phosphorous, application of VAM also enhances plant uptake of other major and minor elements like Zn, B, Ca, Mg, Mn, S and Al from soil (Clark and Zeto, 2000). Additionally, there are reports of other beneficial effects of VAM on plant growth and productivity like increase in draught and salinity resistance, better seedling establishment, suppression of some soil borne pathogens and weeds, and improvement in overall soil structure and health (Gosling *et al.*, 2006; van der Heijden *et al.*, 2008).

AMF are known to form a symbiotic relationship with a range of pulse crops (Pagano *et al.*, 2007). Valsalakumar *et al.* (2007) studied the diversity and distribution of AMF in *Vigna radiata* and found that different species from genus *Glomus* (*G. mosseae* (81%), *G. microcarpum* (24%) and *G. margarita* (24%) are predominant. In a similar study Molla and Solaiman (2009) surveyed the association of AMF in ten diverse leguminous crops and found that AMF from genus *Glomus* and *Scutellospora* are most predominant in chickpea, lentil, black gram and green gram. The application of AMF inoculants in soils increased the growth and yields of legumes significantly under both greenhouse and field conditions. Co-inoculation of AM fungi with *Rhizobium* inoculants have shown synergistic effects and resulted in higher nodulation, N_2 fixation, P uptake, photosynthetic rate and plant biomass in pulses (Geneva *et al.* 2006; Mehdi *et al.*, 2006; Meena *et al.*, 2013). Further, seed production in legumes significantly increased upon co-inoculation of mesorhizobia and AMF in multilocational field trials (Dudeja *et al.*, 2011; Varma *et al.*, 2017).

3.4 Plant Growth-Promoting Rhizobacteria as biofertilizer

Plant growth promoting rhizobacteria (PGPR) include beneficial bacteria that colonize plant roots and enhance plant growth by a wide variety of mechanisms. Their effects on plant growth are mediated by direct or indirect mechanisms. The direct effects are attributed to the higher nutrient availability (Zn, Fe, Mn), production of plant hormones such as auxins, gibberellins and cytokinins as well as siderophores.

A number of studies revealed, increase in the production of organic acids due to microbial inoculation results in the lowering of soil pH around the roots contributing to the solubilisation of different insoluble sources of nutrients like P, K and Zn (Wang *et al.*, 2014). Recent studies have also shown enhancement in uptake of Fe and Zn in chickpea and pigeonpea when inoculated with efficient rhizobacterial strains (Gopalakrishnan *et al.*, 2016; Bhowmik and Das, 2018). Siderophores are low molecular weight, iron-binding compounds which help to sequester iron from the environment and release it inside the cells (Matzanke, 1991). Ability of Fe^{3+} -Fe acquisition through production of siderophore is crucial as it determines the ability of bacteria to colonize plant roots and provide plants with sufficient iron under iron deficient conditions (Crowley, 2006). Production of siderophores by PGPR also prevents multiplication and colonization of pathogenic microorganisms by sequestering Fe^{3+} from the rhizospheric region (Martínez-Viveros *et al.*, 2010).

On the other hand, the indirect effect includes control of soil pathogens through production of hydrogen cyanide (HCN), ammonia, anti microbial compounds, excretion of hydrolytic enzymes (chitinases, glucanases) and elicitation of systemic induced resistance in host plants etc. Chitinases and β-1, 3-glucanases are two main hydrolytic enzymes associated with fungal cell wall lysis. A number of PGPR strains *Pseudomonas aeruginosa, Bacillus subtilis, Ensifer meliloti* and *Rhizobium leguminosarum* having good chitinase and β-1, 3-glucanase activity inhibited growth of *F. oxysporum*, *Macrophomina phaseolina,Sclerotinia sclerotiorum* causing loss of structural integrity of the mycelium, hyphal perforation, lysis, fragmentation and degradation (Akhtar *et al.*, 2010; Kumar *et al.*, 2011; Karimi *et al.*, 2012; Smitha and Singh, 2014).

The well-known PGPR which are being used as biofertilizers in pulses include *Pseudomonas*, *Bacillus*, *Arthrobacter*, *Klebsiella*, *Azotobacter*, *Enterobacter*, and *Burkholderia*. Among these, different species of *Pseudomonas* and *Bacillus* have been reported to possess multiple plant growth promoting activity (Bhowmik and Das, 2018).

Studies suggest that the combination of PGPR strains (two or more) which have diverse mode of plant growth promotion or antagonism against soil-borne pathogens are more effective than single strain inoculum (Nadia *et al.*, 2007; Mazen *et al.*,2008; Shaban and EL-Bramawy, 2011). Akhtar and Siddiqui (2008) also reported that combined application of *Rhizobium* sp. along with *Glomus intraradices* and *Pseudomonas striata* successfully controlled root rot disease in chickpea caused by *Meloidogyne incognita* and *Macrophomina phaseolina*. They also reported significant increase in traits like chlorophyll content, number of pods per plant, nitrogen, phosphorus and potassium contents and over all plant growth. Kumar *et al.* (2010) observed that dual inoculation with *Sinorhizobium fredii* KCC5 and *Pseudomonas fluorescens* LPK2 significantly reduced *Fusarium* wilt in pigeonpea and increased the number of nodules and pods per plant, root and shoot length and plant biomass. They also observed aggressive root colonization, disruption of fungal hyphae and degeneration of fungal conidia which finally lead to suppression of *Fusarium udum.* Hameeda *et al.* (2010) also reported that seed priming with antagonistic *Pseudomonas* sp. CDB 35and *Rhizobium* sp. IC 59 not only reduced chickpea collar rot but also increased nodulation and plant biomass. Shaban and El-Bramawy (2011) reported that dual inoculation with *Rhizobium* and *Trichoderma* reduced damping off and root rot diseases which resulted in the increase of yield components like branches per plant, pods per plant, seeds per pod, mean seed weight and seed yield of broad bean, chickpea and lupine plants. Recent reports on the use of cyanobacteria as stimulatory partners in legume crops have opened up a new niche for research. Cyanobacterial strains such as *Anabaena laxa*, *Calothrix* sp. exhibited improved yields, enhanced nitrogen fixation and leghaemoglobin content while co-inoculated with rhizobial strains (Babu *et al.*, 2015; Bidyarani *et al.*, 2016).

PGPR can also help in increasing abiotic stress tolerance in plants. Under stressed environment, 1-Amino Cyclopropane 1-Carboxylate (ACC) which is an immediate precursor of ethylene biosynthesis accumulates at root tissues and gets oxidized into ethylene by ACC oxidase. This accelerated accumulation of ethylene inhibits nodulation, root-biomass development and can cause pre-mature senescence of nodules under stressed conditions (Glick *et al.*, 2007). PGPR producing ACC deaminase enzyme hydrolyzes ACC into α-ketobutyrate and ammonia and utilize them as carbon and nitrogen sources. This reduces the negative effect of ethylene and improves plant growth under stressed condition (Swarnalakshmi *et al.*, 2016).

4. BIOFERTILIZER FORMULATIONS

Biofertilizers are living microorganisms and unlike chemical fertilizers; they themselves are not the source of nutrients. Rather they help in driving the nutrient cycle in soil and increase the nutrient availability in plant rhizosphere region. Proper survival of microbes during transport, within soil and its establishment in root zone is utmost important for success of any biofertilizer technology (Renjith *et al.*, 2020). Thus a formulation typically consists of viable bacteria in a suitable carrier together with additives that aid in stabilization and protection of microbial cells during storage, transport and at the target. The formulation should also be easy to handle and to apply so that it is delivered to target in most appropriate manner and form. Commercial microbial formulations used now-a-days are mainly of two types, solid (carrier based) and liquid.

Solid carrier based biofertilizer is prepared by mixing broth culture containing high microbial population with a suitable carrier material. A number of factors determine the choice of carrier material like: (i) it should allow the addition of bacterial nutrients, (ii) it must have a high water-holding capacity, (iii) it should allow easy sterilization, (iv) it must have a good pH buffering capability, (v) it must be non-pollutant and biodegradable and (vi) it must allow easy handling by the farmer (Garcia-Fraile *et al.*, 2015; Renjith *et al.*, 2020). A diverse array of materials like peat, charcoal, volcanic pumice, inert materials (perlite, vermiculite, bentonite) are used as carrier all over the world (Stephens and Rask, 2000; Temprano *et al.*, 2002; Malusa *et al.*, 2012). Major disadvantages of carrier based bio-fertilizers are their short shelf life and poor quality because of poor survival of the organisms under adverse conditions, labour intense manufacturing process, lower cell titer and high risk of contamination (Kumaresan and Reetha, 2011; Velieni and Brahmaprakash, 2011).

Liquid biofertilizers are aqueous, oil, or polymer-based liquid formulations carrying desired microorganisms and their nutrients along with cell protectants and additives which provide longer shelf life and greater cell titer under adverse conditions (Brahmaprakash and Sahu, 2012). Some of the polymers which are presently used in preparation of liquid inoculants include polyvinyl pyrrolidone (PVP), methyl cellulose, polyvinyl alcohol, polyethylene glycol, gum Arabica, trehalose, glycerol, sodium alginate etc. (Tittabutr *et al.*, 2007; Buntic *et al.*, 2019; Anjali *et al.*, 2019). Liquid inoculants could be produced with minimum labour, space and energy and also the quantity of inoculum required is less compared to carrier based formulations, hence easier for farmers to handle. The liquid inoculants developed can maintain population of *Rhizobium* sp., *Azotobacter* sp., *Azospirillum* sp. and PSB up to the level of 10^8 cells per ml (Velieni and Brahmaprakash, 2011).

Application of biofertilizers has shown increase in nutrient use efficiency and crop productivity in pulses. Kyei-Boahen *et al.* (2002) showed 24.7% higher yield when liquid biofertilizer was used in chickpea crop against control. Hegde (2002) recorded 12-15% increase in yield in pigeonpea and chickpea through application of liquid biofertilizer. Biswas and Bhowmick (2007) have studied the comparative effect of carrier based and liquid *Rhizobium* inoculants in urdbean. They reported 9.6% and 13.1% increase in grain yield respectively compared to uninoculated control. The combined application of beneficial microbes such as *Rhizobium*, PSB and PGPR can perform the dual role of providing nutrients and protecting pulse crops from harmful pathogens. Some of the microbial biofertilizers used in pulse production has been listed in Table 2.

Table 2. Microbial biofertilizers used in pulse production

S. No.	Groups	Examples	Typical benefit	References
1. ***Nitrogen (N_2) fixing Biofertilizers***				
	Free-living	*Azotobacter*	10-15% yield increase, adds 20- 25 kg N/ha	Dudeja *et al.* (2011); Wani *et al.* (2013)
	Symbiotic	*Mesorhizobium* sp., *Ensifer meliloti, Rhizobium leguminosarum* bv. *Viceae, Rhizobium leguminosarum* bv. *phaseoli*	10-25% yield increase, 50-200 kg N/ha.	Sharma *et al.* (2010); Brahmaprakash and Hegde (2005); Dhakal *et al.* (2016)
2. ***P-Solubilizing Biofertilizers***				
	Bacteria	*Bacillus megaterium* var. *phosphaticum, Bacillus circulans, Pseudomonas striata*	5-30% yield increase	Khan *et al.* (2009), Umamaheswari *et al.*(2013)
	Fungi	*Aspergillus awamori Aspergillus niger*		Wang *et al.* (2014)
3. ***AM Fungi***				
	Arbuscular mycorrhiza	*Glomus* sp., *Gigaspora* sp., *Acaulospora* sp., *Scutellospora* sp., *Sclerocystis* sp.	20-40% yield increase; enhances uptake of P, Zn, S and water.	Mehrvarz *et al.* (2008); Jha *et al.* (2012)
4. ***Plant growth-promoting biofertilizers***				
	Zinc solubilizers	*Bacillus* sp.	Increased zinc availibility	Vaid *et al.* (2014)
	Phytohormone production	*Pseudomonas aeruginosa, Pseudomonas fluorescens, Azotobacter* sp., *Bacillus* sp.,	Enhanced plant growth	Mehrvarz *et al.* (2008); Shahab *et al.* (2009), Joseph *et al.* (2012)
	Biocontrol	*Pseudomonas aeruginosa, Bacillus subtilis*	Protection from soil borne pathogen	Karimi *et al.*(2012)

5. CURRENT BIOFERTILIZERS PRODUCTION SCENARIO IN INDIA

In India, systematic study on biofertilizers was started by N.V. Joshi in 1920 through isolation of nodule bacteria from different crops (Panda, 2011). First commercial production of *Rhizobium* biofertilizer in India began in 1956, and with introduction of soybean in 1960, large scale production started (Bhattacharjee and Dey, 2014).Today production of biofertilizers in India has increased from 25, 065 metric ton (MT) in year 2008-09 to 1, 21, 066 metric ton in year 2017-18 (NCOF Annual report 2017-18). It has been estimated that in India the money spent on biofertilizers and biopesticides is around US$ 1.5 billion (Garcia-Fraile *et al.*, 2015). With the increasing trend of organic farming and environmental awareness, the use of biofertilizers is expected to increase in the coming years.Till now carrier based solid biofertilizers are more popular in India. Phosphate solubilizing bacteria is the most widely produced biofertilizer in India closely followed by *Azotobacter* and *Azospirillum* (Table 3). Due to its improved quality and longer shelf life liquid biofertilizers are rapidly gaining popularity among farmers. Among all the liquid biofertilizer PSB and NPK biofertilizer are most popular.

Table 3. Different types of biofertilizer produced in India (2017-18)

Type of biofertilizer	Carrier Based (MT)	Liquid Based (KL)
Azotobacter	13818.122	1374.88
Azospirillum	14821.42	1286.331
Rhizobium	10725.55	785.652
Phosphorous Solubilizing Bacteria (PSB)	35768.45	2416.92
Potash mobilizing bacteria (KMB)	14206.24	876.307
Zinc Solubilizing Bacteria (ZSB)	3370.69	197.611
VAM	13724.41	35.13
Acetobacter	1390.99	170.527
NPK biofertilizer	6558.07	1385.446
Others	6682.6	504.24
Total	**121066.54**	**9033.06**

Source: National Centre of Organic Farming, Department of Agriculture, Cooperation and Farmers Welfare (Annual report 2017-18)

In zone wise biofertilizer production south-zone comprises more than 60% of biofertilizer production. Seven states Karnataka, Tamil Nadu, Maharashtra, Kerala, Madhya Pradesh, Gujarat and Andhra Pradesh accounts for more than 80% of the total biofertilizer production. The state-wise contribution in the production of carrier-based biofertilizer in India during 2017–18 (Fig. 1) indicates that Karnataka ranks first in the production of carrier-based formulation, followed by Tamil Nadu and Maharashtra. However, Gujarat is leading in the production of liquid-based biofertilizers, followed by Maharashtra (Fig. 2).

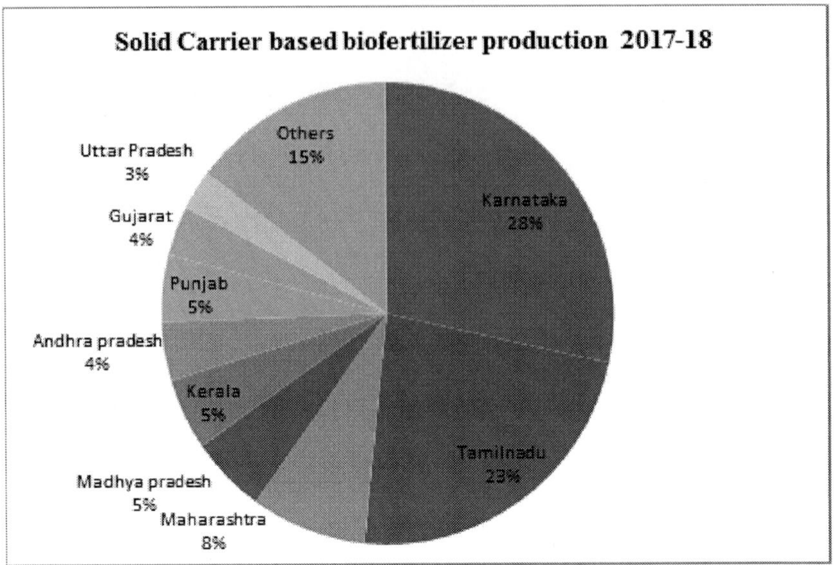

Fig. 1. State-wise contribution to the production of solid carrier based biofertilizers in year 2017-18

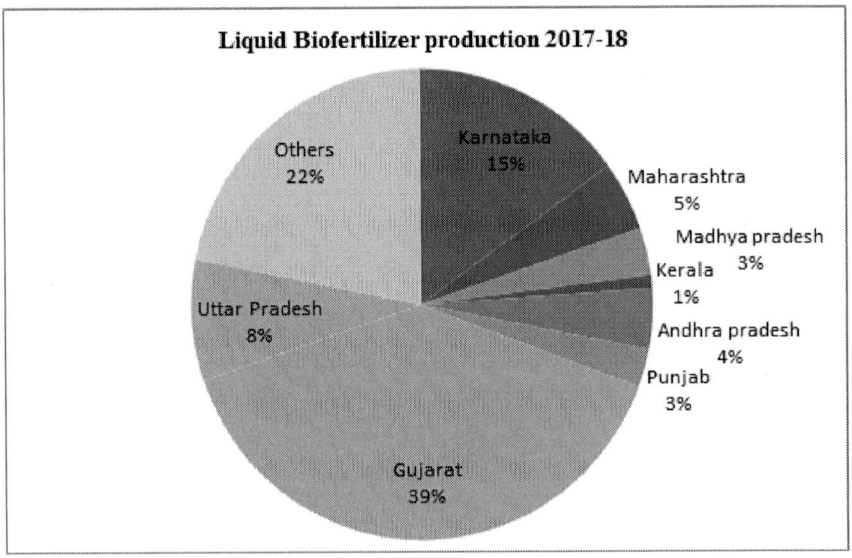

Fig. 2. State-wise contribution to the production of liquid-based biofertilizers in year 2017-18

The Government of India (GOI) is promoting production of biofertilizers in the country through various programs under several schemes like National Mission on sustainable Agriculture (NMSA), Mission for Integrated Development of Horticulture (MIDH), Rashtriya Krishi Vikas Yojana (RKVY), Network Project on Organic Farming under ICAR etc. Several ICAR Institutes ((ICAR-IARI, ICAR-IIHR, ICAR-NBAISM, ICAR-CPCRI, ICAR-DGR) and State Agricultural Universities (CSSHAU, Hisar; PAU, Ludhiana; GBPUA&T, Pantnagar; TNAU, Coimbatore; UAS, Bangalore; UAS, Dharwad; OUAT,

Bhubaneshwar; KAU, Trissur and JNKVV, Jabalpur) are involved in active research and development of liquid biofertilizers for various crops. Beside government institutes there are over 100 major private biofertilizer production companies in the country (Biomax, Ajay Biotech Ltd., Madras Fertilizers Ltd., Gujarat State Fertilizers & Chemicals Ltd., Camson Bio Technologies Ltd., Rashtriya Chemicals & Fertilizers Ltd).

6. CHALLENGES IN RAPID ADOPTION OF BIOFERTILIZER TECHNOLOGY

Although the biofertilizer technology is known for last few decades, the pace of adoption in farmer's field is quite slow. The complaint from farmers regarding the efficiency of biofertilizer is not uncommon and low quality inoculants, lack of proper storage and distribution facility between production and field application could be the reasons behind inconsistent results in field (Brar *et al.*, 2012). Often microbial biofertilizers are location and crop specific, so organism selected from one region is best adapted to that region but it may not perform well in other agro-climatic zone (Panda, 2013). Proper authentication of microbes is necessary for maintaining the quality of biofertilizer. PCR based techniques can be used at different stages of commercial production for authentication of microbial strains. (Balachander, 2012). Apart from that, lack of strict regulatory mechanisms results in low quality products in the market. Most studies suggest that biofertilizers sold in markets are contaminated and have a low count of microorganisms (Mazid and Khan, 2014). Lack of adequate communication between commercial producers and end-users (farmers) creates obstacle in rapid adoption of technology. Microbes are living organism and demand of biofertilizers is seasonal, so proper storage and distribution facility has to be developed to sustain the quality of biofertilizer (Pindi, 2012; Pindi and Satyanarayana, 2012).

7. CONCLUSION

Biofertilizers provide an excellent solution to improve soil health and productivity in a sustainable manner. PGPR bacteria promote plant growth not only by supplying nutrients to the plant, but also by producing phyto-hormones, inducing stress resistance, or preventing pathogen-induced plant diseases. With increase in popularity of organic farming, demand for quality biofertilizers will increase rapidly. Proper governmental policies and well coordinated efforts from researches, agronomists and farmers are much needed for wide adoption of biofertilizer technologies and its success in farmer's field.

8. FUTURE PROSPECTS

With the increased popularity of bio-inoculants, new technologies have emerged focusing mainly towards cost effectiveness, better stability and longer shelf life. Water-in-oil emulsions technology for developing liquid formulations is beneficial for those organisms which are particularly sensitive to desiccation (Vandergheynst *et al.*, 2007). Whereas biofilm based formulations help in survival and better establishment of microbes in root zone under adverse soil conditions (Jayasinghearachchi and Seneviratne, 2004). Application of nanotechnology to trap bacterial cells in nanostructures leads to improved stability and high surface area. Nano-formulations may contribute to enhanced stability of biofertilizers with respect to desiccation, temperature, and UV inactivation (Khot *et al.*, 2012; Malusa *et al.*, 2012). Biofertilizer formulations for precision agriculture in the form of mixed inoculants for major nutrients are in good demand. The liquid formulation that can be easily supplied through biofertigation, can deliver the organisms directly to the root zone of the crop. As the agrochemicals may be toxic to microbial cells, study on temporal and spatial differentiation between biological and chemical inputs of precision farming has to be focused (Balachander, 2012).

REFERENCES

Aggarwal, A., Kadian, N., Tanwar, A., Yadav, A. and Gupta, K.K. (2011) Role of arbuscular mycorrhizal fungi (AMF) in global sustainable development. *Journal of Applied and Natural Science* 3, 340–351

Akhtar, M.S. and Siddiqui, Z.A. (2008) Biocontrol of a root-rot disease complex of chickpea by *Glomus intraradices*, *Rhizobium* sp. and *Pseudomonas striata. Crop Protection* 27, 410–417

Akhtar, M.S., Shakeel, U. and Siddiqui, Z.A. (2010) Biocontrol of *Fusarium* wilt by *Bacillus pumilus, Pseudomonas alcaligenes* and *Rhizobium* sp. on lentil. *Turkish Journal of Biology*34, 1–7.

Anjali, Sharma, P. and Nagpal, S. (2019) Effect of Liquid and Charcoal Based Consortium Biofertilizers Amended with Additives on Growth and Yield in Chickpea (*Cicer arietinum* L.). *Legume Research* 4131, 1-12. DOI: 10.18805/LR-4131

Babu, S., Prasanna, R., Bidyarani, N. and Shivay, Y.S. (2015) Synergistic action of PGP agents and *Rhizobium* spp. for improved plant growth, nutrient mobilization and yields in different leguminous crops. *Biocatalysisand Agricultural Biotechnology* 4, 456-464.

Baddeley, J., Jones, S., Topp, C., Watson, C., Helming, J. and Stoddard, F. (2013) Biological nitrogen fixation (BNF) by legume crops in Europe. *Legume Futures Report* 1.5.

Balachandar, D. (2012) Biofertilizers–What Next? *Journal of Biofertilizers and Biopesticides* 3, 4.

Balachandran, D. and Nagarajan, P. (2002) Dual inoculation of Rhizobium and phosphobacteria with phosphorus on black gram cv. Vamban 1. *Madras Agricultural Journal* 89, 691–693.

Berg, G., Zachow, C., Müller, H., Phillips, J. and Tilcher, R. (2013) Next-generation bio products sowing the seeds of success for sustainable agriculture. *Agronomy* 3, 648–656.

Bhardwaj, D., Ansari, M.W., Sahoo, R.K. and Tuteja, N. (2014) Biofertilizers function as key player in sustainable agriculture by improving soil fertility, plant tolerance and crop productivity. *Microbial Cell Factories*13, 66. doi: 10.1186/1475-2859-13-66

Bhattacharyya, P.N. and Jha, D.K. (2012) Plant growth-promoting rhizobacteria (PGPR): emergence in agriculture. *World Journal of Microbiology and Biotechnology* 28(4), 1327–1350.

Bhowmik, S.N. and Das, A. (2018) Biofertilizers: A Sustainable Approach for Pulse Production, in *Legumes for Soil Health and Sustainable Management* (rds) RS Meena, A Das, GS Yadav, R. Lal, Springer. 445-485 pages.

Bidyarani, N., Prasanna, R., Babu, S., Hossain, F. and Saxena, A.K. (2016) Enhancement of plant growth and yields in Chickpea (*Cicer arietinum* L.) through novel cyanobacterial and biofilmed inoculants. *Microbiological Research* 188, 97-105.

Biswas, P.K. and Bhowmick, M.K. (2007) Effect of liquid and carrier based *Rhizobium* inoculants on growth, nodulation and seed yield of Urdbean. *Journal of Crop and Weed* 3(2), 7-9.

Bohlool, B.B., Ladha, J.K., Garrity, D.P. and George, T. (1992) Biological nitrogen fixation for sustainable agriculture: A perspective. *Plant and Soil* 141, 1-11.

Brahmaprakash, G.P. and Hegde, S.V. (2005) Nitrogen fixing in pigeonpea. In: Ali M, Shivkumar (eds) Advances in pigeonpea research. Indian Institute of Pulses Research, Kanpur.

Brahmaprakash, G.P. and Sahu, G.P. (2012) Biofertilizers for Sustainability. *Journal of the Indian Institute of Science* 92 (1), 38-62.

Brar, S.K., Sarma, S.J. and Chaabouni, E. (2012) Shelf-life of Biofertilizers: an accord between formulations and genetics. *Journal of Fertilizers & Pesticides* 3(5). DOI: 10.4172/2155-6202.1000e109

Buntić, A.V., Stajković-Srbinovi, O.S., Knežević, M.M., Kuzmanović, D.Z., Rasulić, N.V. and Delić, D.I. (2019) Development of liquid rhizobial inoculants and pre-inoculation of alfalfa seeds. *Archives of Biological Sciences* 71, 379-387.

Clark, R.B. and Zeto, S.K. (2000) Mineral acquisition by arbuscular mycorrhizal plants. *Journal of Plant and Nutrition* 23, 867-902.

Cristina, L., Pérez, S.L., Rafael, Z.A. and Jorge, D. (2013) Short-term effects of organic and inorganic fertilizers on soil microbial community structure and function. *Biology and Fertility of Soils* 49, 723-733.

Crowley, D.E. (2006) Microbial Siderophores in the Plant Rhizosphere, in *Iron Nutrition in Plants and Rhizospheric Microorganisms* (eds) LLBarton, JAbadia, Springer Netherlands, Dordrecht. 169-198 pages.

DES. (2020) Agricultural Statistics At A Glance 2019. Directorate of Economics and Statistics. Department of Agriculture, Cooperation and Farmers Welfare; Ministry of Agriculture and Farmers Welfare, Government of India.

Dhakal, Y., Meena, R.S. and Kumar, S. (2016) Effect of INM on nodulation, yield, quality and available nutrient status in soil after harvest of green gram. *Legume Research* 39(4), 590-594

Dudeja, S.S., Singh, N.P., Sharma, P., Gupta, S.C., Chandra, R., Dhar, B., Bansal, R.K., Brahmaprakash, G.P., Potdukhe, S.R., Gundappagol, R.C., Gaikawad, B.G. and Nagaraj, K.S. (2011) Biofertilizer technology and pulse production, *Bioaugmentation, biostimulation and biocontrol, soil biology*(eds) A Singh, Springer, Berlin

García-Fraile, P., Menéndez, E. and Rivas, R. (2015) Role of bacterial biofertilizers in agriculture and forestry. *AIMS Bioengineering* 2(3), 183-205.

Geneva, M., Zehirov, G., Djonova, E., Kaloyanova, N., Georgiev, G. and Stancheva, I. (2006) The effect of inoculation of pea plants with mycorrhizal fungi and *Rhizobium* on nitrogen and phosphorus assimilation. *Plant Soil and Environment* 52, 435-440.

Glick, B.R. (2014) Bacteria with ACC deaminase can promote plant growth and help to feed the world. *Microbiology Research* 169(1), 30-39.

Glick, B.R., Todorovic, B., Czarny, J., Cheng, Z., Duan, J. and McConkey, B. (2007) Promotion of plant growth by bacterial ACC deaminase. *Critical Review in Plant Sciences*26, 277-242.

Gopalakrishnan S, Sathya A, Vijayabharathi R, Varshney RK, Gowda CLL, Krishnamurthy L (2015) Plant growth promoting rhizobia: challenges and opportunities. *3 Biotech* 5, 355-377.

Gopalakrishnan, S., Vadlamudi, S., Samineni, S. and Sameer Kumar, C.V. (2016) Plant growth, promotion and biofortification of chickpea and pigeonpea through inoculation of biocontrol potential bacteria, isolated from organic soils. Springer Plus 5:1882.

Gosling, P., Hodge, A., Goodlass, G. and Bending, G.D. (2006) Arbuscular mycorrhizal fungi and organic farming. *Agriculture Ecosystem &Environment* 113, 17-35.

Hameeda, B., Harini, G., Rupela, O.P., Kumar Rao, J.V.D.K. and Reddy, G. (2010) Biological Control of Chickpea Collar Rot by Co-inoculation of Antagonistic Bacteria and Compatible Rhizobia. *Indian Journal of Microbiology* 50(4), 419-424.

Hegde, S.V. (2002) Liquid biofertilizers in Indian agriculture. *Biofertil Newslett* 10, 17-25.

Herridge, D.F., Peoples, M.B. and Boddey, R.M. (2008) Marschner review: global inputs of biological nitrogen fixation in agricultural systems. *Plant and Soil* 311, 1-18.

Idriss, E.E., Makarewicz, O., Farouk, A., Rosner, K., Greiner, R., Bochow, H., Richter, T. and Borriss, R. (2002) Extracellular phytase activity of *Bacillus amyloliquefaciens FZB45* contributes to its plant-growth-promoting effect. *Microbiology*148(Pt 7), 2097-2109.

Jayasinghearachchi, H.S. and Seneviratne, G. (2004) A *bradyrhizobial- Penicillium* spp. biofilm with nitrogenase activity improves N_2 fixing symbiosis of soybean. *Biology and Fertility of Soil* 40, 432-434.

Jha, M.N., Kumar, P. and Chourasia, S.K. (2012) Hope, hype and reality of biofertilizer. *Fertilizer Technology* 121, 448-480

Joseph, B., Patra, R.R. and Lawrence, R. (2012) Characterization of plant growth promoting rhizobacteria associated with chickpea (*Cicer arietinum* L.). *International Journal of Plant Production* 1(2), 141-152.

Karimi, K., Amini, J., Harighi, B. and Bahramnejad, B. (2012) Evaluation of biocontrol potential of *Pseudomonas* and *Bacillus* spp. against *Fusarium* wilt of chickpea. *Australian Journal of Crop Science* 6(4), 695-703.

Khan, M.Z., Zaidi, A., Wani, P.A. and Oves, M. (2009) Role of plant growth promoting rhizobacteria in the remediation of metal contaminated soils. *Environmental Chemistry Letters* 7(1), 1-19.

Khare, E. and Arora, N.K. (2015) Effects of soil environment on field efficacy of microbial inoculants, in *Plant Microbes Symbiosis: Applied Facets* (Eds.) N.K. Arora. Springer, India. 37-75 pages.

Khot, L.R., Sankaran, S., Maja, J.M., Ehsani, R. and Schuster, E.W. (2012) Applications of nanomaterials in agricultural production and crop protection: A review. *Crop Protection* 35, 64-70

Kloepper, J.W. and Schroth, M.N. (1978) Plant growth-promoting rhizobacteria on radishes. Proc. 4th Intern. Conf. Plant Pathgen. *Bacteria* (Angers, France: Station De Pathologie Végétale Et Phytobactériologie, INRA) 2, 879-882.

Kumar, H., Bajpai, V.K., Dubey, R.C., Maheshwari, D.K. and Kang, S.C. (2010) Wilt disease management, enhancement of growth, and yield of *Cajanus cajan* var Manak by bacterial combinations amended with chemical fertilizer. *Crop Protection* 29(6), 591-598.

Kumar, H., Dubey, R.C. and Maheshwari, D.K. (2011) Effect of plant growth promoting rhizobia on seed germination, growth promotion and suppression of *Fusarium* wilt of fenugreek (*Trigonellafoenum graecum* L.). *Crop Protection* 30, 1396-1403.

Kumar, R. and Chandra, R. (2008) Influence of PGPR and PSB on *Rhizobium leguminosarum* Bv. *viciae* strain competition and symbiotic performance in lentil. *Crop Research* 4(3), 297-301.

Kumaresan, G. and Reetha, D. (2011) Survival of *Azospirillum brasilense* in liquid formulation amended with different chemical additives. *Journal of Phytopathology* 3(10), 48-51.

Kyei-Boahen, S., Slinkard, A.E. and Walley, F.L. (2002) Evaluation of rhizobial inoculation methods for chickpea. *Agronomy Journal* 94, 851-859.

Mahdi, S.S., Hassan, G.I., Samoon, S.A., Rather, H.A., Dar, S.A. and Zehra, B. (2010) Bio-fertilizers in organic agriculture. *Journal of Phytology* 2(10), 42-54.

Malusá, E. and Vassilev, N. (2014) A contribution to set a legal framework for biofertilisers. *Applied Microbiology and Biotechnology* 98(15), 6599-6607.

Malusa, E., Sas-Paszt, L. and Ciesielska, J. (2012) Technologies for Beneficial Microorganisms Inocula Used as Biofertilizers. *The Scientific World Journal* 2012, 1-12.

Martínez-Viveros, O., Jorquera, M.A., Crowley, D.E., Gajardo, G. and Mora, M.L. (2010) Mechanisms and practical considerations involved in plant growth promotion by rhizobacteria. *Journal of Soil Science and Plant Nutrition* 10, 293-319.

Matzanke, B. (1991) Structures, coordination chemistry and functions of microbial iron chelates CRC Handbook of Microbial Iron Chelates:15-64.

Mazen, M., El-Batanony, N.H., Abd El-Monium, M. and Massoud, O. (2008) Cultural filtrate of *Rhizobium* spp. and arbuscular mycorrhiza are potential biological control agents against root rot fungal diseases of faba bean. *Global Journal of Biochemistry and Biotechnology* 3, 32-41.

Mazid, M. and Khan, T.A. (2014) Future of Bio-fertilizers in Indian Agriculture: An Overview. *International Journal of Agricultural and Food Research* 3(3), 10-23.

Meena, K.K., Meena, R.S. and Kumawat, M.S. (2013) Effect of sulphur and iron fertilization on yield attribute, yield, nutrient uptake of mungbean (*Vigna radiata* L.) *Indian Journal of Agricultural Sciences* 83(4), 108-112.

Mehdi, Z., Nahid, S.R., Alikhani, H.A. and Nasser, A. (2006) Responses of lentil to co-inoculation with phosphate-solubilizing rhizobial strains and arbuscular mycorrhizal fungi. *Journal of Plant and Nutrition* 29, 1509-1522.

Mehrvarz, S., Chaichi, M.R. and Alikhani, H.A. (2008) Effects of phosphate solubilizing microorganisms and phosphorus chemical fertilizer on yield and yield components of barley (*Hordeum vulgare* L.). *American-Eurasian Journal of Agriculture and Environmental Sciences* 3(6), 822-828.

Molla, M.N. and Solaiman, A.R.M. (2009) Association of arbuscular mycorrhizal fungi with leguminous crops grown in different agro-ecological zones of Bangladesh. *Archives of Agronomy and Soil Science* 55, 233-245.

Motsara, M.R., Bhattacharyya, P. and Srivastava, B. (1995) Biofertilizer technology, marketing and usage-A source book-cum-glosarry. Fertilizer Development and Consultation Organisation, New Delhi.

Nadia, H., Massoud, O., Mazen, M. and El-Monium, M.A. (2007) The inhibitory effects of cultural filtrates of some wild *Rhizobium* spp. on some faba bean root rot pathogens and their antimicrobial synergetic effect when combined with *Arbusclar mycorrhiza* (AM). *World Journal of Agricultural Sciences* 3, 721-730.

Nobbe, F. and Hiltner, L. (1896) U.S. Patent 570 813. Inoculation of the soil for cultivating leguminous plants.

Pagano, M.C., Cabello, M.N. and Scotti, M.R. (2007) Phosphorus response of three native Brazilian trees to inoculation with four arbuscular mycorrhizal fungi. *Journal of Agricultural Technology* 3, 231-240.

Panda, H. (2011) Manufacture of Biofertilizer and Organic Farming. Asia Pacific Business Press Inc. Pp. 103-121.

Panda, H. (2013) Handbook on Organic Farming and Processing. Asia Pacific Business Press Inc. Pp. 149-152

Pindi, P.K. (2012) Liquid Microbial Consortium for Soil Health. *Journal of Biofertilizers and Biopesticides* 3, e102. doi:10.4172/2155-6202.1000e102

Pindi, P.K. and Satyanarayana, S.D.V. (2012) Liquid Microbial Consortium- A Potential Tool for Sustainable Soil Health. *Journal of Biofertilizers and Biopesticides*3:124. doi:10.4172/2155- 6202.1000124.

Renjith, P.S., Sheetal, K.R., Kumar, S., Choudhary, J. and Prasad S. (2020) Microbial and Biotechnological Approaches in the Production of Biofertilizer, in *Environmental Microbiology and Biotechnology*(eds), A Singh,S Srivastava, D Rathore, D Pant, Springer, Singapore. https://doi.org/10.1007/978-981-15-6021-7_10

Richardson, A.E. (2001) Prospects for using soil microorganisms to improve the acquisition of phosphorous by plants. *Australian Journal of Plant Physiology* 28(9), 897-906.

Savci, S. (2012) An Agricultural pollutant: chemical fertilizer. *International Journal of Environent Science and Development* 3, 76-80.

Shaban, W. and El-Bramawy, M. (2011) Impact of dual inoculation with *Rhizobium* and *Trichoderma* on damping off, root rot diseases and plant growth parameters of some legumes field crop under greenhouse conditions. *International Research Journal of Agricultural Science and Soil Science* 1, 98-108.

Shahab, S., Ahmed, N. and Khan, N.S. (2009) Indole acetic acid production and enhanced plant growth promotion by indigenous PSBs. *African Journal of Agricultural Research* 4(11), 1312-1316.

Sharma, M.P., Sharma, S.K. and Dwivedi, A. (2010) Liquid biofertilizer application in soybean and regulatory mechanisms. *Agriculture Today* 44-45.

Sharma, S.B., Sayyed, R.Z., Trivedi, M.H. and Gobi, T.A. (2013) Phosphate solubilizing microbes: sustainable approach for managing phosphorus deficiency in agricultural soils. Springer Plus 2, 587.

Shukla, M., Patel, R.H., Verma, R., Deewan, P. and Dotaniya, M.L. (2013) Effect of bio-organics and chemical fertilizers on growth and yield of chickpea (*Cicer arietinum* L.) under middle Gujarat conditions. *Vegetos*. 26, 183-187.

Smitha, M. and Singh, R. (2014) Biocontrol of Phytopathogenic Fungi using Mycolytic Enzymes produced by Rhizospheric Bacteria of *Cicer arietinum*. *Indian Journal of Agricultural Biochemistry* 27, 215-218.

Stephens, J.H.G. and Rask, H.M. (2000) Inoculant production and formulation. *Field Crops Research* 65, 249-258.

Swarnalakshmi, K., Yadav, V., Senthilkumar, M. and Dhar, D.W. (2016) Biofertilizers for higher pulse production in India: scope, Accessibility, and challenges. *Indian Journal of Agronomy* 61, S173-S181.

Tagore, G.S., Namdeo, S.L., Sharma, S.K. and Kumar, N. (2013) Effect of *Rhizobium* and phosphate solubilizing bacterial inoculants on symbiotic traits, nodule leghemoglobin, and yield of chickpea genotypes. *International Journal of Agronomy* 2013:1–8. Article ID 581627, 8 pages.

Temprano, F., Albareda, M., Camacho, M., Daza, A., Santamaría, C. and Rodríguez-Navarro, N.D. (2002) Survival of several *Rhizobium/Bradyrhizobium* strains on different inoculant formulations and inoculated seeds. *International Microbiology* 5, 81-86.

Tittabutr, P., Payakapong, W., Teaumroong, N., Singleton, P.W. and Boonkerd, N. (2007) Growth, survival and field performance of bradyrhizobial liquid inoculant formulations with polymeric additives. *Science Asia* 33, 69-77.

Umamaheswari, T., Anbukkarasi, K., Hemalatha, T. and Chendrayan, K. (2013) Studies on phytohormone producing ability of indigenous endophytic bacteria isolated from tropical legume crops. *International Journal of Current Microbiology andApplied Sciences* 2(6), 127-136.

Vaid, S.K., Kumar, B., Sharma, A., Shukla, A.K. and Srivastava, P.C. (2014) Effect of zinc solubilizing bacteria on growth promotion and zinc nutrition of rice. *Journal of Soil Science and Plant Nutrition* 14, 889-910.

Valsalakumar, N., Ray, J.G. and Potty, V.P. (2007) Arbuscular mycorrhizal fungi associated with green gram in south India. *Agronomy Journal* 99, 1260-1264.

van der Heijden, M.G.A., Rinaudo, V., Verbruggen, E., Scherrer, C., Bàrberi, P. and Giovannetti, M. (2008) The significance of mycorrhizal fungi for crop productivity and ecosystem sustainability in organic farming systems. In: 16th IFOAM organic world congress, Modena

Vance, C.P. (2001) Symbiotic Nitrogen Fixation and Phosphorus Acquisition.Plant Nutrition in a World of Declining Renewable Resources. *Plant Physiology* 127, 390-397.

Vandergheynst, J., Scher, H., Guo, H.Y. and Schultz, D. (2007) Water-in-oil emulsions that improve the storage and delivery of the biolarvacide *Lagenidium giganteum*. *Biological Control* 52, 207-229.

Varma, D., Meena, R.S. and Kumar, S. (2017) Response of mungbean to fertility and lime levels under soil acidity in an alley cropping system in Vindhyan Region, India. *International Journal of Chemical Studies* 5(2), 384-389.

Velieni, S. and Brahmaprakash, G.P. (2011) Survival and phosphate solubilizing ability of Bacillus megaterium in liquid inoculants under high temperature and desiccation stress. *Journal of Agricultural Science and Technology* 13, 795-802.

Vessey, J.K. (2003). Plant growth promoting rhizobacteria as bio-fertilizers. *Plant and Soil* 255, 571-586.

Walpola, B. and Yoon, M.H. (2013) Phosphate solubilizing bacteria: assessment of their effect on growth promotion and phosphorous uptake of mung bean (*Vigna radiata* [L.] R. Wilczek). *Chilean Journal of Agricultural Research* 73(3), 275–281

Wang, H., Shen, L., Li-mei, Z., Ji-zong, Z., Tia-nzi, R., Bin-quan, F. and Hong-bin, L. (2014) Preparation and utilization of phosphate biofertilizers using agricultural waste. *Journal of Integrative Agriculture* 14(1), 158-167.

Wani, S.A., Chand, S. and Ali, T. (2013) Potential Use of *Azotobacter chroococcum* in Crop Production: An Overview. *Current Agricultural Research Journal*1 (1), 35-38.

Zhang, L., Fan, J., Ding, X., He, X., Zhang, F. and Feng, G. (2014) Hyphosphere interactions between an arbuscular mycorrhizal fungus and a phosphate solubilizing bacterium promote phytate mineralization in soil. *Soil Biology and Biochemistry* 74, 177-183.

CHAPTER 13

Weed management in pulse-based conservation agriculture system

C.P. Nath[1*], Narendra Kumar[1], Debarati Datta[2], T.K. Das[3], Asik Dutta[1], K.K. Hazra[1] and C.S. Praharaj[1]

1. *ICAR–Indian Institute of Pulses Research, Kanpur 208 024*

2. *ICAR–Central Research Institute for Jute and Allied Fibers, Barrackpore 700 120*

3. *ICAR–Indian Agricultural Research Institute, New Delhi 110 012*

*Corresponding author email: cpnath4@gmail.com

Abstract

The setbacks of conventional agriculture demands shift in agriculture system and thus, conservation agriculture (CA) becomes the best feasible option. CA is gaining popularity as it brings sustainability of the production system without compromising crop and soil productivity. However, adoption of CA drastically influences the weed population differently over conventional agriculture. Minimum disturbance of soil results in weed emergence from the top layer and accumulation of weed seeds in the seed bank. Again, shift in weed flora and resistance of herbicides towards weed poses great menace for its control. Thus, weed management in CA possesses great challenge for farmers. In zero tillage, there is increased emergence of perennial weeds which can be suppressed by use of crop residue. This crop residue when spread uniformly with appropriate quantity, can provide a competitive advantage for crop over the weed and also help in moisture retention, lowering of soil temperature and increase in soil organic matter (SOM). Again, crop residue incorporation followed by the application of post-emergence herbicide is found more effective than pre-emergence herbicide. Moreover, integrated weed management (IWM) is the best way to manage weeds effectively in an eco-friendly and cost-effective manner under CA which comprises crop establishment, crop rotations, use of cover crops and crop residues as mulch with a combination of pre- and post-emergence herbicide specific to pulse crops.

Keywords: Conservation agriculture, Herbicide, Integrated weed management, Tillage, Weed shift

1. INTRODUCTION

Global demand for food, feed, fibre and bio-energy due to exponential increase in population had enhanced the problem of malnutrition and poverty. This shifts the focus on intensive agriculture for increasing agricultural productivity and associated factor productivities

(Kassam *et al.*, 2015). But, this faulty intensive production system based on the principles of yield maximization has been plagued with multiple constraints which threaten the sustainability of the agro-ecosystem through groundwater over exploitation, development of herbicide resistance weed, contamination of soil, water and air, deterioration of soil health, multi-nutrient deficiency. Widespread resource degradation problems, escalating cost of inputs like fertilizer under conventional agricultural production system, and the need of making agriculture more competitive makes conservation agriculture more imperative.

Conservation agriculture (CA) based crop management technologies are said to be more efficient, use less input, improve production and income and address the emerging problems (Gupta and Seth, 2007). Additionally, secondary drivers like availability of new farm machinery; availability of new biocide molecules for efficient weed, insect, pest and disease control; ever-decreasing labour force, increasing production costs, energy shortages, erosion losses, pollution hazards and escalating fuel cost have accelerated change in thinking of researchers, policy makers and farmers to adopt modified methods for cultivation of crops aimed at improving productivity and resource-use efficiency (Jat *et al.*, 2011). The CA practices are designed to achieve agricultural sustainability by implementation of sustainable management practices that minimize environmental degradation and conserve resources while maintaining high-yielding, profitable systems, and also improve the biological functions of the agro-ecosystem with limited mechanical practices and judicious use of external inputs. It is characterized by three linked principles, viz. (i) continuous minimum mechanical soil disturbance, (ii) permanent organic soil cover, and (iii) diversification of crop species grown in sequences and/or associations. A host of benefits can be achieved through employing components of CA, including reduced soil erosion and water runoff, increased productivity through improved soil quality, increased water availability, increased biotic diversity, and reduced labour demands. However, weeds are the major biotic constraint in CA, posing as a great challenge towards its adoption. Giller *et al.* (2009) argued that weeds are 'Achilles heel' as they can affect yield and sustainability of CA systems. Effective control of weeds is a major impediment to CA productivity as weed infestations compromise crop yields (Kumar *et al.*, 2008; Das *et al.*, 2020).

2. WEEDS AND CA

Weed management is an essential part of the agriculture production system and CA requires special attention for its management (Das et al., 2018; Nandan *et al.*, 2018a; Nath *et al.*, 2018). Based on habitat, weeds act differently. Weed infestation show a drastic change due to continuous adoption of different cultivation practices such as sowing technique, tillage, method of weed control, residue management, cropping system and application of inputs. Continuous adoption of a particular factor over the years may either increase or decrease the infestation of different weed species depending on several factors.

2.1 Vertical weed seed distribution

Different tillage systems disturb the vertical distribution of weed seeds in the soil, in different ways. Weed management in CA depends upon good agronomical practices, use of herbicide and tillage level and largely on a good understanding of the dynamics of the weed seed bank in the soil. Seeds infiltrate the soil via very slow processes (cracks, fauna, freeze-dry cycles), resulting in an accumulation of weed seeds (60–90%) in the top 5 cm of the soil (Fig. 1). In the CA system, during initial years higher the weed influx, small-seeded annual and biennial weeds get favoured for germination and growth as most of the seeds remain on the surface whereas, dormant seeds buried in soil remains dormant due to minimum soil disturbance against the conventional system (Chauhan *et al.*, 2006). Contrary to this, in spite of small seed size, little canary grass has shown a remarkable reduction in their population under zero tillage (ZT) compared to conventional tillage (CT) system in the Indo-Gangetic Plains. This may be attributed to (i) higher soil strength in ZT because of crust development in the absence of tillage, which can mechanically impede seedling emergence (Chhokar *et al.* 2007; Nandan et al., 2018b), (ii) less soil temperature fluctuation under ZT (Gathala *et al.* 2011; Das *et al.*, 2014), or (iii) relatively lower levels of light stimuli, N mineralization and gas exchange under ZT, all of which are known to stimulate germination of many weed species under CT system (Franke *et al.*, 2007).

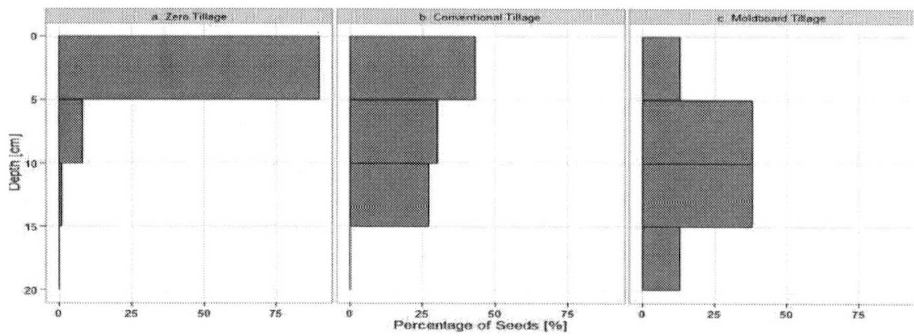

Fig. 1. Theoretical seed distribution in year one following seed rain in (a) zero tillage systems, (b) conventional tillage to a depth of 15 cm, (c) mouldboard tillage to a depth of 20 cm, based on equations from Mohler (1993).

2.2 Dominance, composition and diversity of weed type

In CA perennial weeds tend to dominate over annual broad-leaved and grasses. This indicates that in CA there is the shift in weed flora from docile weeds to obnoxious perennial weeds such as bermudagrass (*Cynodon dactylon* L.) and mexican clover (*Richardia scabra* L.) (Shahzad *et al.*, 2016). Perennial weeds thrive in reduced or no-tillage systems because the root system is not disturbed and herbicides used to control annual weeds are not effective on perennial weeds. Perennial monocots are considered a greater threat than perennial dicots in the adoption of reduced tillage systems. Conservation tillage may encourage these perennial reproductive structures by not burying them to depths that are unfavourable for emergence or by failing to uproot and kill them. Zero tillage brings about a paradigm shift in weed growth, requiring clear understanding and formulating a strategy for their management. For example, the infestation of awnless barnyardgrass, rice flatsedge, Indian Sorrel, nut sedge, field bindweed, crabgrass, crowfootgrass has been found to increase; while others like little canary grass, wild oat and lambs quarters, bermuda grass, Italian ryegrass showed decline under ZT compared with CT. Some weed species are not affected by tillage systems followed. For example, although emergence of awnless barnyard grass (*Echinochloa colona*) and rice flatsedge (*Cyperus iria*) was higher under continuous ZT than continuous CT or rotational tillage systems (ZT– CT and CT– ZT); no such tillage effect was noticed on pink node flower (*Caesulia axillaris*). Higher seedling emergence of awnless barnyard grass (*E. colona*) and rice flatsedge (*C. iria*) under continuous ZT was attributed to their small seed size, which failed to germinate when buried deeply in CT (Mishra and Singh, 2012). Infestation of *Phalaris minor* is a serious problem in wheat grown after rice in north- western India (Das and Yaduraju, 2002). This has increased due to continuous adoption of rice-wheat system and use of same or similar herbicides. New herbicides with a different mode of action are being advocated these are also sometimes proving ineffective for control of *P. minor*. Modifying cultivation practices may help in reducing its infestation. Results from on-farm trials at several locations in Haryana, India revealed that population density of *P. minor* was considerably lower and grain yield of wheat was comparatively higher under ZT than CT.

2.3 Shift in weed flora

The shift in weed flora takes place from the transformation of conventional to conservation tillage system (Singh *et al.*, 2017). Tillage provides different habitat for weeds by manipulating and changing the microclimate of soil and affects weeds by uprooting, dismembering, and burying them deep enough to prevent emergence (Baghel *et al.*, 2020; Nath *et al.*, 2015). Ploughing also moves weed seeds both vertically and horizontally, and changes the soil environment; thereby promoting or inhibiting weed seed germination and emergence. Under ZT system, gramineous weeds are favoured more over the other weed species and spread more easily that mimic pasture or roadside surroundings (Nichols *et al.*, 2015). Annual grasses increase gradually whereas annual dicotyledonous weeds population decreases (Tuesca *et al.*, 2001). In contrary to this, Mekonnen and Markos (2016) found that the family of broad-leaved weeds were to be the most abundant under CA system. Long-term field experiment and farmer surveys viewed change in the weed continuum in ZT wheat with lesser soil disturbance and found that broad-leaved weeds density gets increased (Ramesh, 2015). In CA, weeds species tolerant to shade, wet condition and low temperature can flourish more than the other weed species and have the capacity to be troublesome in reduced tillage. Increased weed infestation was recorded in aerobic direct-seeded rice than puddled condition.

2.4 Germination of weed seed

Tillage reduces resistance to root and seedling penetration, which affects the growth and establishment of germinated weed seeds (Verhulst *et al.*, 2010; Nichols *et al.*, 2015) (Fig. 2). The reduced resistance in tilled soils translates to a higher probability of a germinated seed successfully emerging. Tilled soils also allow seedlings to emerge from deeper in the soil compared to un-tilled soils (Franke *et al.*, 2007). In addition to seedling emergence, seedling establishment is affected by tillage. If located directly on the surface of un-tilled soils, the radicle of germinated weed seeds may have difficultly penetrating ZT soil surfaces, resulting in lethal germination. Surface residues can affect seed germination via physical and chemical changes in the seed environment. The two main physical effects include a reduction in light and soil surface insulation. Insulation of the soil surface has implications for both soil temperature and moisture. Even under heavy crop residue loads, most seeds on the soil surface receive sufficient light to trigger germination. Surface residue decreases the daily maximum soil temperature but has little effect on the daily minimum (Teasdale and Mohler, 1993) resulting in two changes: cooler average soil temperatures and less drastic fluctuations. Most agronomic crops and many weeds require soil temperatures above a certain threshold in order to germinate—lower average soil temperatures would therefore delay germination of both (Wicks *et al.*, 1994). Some weed species' germination is enhanced by larger temperature fluctuations (Liebman and Mohler, 2001); the buffered soil temperature could therefore reduce germination rates in addition to causing later germination. Surface residues change the chemical environment of the weed seed via allelopathy. Allelopathic compounds can be released by live plants or when residues decompose. Allelopathic effects from crop residue tend to have more pronounced effects on small seeds. This may be due to several factors but in general results in preferential suppression of weed growth compared to that of large-seeded crops (Liebman and Mohler, 2001).

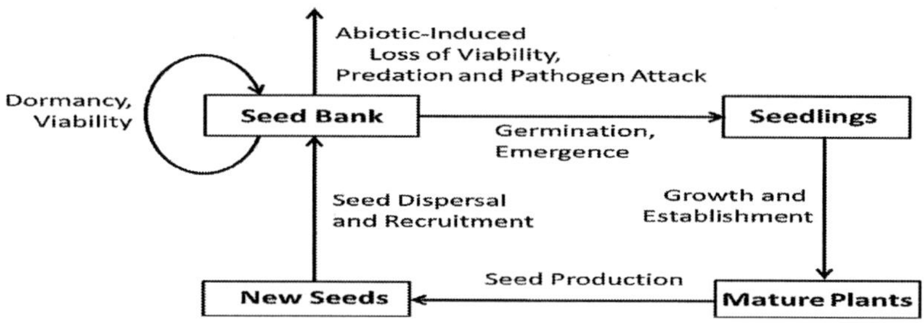

Fig. 2. Simplified conceptual representation of stocks and flows of an annual weed's life cycle (Nichols et al., 2015)

2.5 Weed seed predation and viability

CA systems may favour population growth of harvester ants by not damaging the nests, and may minimize the redistribution of weed seeds stored in superficial chambers (Baraibar *et al.,* 2009). Weed seed predation can be encouraged to manage weeds in CA as it can substantially reduce the size of the weed seed bank (Nath *et al.*, 2017). Predators prefer certain kinds of seeds, e.g. the ant species, tropical fire ant (*Solenopsis geminate*) prefers grass weed seeds over broadleaf weed seeds. Vertebrate and large invertebrate predators usually prefer larger seeds. Such selectivity in seed consumption may result in shifts in weed population. Surface residue may indirectly encourage seed predation by providing foraging and nesting habitat for predators (Baraibar *et al.*, 2009). Residue on the soil surface provides an insulated soil-atmosphere boundary that will decrease evaporative losses and maintain humidity. The increased micro-flora activity and biomass under residue (Yang *et al.*, 2013) would seem to encourage higher rates of seed losses under residue due to decay.

3. STRATEGIES OF WEED MANAGEMENT IN CA

Management of weeds is a major issue in agricultural production system, particularly under CA where the infestation is likely to be higher than conventional intensive–tillage. Understanding ecology, seed bank and dynamics of specific weed flora is essential for developing effective management strategies in divergent situations. Weed control in CA is a greater challenge than in conventional agriculture because there is no weed seed burial by tillage operations (Chauhan *et al.*, 2012). The behaviour of weeds and their interaction with crops under CA is complex and not fully understood. In the past, attempts to implement CA have often resulted in a yield penalty because reduced tillage failed to control weed interference. However, the recent development of post-emergence broad-spectrum herbicides provides an opportunity to control weeds in CA. Crop yields can be similar for conventional and conservation tillage systems if weeds are controlled and crop stands are uniform. Various approaches employed to successfully manage weeds in CA systems includes preventive measures, cultural practices (tillage, crop residue as mulches, intercropping, cover cropping, competitive crop cultivars), use of herbicide-tolerant cultivars and herbicides.

3.1 Preventive measures

Preventive measures are the first and most important steps to manage weeds, in general and especially under CA, as the presence of even a small quantity of weed seeds may cause a serious infestation in the forthcoming seasons. Preventive weed control encompasses all measures taken to prevent or arrest the introduction and arrest of weeds. Weed seeds resembling the shape and size of crop seeds are often the major source of contamination in crop seeds which usually occurs at crop harvesting stage. This can be prevented by the use of certified weed seed free crop, using clean implements for farming, well decomposed compost and removal of weeds near irrigation ditches, fence rows, etc. prior to seed setting.

3.2 Cultural practices

For sustainable and successful weed management a system must be created that reduces weed establishment and minimizes weed competition with crops. Further, management practices, viz. tillage, mulching, inter- cultivation, intercropping, cover crops, crop rotation/diversification and other agro- techniques–should be given due emphasis in managing weeds under CA. One of the pillars of CA is ground cover with dead or live mulch, which leaves less time for weeds to establish during fallow or a turnaround period. Some other common problems under CA include emergence from recently produced weed seeds that remain near the soil surface, lack of disruption of perennial weed roots, interception of herbicides by thick surface residues, and a change in the timing of weed emergence. Shrestha *et al.* (2002) concluded that long-term changes in weed flora are driven by an interaction of several factors, including tillage, environment, crop rotation, crop type, and timing and type of weed management practice.

3.3 Tillage

Differential distribution of seeds in the soil profile leads to changes in weed population dynamics. Weed seeds buried deep germinate but fail to emerge due to the thick soil layer above it, resulting in death of the weed seedling. Tillage stimulates weed germination and emergence of many weed seeds through brief exposure to light. ZT wheat in a rice–wheat system reduces littlie seed canary grass (*P. minor*) infestation, which is highly competitive and can cause drastic wheat yield reductions under heavy infestation, but it favours the infestation of toothed dock (*Rumex dentatus* L.) and cheeseweed mallow (*Malva parviflora* L.) (Chhokar *et al.*, 2007) and wild oat (Mishra *et al.*, 2005). Cheeseweed mallow is favoured by shallow seed burial and scarification leading to more weed population under a ZT system. The findings of a long-term experiment with four tillage systems adopted for 12 consecutive years in a continuous winter wheat or a pigeon bean–winter wheat rotation showed that total weed seedling density in ZT, minimum tillage using rotary harrow (15 cm depth), and chisel ploughing (45 cm depth) was relatively higher in the 0–15, 15–30, and 30–45 cm soil layers, respectively (Barberi and Lo Cascio, 2001). The impact of tillage on weed infestation varies depending upon the weed seed morphology *vis-a-vis* agro-climatic situations. For example, the benefit of ZT in reducing the *P. minor* population was relatively lower under late-sown conditions (Lathwal and Malik, 2005). DSR–wheat system with continuous ZT reduced the population of wild oat and lamb's quarter in wheat (Mishra and Singh, 2012). Some authors observed a small difference in weed populations between conventional and ZT fields, while relatively less weeds were reported in ZT wheat from the Indo-Gangetic Plains (Hobbs and Gupta, 2001). Franke *et al.* (2007) observed that emergence rate of all three flushes of *P. minor* in wheat sown on the same date were lower in ZT compared with CT. The first emergence flush which was the most important flush affecting crop–weed competition was about 50% lower in ZT than in CT (Franke *et al.*, 2007; Susha *et al.*, 2018). Chhokar *et al.* (2007) estimated 39% lower biomass of littleseed canarygrass (based on 15 field observations) under ZT compared with CT because of lower density. ZT, when combined with residue retention on the surface and early sowing, results in further suppression of littleseed canarygrass and other weeds of wheat. Significantly lower density of *C. iria* was recorded under ZT (DSR)+*Sesbania* with or without retention of previous season crop residue compared to CT (DSR) or TPR. Whereas, ZT (DSR)+ *Sesbania* with or without crop residue recorded higher population of C. *axillaris.* CT (TPR) recorded lowest population of *P. minima* and *D. retroflexa* during rice. So far as the total weed population and weed dry matter accumulation is concerned, lowest total weed density was recorded with ZT (DSR)+*Sesbania* without residue retention, but it was statistically at par with TPR. However, CT (DSR) being at par with ZT (DSR) without retention of residue of previous season crop recorded significantly lower weed dry matter production.

3.4 Method of crop establishment

Furrow Irrigated Raised-Bed System (FIRBS) and ridge tillage systems are the form of reduced and conservation tillage, respectively, that appear to overcome weed control problems associated with conventional and NT systems. Bed planting also reduces the weed infestation by burial the weed seeds deep at the time of bed preparation. Besides improved weed management, FIRBS improves input use-efficiency. Raised bed planting of wheat provides an opportunity for mechanical weeding and offers irrigation water saving over flooding method in wheat. Chauhan *et al.* (1998) obtained reasonably good control of little seed canary grass in wheat on raised beds but broad-leaved weeds in furrows were not controlled. The weed seeds lying on the top of bed will show poor germination and their growth will be comparatively less due to less availability of irrigation water on the top of bed. This method also facilitated mechanical weeding as the area in the furrows could easily be cultivated and even manual weeding could be done. When crop plants are 40 cm tall, soil is excavated from the furrows and is moved back to the ridge crest, thereby affecting weeds, weed control and the crop–weed interaction. Reshaping the bed before planting of wheat can kill the first flush of *P. minor* seedlings.

3.5 Stale seedbed method

No-till stale seedbed practice can help to reduce weed pressure in CA systems. In this technique, the field is irrigated 10–15 days prior to actual seeding to favour the germination of weed seeds lying on the soil surface. Emerged weeds are then destroyed by the application of non-selective herbicides like glyphosate, paraquat or ammonium glufosinate. It depletes the seed bank in the surface layer of the soil and reduces subsequent weed emergence. Where light rains occur for an extended period before the onset of the monsoon or irrigation is available, it may be possible to kill several flushes of weed growth before planting. However, this practice may not be exploited where the season available for crop growth is short, which may reduce the yield potential of the crop. The main advantage of the stale seedbed practice is that the crop emerges in a weed-free environment, with a competitive advantage over late-emerging weed seedlings. Stale seedbeds reduce weed populations in direct-seeded rice (Rao *et al.,* 2007), and may be especially effective when combined with no- till practices (Chauhan *et al.,* 2006). This practice is very effective in ZT wheat in the north-western Indo-Gangetic Plains (Mahajan *et al.,* 1999).

3.6 Crop residues

Crop residues comprise organic material like live/green mulch or crop/plant residue and sometimes non-living materials such as plastic sheets used in various cropping systems. Crop residues, its quantity and allelopathic property effect the weed seed germination and emergence. Under crop residue, weed density was reduced by nearly 50 to 75% (Mohler and Teasdale, 1993). In CA, cover crop on the soil surface suppresses weed seed germination by decreasing the light transmission and their allelopathic effect (Choudhary and Kumar, 2014). Delayed weed emergence provides crop to take competitive advantage over weeds which have less impact on crop yield loss (Chauhan and Johnson, 2010). Chhokar *et al.* (2009) observed that 2.5 t ha^{-1} rice residue mulch was not effective in suppressing weeds, but 5.0 and 7.5 t ha^{-1} residue mulch reduced weed biomass by 26 to 46 %, 17 to 55 %, 22 to 43 %, and 26 to 40% of *P. minor*, *Oxalis corniculata*, *Medicago sativa* and *Setaria glauca*, respectively, compared with ZT without residue. In dryland areas, the amount of available crop residue may be insufficient to substantially suppress weed germination and growth (Chauhan and Johnson, 2010). Further, certain crops like oilseeds and pulses produce less biomass than cereals. Therefore, the effects of crop residue on the weed population depend on the region, crop and rainfall. There is a need to integrate herbicide use with residue retention to achieve season-long weed control. In high-residue situations, it is important that residue does not hinder crop emergence.

3.7 Intercropping

Intercropping involves growing a smother crop between rows of the main crop to minimise the competition for resources between the two and hence can be used as an effective weed control strategy in CA. Use of short-duration, quick-growing, and early-maturing legume crops with long-duration and wide-spaced crops leads to quickly ground cover, provides ecological diversity and higher total weed suppressing ability than sole cropping. For example, alfalfa+barley, alfalfa+oats, fababean+red clover, maize+italian ryegrass/ perennial ryegrass, maize + red clover/hairy vetch, maize/cassava+cowpea/peanut/

sweet potato, pigeonpea+urdbean /mungbean/ soybean/cowpea/sorghum, rice+*Azolla pinnata*, sorghum+cowpea/mungbean/ peanut/soybean, chickpea+mustard, etc. are some successful weed suppressing intercropping systems. Success of intercropping relies on the best match between the requirements of the component species for light, water and nutrients, which increases resource use. Total weed growth reduced under intercropping combinations of chickpea+mustard over the sole chickpea crop without losing productivity of the main crop (Rathi *et al.,* 2007). Compared with the sole crop, increased canopy cover and decreased light availability for weeds in maize–legume intercropping was responsible for the reduction in weed density and dry matter (Kumar *et al.,* 2010).

3.8 Brown manuring

Sesbania can be grown with rice as a co-culture to suppress weeds, and in addition to weed control it can also fix large amounts of N (Ladha *et al.,* 2000; Susha *et al.*, 2018). Sesbania intercropping for 25–30 days in a dry-seeded rice under CA followed by killing of *Sesbania* using 2,4-D or mechanical means was effective in controlling weeds, but the contribution from N fixation was small because of intercropping and short growth duration. This brown manuring practice is highly beneficial resource conservation technology for soil and water conservation, weed control and nutrient supplementation in maize (Sharma *et al.,* 2010).

3.9 Cover cropping

Inclusion of cover crops in a rotation between two main crops is a good preventive measure when developing a weed management strategy. Cover crops are sustainable tools to manage weeds, optimize the use of natural resources, and reduce water runoff, nutrient leaching and soil erosion. Competition from a strong cover crop can virtually shut down the growth of many annual weeds and reproduction of perennial weeds that are more difficult to suppress. Weed suppression is exerted partly through resource competition for light, nutrients and water during the cover crop growing cycle, and partly through physical and chemical effects that occur when cover crop residues are left on the soil surface as a dead mulch or ploughed down. Several *Brassica* spp. could be useful allelopathic cover crops because these are winter-hardy and can be grown almost anywhere. Rye residue contains good amounts of allelopathic chemicals, viz. isothiocyanate benzyl and isothiocyanate allyl. When left undisturbed on the soil surface, these chemicals leach out and prevent germination of small-seeded weeds. The magnitude of allelopathic influence depends on allelopathic crops as well as on target weeds in a crop-weed environment. Crop allelopathy against weeds may be exploited as a useful tool to manage weeds under CA. Several crops are able to strongly suppress weeds, such as alfalfa, barley, black mustard, buckwheat, rice, sorghum, sunflower and wheat; either by exuding allelochemical compounds from living plant parts or from decomposing residues. The growing need for sustainable agricultural systems has necessitated increased cover crop research to better utilize these covers for effective weed control. Weed pressure in CA can be reduced by including short-duration legume crops e.g. mungbean, cowpea, *Sesbania,* etc., during the fallow period between harvesting wheat and planting rice. In India, *Sesbania* grown as a cover crop produced green biomass up to 30 t ha^{-1} in 60 days, and controlled most of the weeds (Mahapatra *et al.,* 2004). Perennial grasses such as cogon grass (*Imperata cylindrica* (L.) *P. Beauv.)*

and *bermuda grass (Cynodon dactylon* (L.) *Pers.),* and other problem weeds like *Striga* spp. and Siam weed (*Chromolaena odorata* (L.) can be suppressed by one or two seasons of cover crops. In CA, a number of cover crops, including legumes (alfalfa, Sesbania, sunhemp, clover, soybean, lupin and cowpea) and non-legumes (sunflower, rapeseed, rye, buckwheat and sudan grass) could be exploited to suppress and smother various weeds.

3.10 Crop diversification

Crop rotation brings diversification of crop and breaks the cycle of dominating weed flora under monoculture (Rahman, 2017). It alters selection pressures *via* three mechanisms *viz.* altering management *e.g.*, agronomical means, different patterns of resource competition, and allelopathy. Every crop has unique architecture and requires variable management techniques that generate different microclimate. The type of crop canopy filters the incoming solar radiation that can inhibit the germination of most weed species. Different crops require different cultural practices, which help to disrupt the growing cycle of weeds, and prevent any weed species to dominate. For example, Johnson grass generally becomes a predominant weed in a continuous maize system but may be controlled by rotating with cotton. Cropping sequences provide varying patterns of resource competition, allelopathic interference, soil disturbance and mechanical damage, and thus provide an unstable environment that prevents the proliferation and dominance of a particular weed, and discourages growth and reproduction of troublesome weed species. The prolonged cultivation of the rice–wheat system in north-western India has resulted in increased population of sedges and grassy weeds. The diversification of the system even for a short period and intensification by including summer legumes/green manuring decreased the weed menace. Certain crop-associated weed species e.g. barnyard grass in rice, wild oat and little seed canary grass in wheat, dodder (*Cuscuta* spp.) in alfalfa etc., may be discouraged by following a rotation of crops with contrasting growth and cultural requirements. In case, where sugarcane is taken followed by one ratoon, littleseed canary grass population goes down considerably. Replacing wheat with other crops like Egyptian clover (*Trifolium alexandrinum* L.), potato (*Solanum tuberosum* L.), sunflower (*Helianthus annuus* L.) and annual rape (*Brassica napus* L.) for 2–3 years in a rice–wheat cropping system significantly reduced the population of littleseed canary grass.

A rice–wheat rotation suppressed the establishment and growth of wild oat in wheat, while a maize–wheat rotation resulted in a gradual build-up of wild oat. The inclusion of sesame in several cropping sequences reduced the aerial growth of nutsedge (Varshney, 2000). Rice-fallow-sugarcane- ratoon sugarcane- sunflower- rice-wheat - sugarcane is a long duration (4 year) rotation which is common in the northeast district of Haryana (India). This rotation offers little opportunity for *P. minor* to proliferate. Other rotations include rice-potato-sunflower, rice-mustard-sugarcane and rice-potato-onion (Chhokar *et al.*, 2008). Inclusion of berseem (*Medicago sativa*) in the rice wheat cropping system helped to reduced seed bank of *P. minor* within a lesser period of time because the emerged plants of *P. minor* were cut with each cutting of berseem and these were not given any opportunity to set and shed seeds in field (Singh *et al.*, 1999). Similarly in potato based rotations uprooting of germinated *P. minor* plants takes place with earthing up or digging operations. Parasitic weeds can be successfully managed by rotating the host crop with trap crops, as they induce germination of weed seeds but are themselves not parasitized. The added advantage of the crop rotation is that it also allows growers to use new herbicides that may control problematic weeds.

3.11 Cultivar selection

The competitive ability of a crop variety is reflected either by its ability to reduce weed growth and seed production or to tolerate weed interference and maintain higher levels of grain yield. Although there is conflicting evidence as to which crop characteristics contribute most to competitiveness, several studies have highlighted the role of rapid germination and emergence, vigorous seedling growth, rapid leaf expansion, rapid canopy development, extensive root systems, and also production of allelopathic compounds by the crop. A quick growing and early canopy-producing crop is a better competitor against weeds than crops lacking these characters. Plant height is usually correlated with weed suppression but it is often negatively correlated with crop yield and positively correlated with sensitivity to lodging. Therefore, development of weed competitive cultivars without sacrificing yield potential is essential for integrated weed management. Designing breeding programs to select for competitive ability under CA is challenging due to the complexity of characteristics and large variation between location and year, but development of such varieties would be highly beneficial not only for weed control, but for other CA-specific characteristics. Herbicide-tolerant crops must be used in conjunction with other weed control methods, particularly rotational use of herbicidal mode-of-actions to avoid resistance issues.

3.12 Proper planting geometry

Crop geometry, including row spacing and planting pattern, can also influence crop–weed competition. Narrow row spacing brings variation in microclimate, viz. light intensity, evaporation and temperature at soil surface. Crops grown in narrow rows start competing with weeds at an earlier stage than those in wide rows because of more rapid canopy closure and better root distribution. Narrow row widths and a higher seeding density will reduce the biomass of late-emerging weeds by reducing the amount of light available for weeds located below the crop canopy. Reduced growth of weeds was reported due to increased population and decreased spacing in rice (Ghuman *et al.*, 2008). Narrow row spacing (15 cm) reduced *Phalaris minor* biomass by 16.5% compared with normal spacing of 22.5 cm (Mahajan and Brar, 2002). Higher seed rate of 150 kg ha^{-1} was found helpful in reducing populations of *Phalaris minor*, *Oxalis corniculata*, and *Melilotus alba* compared with a normal seed rate of 125 kg ha^{-1}.

3.13 Appropriate planting time

Planting time influences the occurrence and manifestation of weed species. Thus, sowing time should be manipulated in such a way that ecological conditions for the germination of weed seeds are not met. In the north-western part of the Indo-Gangetic Plains, farmers advance wheat seeding by 2 weeks to get a head start over the noxious weed littleseed canary grass and provide higher yield (Chauhan *et al.*, 2012). Similarly, delayed sowing of lentil and chickpea reduced the infestation of *Orobanche* (Linke and Saxena 1989). However, this is not a viable approach in all cases as delayed sowing may also result in reduced yield.

Sinha *et al.* (1988) reported that early sowing and closer row spacing reduced weed growth and increased dry matter accumulation, but also resulted in lower seed yield of pigeonpea. Lenssen (2008) reported that early planting of barley resulted in a small accumulation of weed biomass, and no weed seed production, while delayed planting resulted in decreased forage yield with high amounts of weed biomass and seed production, especially in ZT.

3.14 Resource management

Fertilizer: In general weeds have more aggressive nutrient uptake compared to crops, therefore altering timing, placement, and source of fertilizers in order to preferentially provide the crop with better access to nutrients is desirable. In soils with low background levels of fertility, banding of fertilizers can reduce weed biomass compared to broadcasting, with deep banding being more effective than surface banding (Liebman and Mohler, 2001; Derksen *et al.*, 2002). The source of fertilizer can also favour certain weeds and therefore offers an opportunity to shift weed species. Similarly, placement of fertilizer in the crop root zone can shift weed–crop competition in favor of the crop. Under ZT, seed drills can place basal applications of fertilizer below the seeds, thereby suppressing weeds, compared with a farmer's practice of broadcasting seeds and fertilizers. Some of the nutrient management strategies to reduce early competition from weeds include: placement of phosphate fertilizer especially, basal nitrogen application as Neem cake/ Karanja cake, and delaying urea application by 7-10 days.

Water: In irrigated environments, spatial and temporal variation of soil moisture offers opportunities for weed control. When the top layer of soil is dry, planting large-seeded crops into deep soil moisture can provide crops with an initial advantage over weeds (Liebman and Mohler, 2001). Another option under these conditions is to apply irrigation to germinate weeds, terminate them using herbicide, then plant the crop into the clean seed bed (Chauhan *et al.*, 2012; Mulvaney *et al.*, 2014). The type of irrigation used can also change the location and density of weeds. Because wheat can germinate under drier conditions than can many weeds, sowing under dry conditions can facilitate reduced weed emergence and competition.

3.15 Use of suitable farm machinery

Observations from farmers' fields across Punjab showed that the Happy Seeder (zero tillage) and rotavator (reduced tillage) are efficient methods for control of weeds as well as for *in situ* management of paddy straw (Kang, 2013). The average reduction in the weed population in the happy seeder-sown wheat crop over the rotavator and farmer's practice was 26.5 and 47.7%, respectively. However, the reduction in weed population in the rotavator-sown crop was 29.3% over the farmer's practice (Singh *et al.*, 2013). Advanced versions of the Happy Seeder, *viz.* turbo seeder, PCR planter and easy seeder are being developed for more efficient sowing and fertilizer placement. These machines could be used under CA systems both for seeding as well as managing weeds. Weed populations in wheat were recorded under precisely leveled fields (200 no. m^{-2}) compared to traditional leveled fields (350 no. m^{-2}) (Jat *et al.*, 2003). Precision land leveling may reduce up to 75% of the labour requirement needed for weeding operations (Rickman, 2002).

3.16 Chemical weed management

Herbicides are an integral part of weed management in CA. However, to sustain CA systems, herbicide rotation and/or integration of weed management practices is preferred as continuous use of a single herbicide over a long period of time may result in the development of resistant biotypes, shifts in weed flora and negative effects on the succeeding crop and environment. Minimum or ZT system under CA has obligated farmers to be more dependent on herbicides for effective weed control (Eslami, 2014). Its efficacy under CA system depends on the suitability of herbicide, application time (either pre- or post-emergence) and the amount of crop residue on the soil surface. In CA, the diverse weed flora that emerges in the field after harvesting the preceding crop must be killed using non-selective herbicides like glyphosate, paraquat and ammonium- glufosinate. Unlike in a conventional system, crop residues present at the time of herbicide application in CA systems may decrease the herbicide's effectiveness as the residues intercept herbicide droplets and reduce the amount of herbicide that reaches the soil surface. Proper selection of herbicide formulations for application under CA is necessary to increase their efficacy. For example, pre-emergence herbicides applied as granules may provide better weed control than liquid-forms in no-till systems. Climatic conditions and herbicide application methods significantly affect herbicide persistence under CA systems. Crop residues can intercept 15–80% of the applied herbicides which may result in reduced efficacy of herbicides in CA systems (Chauhan *et al.*, 2012). Weed control by herbicide application was better in the CT system (80–96%) than in the ZT system (50–61%) (Chauhan and Opena, 2012). Several selective post-emergence herbicides, some of which are low dose and high- potency molecules, are now available to effectively manage weeds in major field crops like rice, wheat, soybean etc. under CA. Wolf *et al.* (2000) observed that the quantity of spray lodged on smooth pigweed (*Amaranthus hybridus* L.) was reduced by 38–52% by standing wheat stubble depending upon the spray travel speed. Post- emergence herbicides should be applied once the weeds become established, since the timing of weed emergence is less uniform in CA systems than in conventional-tilled systems.

Table 1. Promising herbicides for weed control in different field crops under CA.

Crop	Herbicide	Dosage (g a.i./ha)	Time of application (DAS)
Rice	Bispyribac-Na	25	15-25
	Ethoxysulfuron	20	3-5
	Pyrazosulfuron-ethyl	25	15-20
	Fenoxaprop-p-ethyl	60	30-35
Wheat	Metsulfuron-methyl	04	20-25
	Clodinafop-propargyl	60	30-35
	Sulfosulfuron + Metsulfuron	25+2	25-30
Maize	Halosulfuron	100	15-20
	Tembotrione	100	15-20
Soyabean	Imazethapyr	100	20-25
	Quizalafop-ethyl	50	15-20
Cotton	Quizalafop-ethyl	50	15-20
	Pyrithriobac-Na	60	30-35

3.17 Integrated weed management

Considering the diversity of weed problems in CA systems, no single method of weed control, viz. cultural, mechanical or chemical, provides the desired level of weed control. Therefore, a combination of different weed management strategies should be evaluated to widen the weed control spectrum and efficacy for sustainable crop production. The IWM system is not meant to replace selective, safe and efficient herbicides but is a sound strategy to encourage judicious use of herbicides along with other safe, effective, economical and eco-friendly control measures (Datta *et al.*, 2017). Weed control efficiency of applied herbicides and crop competitiveness against weeds could be improved by combining good agronomic practices, timeliness of operations, fertilizer and water management, and retaining crop residues on the soil surface. For example, effective ryegrass control (up to 97%) has been observed in a ZT stubble-retained system by using soluble herbicides and minimal disturbance seeders (Crabtree, 1999). Similarly, integrating superior genotypes with a high seeding rate and early weed control lead to a 40% yield increase compared with the combination of weaker genotype, low seeding rate and delayed weed control (Harker *et al.,* 2003).

4. CONCLUSION

Over the coming years, agriculture, particularly smallholder agriculture in developing countries, will face a convergence of pressures, including a growing population, increased migration, and scarcity of labour, reduced land productivity, climate volatility and food insecurity. The sustainability of food and agricultural systems depends on not depleting natural resources; soils, especially, have been degraded by intensive crop production which has also jeopardized future food production in these areas. Much needs to be done to prevent further losses and to enhance the status of natural resources. Conservation agriculture (CA) is a response to sustainable land management, environmental protection and climate change adaptation and mitigation. It promotes maintenance of a permanent soil cover, minimum soil disturbance, and diversification of plant species. It enhances biodiversity and natural biological processes above and below the ground surface, which contribute to increased water and nutrient use efficiency and to improved and sustained crop production. However, weed management may be critical for successful implementation of CA. Overreliance on herbicide use showed its consequence in terms of environmental pollution, weed shift, and herbicide resistance development in weeds. Growing herbicide tolerant crops using non-selective herbicides is a broad spectrum weed management technique to tackle weed shift, but the same has resulted in evolution of more problematic 'super weed'. These observations indicate the need of integrated weed management technologies involving the time tested cultural practices, viz. competitive crop cultivars, mulches, cover crops, intercrops with allelopathic potential, crop diversification, planting geometry, efficient nutrient and water management, etc., along with limited and site specific herbicide application. The modern seeding equipments, e.g. 'Happy Seeder' technology, that helps in managing weeds through retention of crop residues as mulches, besides providing efficient seeding and fertilizer placement, holds the promise of becoming an integral part of CA system. Further, lack of availability of suitable machineries and timely availability of herbicides could be other bottlenecks towards the popularization of CA, which requires administrative intervention. Fortunately, there are options that can reduce weed pressure and incorporate the idea that weed management, rather than total weed elimination, is the goal, and allow some weeds to play various roles in the agro-ecosystem.

5. FUTURE OUTLOOK

- The conventional agriculture-based crop management systems are gradually undergoing a paradigm shift from intensive tillage to reduced/zero-tillage operations.
- A systematic package of practice for integrated weed, disease or pest control strategies under CA systems is of paramount importance.
- Efforts are needed to understand weed, disease and insect responses to ZT soil and microclimate conditions on a long-term basis. Research should be conducted on soil biological aspects and the rhizosphere environment under contrasting soils and crops with particular emphasis on optimizing fertilizer management.
- Other areas of research includes machinery development for local farming systems, sowing into crop residues, understanding herbicide performance in crop residues with reduced tillage, changes in nutrient cycling and nitrogen demand, leaf and root diseases, etc.
- Since herbicides cannot be eliminated from no-tillage, crop management, degradation pathways, adsorption–desorption and transport processes of herbicides are important research areas. Further, over-reliance on herbicides in a CA system is a concern from an environmental point-of-view.
- A breeding program to transfer the allelopathic genes into modern cultivars to enhance their allelopathic activity for weed suppression may help to reduce over reliance on herbicides.
- The positive impacts should be exploited through systems research to enhance CA crop yields. Information has mostly been generated on the basis of research trials, but more on- farm-level research and development is needed.
- A comprehensive survey is needed to find out the issues resisting the adoption of resource conservation technologies under different agro-ecological regions of the country and accordingly suitable strategies are to be formulated to address those bottlenecks by following the bottom-up approach for wider adoption of CA.

REFERENCES

Baghel, J.K., Das, T.K., Mukherjee, I., Nath, C.P., Bhattacharyya, R., Ghosh, S. and Raj, R., (2020) Impacts of conservation agriculture and herbicides on weeds, nematodes, herbicide residue and productivity in direct-seeded rice. *Soil Tillage Res*. 201, 104634.

Baraiba, B., Westerman, P.R., Carrion, E. and Recasens, J. (2009) Effects of tillage and irrigation in cereal fields on weed seed removal by seed predators. *Journal of Applied Ecology* 46, 380-387

Barberi, P. and Lo Cascio, B. (2001) Long-term tillage and crop rotation effects on weed seed bank size and composition. *Weed Research* 41, 325-340.

Chauhan, B.S., Gill, G. and Preston, C. (2006) Tillage system effects on weed ecology, herbicide activity and persistence: a review. *Australian Journal of Experimental Agriculture* 46, 1557-1570.

Chauhan, B.S., Gill, G.S. and Preston, C. (2007) Effect of seeding systems and dinitroaniline herbicides on emergence and control of rigid ryegrass (*Lolium rigidum*) in wheat. *Weed Technology* 21, 53–58.

Chauhan, B.S. and Johnson, D.E. (2010) Implications of narrow crop row spacing and delayed *Echinochloa colona* and *Echinochloa crusgalli* emergence for weed growth and crop yield loss in aerobic rice. *Field Crops Research* 117, 177-182.

Chauhan, B.S. and Opena, J. (2012) Effect of tillage systems and herbicides on weed emergence, weed growth, and grain yield in dry-seeded rice systems. *Field Crops Research* 137, 56-69.

Chauhan, B.S., Singh, R.G. and Mahajan, G. (2012) Ecology and management of weeds under conservation agriculture: A review. *Crop Protection* 38, 57-65.

Chauhan, D.S., Sharma, R.K., Verma, O.S., Singh, G. and Tyagi, B.S. (1998) Wheat: Research needs beyond 2000AD, Proceeding of international Conference, 12-14 August 1997, Karnal, India, pp. 263-273.

Chhokar, R.S., Sharma, R.K., Jat, G.R., Pundir, A.K. and Gathala, M.K. (2007) Effect of tillage and herbicides on weeds and productivity of wheat under rice– wheat growing system. *Crop Protection* 26, 1689–1696.

Chhokar, R.S., Singh, S., Sharma, R.K. and Singh, M. (2009) Influence of straw management on *Phalaris minor* control. *Indian Journal of Weed Science* 41, 150–156.

Chhokar, R.S., Sharma, R.K., Singh, R.K. and Gill S.C. (2008) Herbicide resistance in littleseed canarygrass (*Phalaris minor*) and its management. Page 106 in Proceedings of the 14th Australian Agronomy Conference. Adelaide, South Australia: Australian Society of Agronomy.

Choudhary, V.K. and Kumar, P.S. (2014) Influence of mulching on productivity, root growth and weed dynamics of maize (*Zea mays*)-based cropping systems. *Indian Journal of Agronomy* 59(3), 364-370.

Crabtree, W. (1999) Stubble, harrows, ryegrass, soil residual herbicides and no-till sowing. In: Stewart V (Ed), Western Australian GRDC crop updates-weed update. Department of Agriculture and Food, Government of Western Australia, Perth, Australia, pp. 35–37.

Das, T.K., Bhattacharyya, R., Sudhishri, S., Sharma, A.R. Saharawat, Y.S., Bandyopadhyay, K.K. Sepat, S. Bana, R.S., Aggarwal, P., Sharma, R.K., Bhatia A., Singh, G., Datta, S.P., Kar, A., Singh, B., Singh, P., Pathak, H., Vyas, A.K. and Jat, M.L. (2014) Conservation agriculture in an irrigated cotton–wheat system of the western Indo-Gangetic Plains: Crop and water productivity and economic profitability. *Field Crops Research* 158, 24–33.

Das, T.K., Nath, C.P., Das, S., Biswas, S., Bhattacharyya, R., Sudhishri, S., Raj, R., Singh, B., Kakralia, S.K., Rathi, N. and Sharma, A.R., (2020) Conservation Agriculture in rice-mustard cropping system for five years: Impacts on crop productivity, profitability, water-use efficiency, and soil properties. *Field Crops Research* 250, 1077-81.

Das, T.K., Saharawat, Y.S., Bhattacharyya, R., Sudhishri, S., Bandyopadhyay, K.K., Sharma, A.R. and Jat, M.L. (2018) Conservation agriculture effects on crop and water productivity, profitability and soil organic carbon accumulation under a maize-wheat cropping system in the North-western Indo-Gangetic Plains. *Field Crops Research* 215, 222-231.

Das, T.K. and Yaduraju, N.T. (2002) Optimization of metribuzin use for controlling isoproturon-resistant *Phalarisminor* Retz. in wheat. *Pesticide Research Journal* 14, 47-56.

Datta, D., Saxena, S.C. and Ghosh, S. (2017) Boosting productivity and profitability of soybean (*Glycine max*) in Uttarakhand by weed management through herbicides and mulch. *Indian Journal of Agronomy* 62(4), 538-540.

Derksen, D.A., Anderson, R.L., Blackshaw, R.E. and Maxwell, B. (2002) Weed dynamics and management strategies for cropping systems in the northern Great Plains. *Agron. J.* 94, 174–185.

Eslami, S.V. (2014) Weed management in conservation agriculture systems. In B. S. Chauhan, G. Mahajan (eds.) Recent Advances in Weed Management. Springer New York Heidelberg Dordrecht, London. pp. 87-124.

Franke, A.C., Singh, S., Mcroberts, N., Nehra, A.S., Godara, S., Malik, R.K. and Marshall, G. (2007) *Phalaris minor* seedbank studies: longevity, seedling emergence and seed production as affected by tillage regime. *Weed Research* 47, 73–83

Gathala, M.K., Ladha, J.K., Kumar, V., Saharawat, Y.S., Kumar, V., Sharma, P.K., Sharma, S. and Pathak, H. (2011) Tillage and crop establishment affects sustainability of south asian rice–wheat system. *Agronomy Journal* 103, 961-971.

Ghuman, R.S., Brar, L.S. and Walia, U.S. (2008) Role of variety and plant geometry on weed management in transplanted rice (*Oryza sativa* L.). *Indian Journal of Weed Science* 40, 137-141

Gupta, R. and Seth, A. (2007) A review of resource conserving technologies for sustainable management of the rice–wheat cropping systems of the Indo-Gangetic Plains (IGP). *Crop Protection* 26, 436–447

Harker, K.N., Clayton, G.W., Blackshaw, R.E., O`Donovan, J.T. and Stevenson, F.C. (2003) Seeding rate, herbicide timing and competitive hybrids contribute to integrated weed management in canola (*Brassica napus*). *Canadian Journal of Plant Science* 83, 433-440

Hobbs, P.R. and Gupta, R. (2001) Resource conserving technologies for wheat in rice – wheat systems. http://apps.cimmyt.org/Research/RG/map/developingworld/res_cons/res_cons/htm

Jat, M.L., Pal, S.S., Subbe Rao, A.V.M. and Sharma, S.K. (2003) Improving resurce use efficiency in wheat through laser land leveling in an Ustochrept of Indo-Gangetic Plain. In: National Seminar on Developments in Soil Science, 68th Annual Convention of the India Society of Soil Science, November 4-8, CSAUAT, Kanpur (UP).

Jat, M.L., Saharawat, Y.S. and Gupta, R. (2011) Conservation agriculture in cereal systems of south Asia: Nutrient management perspectives. *Karnataka Journal of Agricultural Sciences* 24, 100-105

Kang, M.S. (2013) Happy seeder technology is well received by punjab farmers. http://bharatsandesh.com/bharat/index.php?option=com_content&task=view&id=16957&Itemid=27 dt. 02.12.2013

Kassam, A., Friedrich, T., Derpsch, R. and Kienzle, J. (2015) Overview of the worldwide spread of conservation agriculture. *Field Actions Sci. Rep.* 8, 1-11.

Kumar, V., Bellinder, R.R., Gupta, R.K., Malik, R.K. and Brainard, D.C. (2008) Role of herbicide resistant rice in promoting resource conservation technologies in rice–wheat cropping systems in India: a review. *Crop Protection* 27, 290–301.

Ladha, J.K., Dawe, D., Ventura, T.S., Singh, U., Ventura, W. and Watanabe, I. (2000) Long-term effects of urea and green manure on rice yields and nitrogen balance. *Soil Science Society of America Journal* 64, 1993–2001.

Lathwal, O.P. and Malik, R.K. (2005) Effect of zero till seed-cum-fertilizer drill in economizing the cost of cultivation in wheat. *Haryana Journal of Agronomy* 21, 62-64.

Lenssen, A.W. (2008) Planting Date and Preplant Weed Management Influence Yield, Water Use, and Weed Seed Production in Herbicide-Free Forage Barley. *Weed Technology* 22, 486-492.

Liebman, M. and Mohler, C.L. (2001) Ecological Management of Agricultural Weeds. Cambridge: Cambridge University Press. 532pp.

Linke, K.H. and Saxena, M.C. (1989) Proceedings of International Workshop on *Orobanche,* Oberrenchal, Germany, August 1989, pp. 19-22

Mahajan, G., Brar, L.S. and Sardana, V. (1999) Effect of tillage and time of sowing on the ef? cacy of herbicides against Phalaris minor in wheat. (In): Proceeding of 17th Asian Paci? c Weed Science Society Conference, Bangkok, Thailand, pp. 193-198

Mahajan, G. and Brar, L.S. (2002) Integrated management of Phalaris minor in wheat: rationale and approaches—a review. *Agricultural Review* 23, 241–251.

Mahapatra, B.S., Mishra, A. and Kumar, A. (2004) Green manuring: a basic concept and its role in weed control. (In): Training manual: Advances in Weed Management. G.B. Pant University of Agriculture and Technology, Pantnagar, India.

Mekonnen, B. and Markos, D. (2016) Weed population dynamics in four year conservation (CA) and conventional (CN) agriculture plots in southern maize belt of Ethiopia. *Journal of Biology, Agriculture and Healthcare* 6(9), 1-9.

Mishra, J.S. and Singh, V.P. (2012) Tillage and weed control effects on productivity of a dry seeded rice–wheat system on a vertisol in central India. *Soil and Tillage Research* 123, 11–20.

Mishra, J.S., Singh, V.P. and Yaduraju, N.T. (2005) Effect of tillage practices and herbicides on weed dynamics and yield of wheat (*Triticum aestivum*) under transplanted rice (*Oryza sativa*)– wheat system in Vertisols. *Indian Journal of Agronomy* 50, 106-109.

Mohler, C.L. and Teasdale, J.R. (1993) Response of weed emergence to rate of *Vicia villosa* Roth and *Secale cereale* L. residue. *Weed Research* 33, 487–499.

Mohler, C.L. and Teasdale, J.R. (1993) Responseof weed emergence to rate of Viciavillosa Roth and Secalecereale L, residue. *Weed Research* 33, 487-99.

Mohler, C.L. (1993) A model of the effects of tillage on emergence of weed seedlings. *Ecological Applications* 3, 53–73.

Mulvaney, M., Verhulst, N., Herrera, J., Mezzalama, M. and Govaerts, B. (2014) Improved wheat performance with seed treatments under dry sowing on permanent raised beds. *Field Crops Research* 164, 189–198.

Nandan, R., Singh, S.S., Kumar, V., Singh, V., Hazra, K.K., Nath, C.P., Malik, R.K., Poonia, S.P. and Solanki, C.H. (2018b) Crop establishment with conservation tillage and crop residue retention in rice-based cropping systems of Eastern India: yield advantage and economic benefit. *Paddy Water and Environment* 16, 477-492.

Nandan, R., Singh, V., Singh, S.S., Kumar, V., Hazra, K.K., Nath, C.P., Poonia, S.P. and Malik, R.K. (2018a) Comparative assessment of the relative proportion of weed morphology, diversity, and growth under new generation tillage and crop establishment techniques in rice-based cropping systems. *Crop Protection* 111, 23-32.

Nath, C.P., Das, T.K., Rana, K.S., Bhattacharyya, R., Pathak, H., Paul, S., Meena, M.C. and Singh, S.B. (2017) Weeds and nitrogen management effects on weeds infestation and crop productivity of wheat–mungbean sequence in conventional and conservation tillage practices. *Agric. Res*. 6, 33–46.

Nath, C.P., Das, T.K., Rana, K.S., Bhattacharyya, R., Paul, S., Singh, S.B., Meena, M.C. and Hazra, K.K. (2018) Tillage and nitrogen management effects with sequential and ready-mix herbicides on weed diversity and wheat productivity. *International Journal of Pest Management* 64, 303-314.

Nath, C.P., Das, T.K., Rana, K.S., Pathak, H., Bhattacharyya, R., Paul, S., Singh, S.B. and Meena, M.C. (2015) Weed-management and wheat productivity in a conservation agriculture-based maize (*Zea mays*)-wheat (*Triticum aestivum*)-mungbean (*Vigna radiata*) system in north-western Indo-Gangetic plains of India. *Indian Journal of Agronomy* 60, 554-563.

Nichols, V., Verhulst, N., Cox, R. and Govaerts, B. (2015) Weed dynamics and conservation agriculture principles: A review. *Field Crops Research* 183, 56-68.

Rahman, M.M. (2017) Weed management in conservation agriculture. *Advances in Plants and Agriculture Research* 7(3), 302-03.

Ramesh, K. (2015) Weed problems, ecology, and management options in conservation agriculture: issues and perspectives. *Advances in Agronomy* 131, 251-303.

Rao, A.N., Mortimer, A.M., Johnson, D.E., Sivaprasad, B. and Ladha, J.K. (2007) Weed management in direct- seeded rice. *Advances in Agronomy* 93, 155-257.

Rathi, J.P.S., Rathi, P.K. and Singh, O.P. (2007) Studies on integrated weed management technique in chickpea with mustard intercropping system. *Plant Archives* 7, 909-912.

Rickman, J.F. (2002) Manual for land leveling, Rice– wheat Consortium Technical Bulletin Series 5. New Delhi-12, India: Rice– wheat Consortium for the Indo-Gangetic Plains, 24 p

Shahzad, M., Farooq, M. and Hussain, M. (2016) Weed spectrum in different wheat-based cropping systems under conservation and conventional tillage practices in Punjab, *Pakistan. Soil and Tillage Research* 163, 71–79.

Sharma, A.R., Singh, R., Dhyani, S.K. and Dube, R.K. (2010) Effect of live mulching with annual legumes on performance of maize (*Zea mays*) and residual effect on following wheat (*Triticum aestivum*). *Indian Journal of Agronomy* 55, 177-184.

Shrestha, A., Knezevic, S.Z., Roy, R.C., Ball-Coelho, B.R. and Swanton, C.J. (2002) Effect of tillage, cover crop and crop rotation on the composition of weed flora in a sandy soil. *Weed Research* 42, 76-87.

Singh, A., Kang, J.S., Kaur, M. and Goel, A. (2013). Root parameters, weeds, economics and productivity of wheat (*Triticum aestivum*) as affected by methods of planting in-situ paddy straw. *Int. J. Curr. Microbiol. App. Sci.* 2(10), 396-405.

Singh, S., Kirkwood, R.C. and Marshal, G. (1999). A review of the biology and control of *Phalaris minor* Retz. (littleseed canarygrass) in cereals. *Crop Protection* 18,1–16.

Singh, V.P., Barman, K.K., Singh, P.K., Singh, R. and Dixit, A. (2017). Managing weeds in rice (*Oryza sativa*) – wheat (*Triticum aestivum*)-greengram (*Vigna radiata*) system under conservation agriculture in black cotton soils. *Indian Journal of Agricultural Sciences* 87(6), 739-4.

Sinha, A.C., Mandal, B.B. and Jana, P.K. (1988). Physiological analysis of yield variation in irrigated pigeonpea in relation to time of sowing, row spacing and weed control measures. *Indian Agriculturist* 32, 1777-1785.

Susha, V.S., Das, T.K., Nath, C.P., Pandey, R., Paul, S. and Ghosh, S. (2018). Impacts of tillage and herbicide mixture on weed interference, agronomic productivity and profitability of a maize – wheat system in the North-western Indo-Gangetic Plains. *Field Crops Research* 219,180-191.

Teasdale, J.R. and Mohler, C. (1993). Light transmittance, soil temperature, and soil moisture under residue of hairy vetch and rye. *Agronomy Journal* 85, 673–680.

Tuesca, D., Puricelli, E. and Papa, J. (2001). A long-term study of weed flora shifts in different tillage systems. *Weed Research* 41, 369–382.

Varshney, J.G. (2000). Final report of ICAR adhoc research scheme "Nutsedge management in field crops with particular emphasis on pulses", Indian Institute of Pulse Research, Kanpur, pp. 163.

Verhulst, N., Govaerts, B., Verachtert, E., Castellanos-Navarrete, A., Mezzalama, M., Wall, P., Chocobar, A., Deckers, J. and Sayre, K. (2010) Conservation agriculture, improving soil quality for sustainable production systems. In: Lal, R., Stewart, B.A. (Eds.), Advances in Soil Science: Food Security and Soil Quality. pp. 137–208.

Wicks, G.A., Crutchfield, D.A. and Burnside, O.C. (1994) Influence of wheat (*Triticum aestivum*) straw mulch and metolachlor on corn (*Zea mays*) growth and yield. *Weed Sci.* 42, 141-147.

Wolf, T.M., Harrison, S.K., Hall, F.R. and Cooper, J. (2000) Optimizing post-emergence herbicide deposition and efficacy through application variables in no-till systems. *Weed Science* 48, 761-68.

Yang, Q., Wang, X., Shen, Y. and Philp, J. (2013). Functional diversity of soil microbial communities in response to tillage and crop residue retention in an eroded Loess soil. *Soil Science Plant Nutrition* 59, 311–321.

CHAPTER 14

Retrospect and prospects of grass pea cultivation in central India

Mangla Parikh[1]*, S.K. Nair[1], Deepak Chandrakar[2] and Ritu R. Saxena[1]

1. *Department of Genetics and Plant breeding, 2 Department of Agronomy College of Agriculture, Indira Gandhi Krishi Vishwavidyalaya, Raipur (CG) 492 012*

*Corresponding author email: manglachaudhary@rediffmail.com

Abstract

Grass pea is the most important (hardy) cool-season pulse crop of India, occupying an area of 0.58 M ha with an annual production of 0.43 Mt. It is cultivated primarily in Chhattisgarh, Bihar, Madhya Pradesh, Maharashtra and West Bengal. The majority of this acreage (~70%) is shared by Chhattisgarh and the Vidarbha region of Maharashtra, which is a rice growing region where supplemental irrigation is available only for rice. Grass pea is one of the cheapest sources of dietary protein in the developing country. It is an excellent example of an orphan crop adapted to drought and salinity and is largely considered as an 'Insurance Crop' in areas that are prone to abiotic stresses. The flour of grass pea is richly used with the flour of chickpea to make crispy food products. Apart from this, grass pea is also consumed as green leafy vegetables, green pods and for dal purpose. Grass pea has a tremendous potential as a source of multiple stress-tolerant genes, which could be exploited through modern genomic approaches to accelerate crop improvement programme. Chhattisgarh state is a tribal state rich in grass pea biodiversity. Indira Gandhi Krishi Vishwavidhyalaya, Raipur has maintained a total of 1963 grass pea germplasm accessions. Henceforth, under crop improvement focus on this crop is mandatory to screen and identify the potential donors on need based and area specific traits.

Keywords: Chhattisgarh, Lathyrus, Nutritional, ODAP, Stress

1. INTRODUCTION

Pulses are an important group of food crops playing vital role in national food and nutritional security. The share of pulses to total food grain basket is around 9-10% and is inexpensive source of proteins, vitamins and minerals. Grass pea (*Lathyrus sativus* L.), also known as *Khesari,* is one of the oldest Neolithic plants cultivated since long and spread over three continents. It is robust legume/pulse crop considered as one of the most resilient to climate changes with immense economic significance (Lambein *et al*., 2019). It offers an attractive choice for sustainable food production endowed with many intrinsic properties such as tolerance to moisture stress, salinity and requires minimum management, possessing good quality of amino acid composition and resistance to many biotic stresses. Grass pea is grown over large areas in Bangladesh, China, India, Burma, Nepal and Pakistan, including Southern Europe and parts of Africa and South America. The major grass pea cultivating states in India are Chhattisgarh, Bihar, Jharkhand, Maharashtra, Odisha, Assam, West Bengal and Eastern Uttar Pradesh (Khandare *et al.*, 2014). The majority of this acreage (~70%) is shared by Chhatisgarh and Vidarbha region of Maharashtra, which is a rice dominating ecology where supplemental irrigation is available only for rice (Dixit *et al.*, 2016). Consequently, water is not available for subsequent winter crops, making grass pea the only alternative for a crop following rice (Singh and Chandel, 1996). The total area and production of grass pea in the country are 5.11 lakh ha and 4.07 lakh tonnes, respectively. Chhattisgarh ranked the first position both in area and production (66.68 % and 60.54%) followed by Bihar (13.10% and 16.95%) and Madhya Pradesh (Tiwari and Shivhare, 2017).

Grass pea, a nutrient-dense food crops with reduced water demands, is likely to play a key role in alleviating malnutrition problem in India. Grass pea holds tremendous potential as a functional food to improve health conditions associated with cardiovascular disease, hypoxia, and hypertension. The major health concern associated with grass pea consumption is the neurotoxin ODAP (β-N-oxalyl-l-α, β-diaminopropionic acid), which is also known as β-N-oxalyl-amino-L-alanine (BOAA). Instances of lathyrism have been reported from various parts of India (Khandare *et al.*, 2018). It was observed that lathyrism could affect anyone consuming a diet having >25% grass pea for 3-4 months (Asthana, 1996). Its prolonged consumption can lead to the neurological disorder lathyrism in humans and domestic animals. Emerging concern of grass pea as a functional food is likely to cause a dramatic shift in the ways pulses and lathyrism are perceived. The major production constraint in the grass pea is its dominant area under rainfed condition and marginal lands that are generally characterized by poor soil health. Apart from various agro-ecological constraints, the crop also encounters a range of biotic and abiotic factors which reduce yield potential by 15-25%. Inadequate transfer of applicable technologies remains another constraint.

Increasing genetic erosion presents a challenge to sustaining grass pea genetic diversity. There is a pressing need to collect and conserve the genetic variation present across diverse geographical regions. A systematic collection of grass pea in India was initiated in 1967 in Madhya Pradesh. In 1969 germplasm collections were made in different states of India including Bihar, Eastern Uttar Pradesh, West Bengal, and Gujarat, and from tribal areas of Bihar in 1975. More than 1000 accessions were collected from Madhya Pradesh during 1989–1991 (Campbell, 1997). At present, 2720 grass pea accessions are conserved in collections at the ICAR-National Bureau of Plant Genetic Resources (NBPGR), New Delhi. In addition, active collections are being maintained at different research stations including Indira Gandhi Krishi Vishwavidyalaya, Raipur; ICAR-Indian Institute of Pulses Research (IIPR), Kanpur and NBPGR, Akola.

The genetic potential of grass pea could be exploited to enhance food and nutritional security, to provide feed to livestock and to improve soil fertility as green manure in harsh drought-prone environments. Regardless of the availability of low toxic lines, listing grass pea as a toxic plant and banning seed sales in some countries have considerably limited funding for genetic improvement of grass pea through modern breeding techniques as well as genetics and omics tools. As a consequence, sparse genomic resources exist today for this orphan legume, hampering its potential exploitation in crop breeding (Hao *et al.*,

2017). Grass pea is the most important pulse crop of Chhattisgarh region, covering an area of about 214.18 thousand ha (Anonymous, 2018) and accounting for nearly two-third of the total reported area under this crop in India. Its area fluctuates from year to year depending upon the distribution of rainfall. It is predominantly grown as a relay crop, popularly known as *utera*, in rice fields purely under rainfed conditions. Wide fluctuations in its productivity are observed depending upon the occurrence of winter rains. It is a rich source of protein and is used as a pulse by the poor sections of the society. It is widely used as an adulterant in varying proportions in chickpea and pigeonpea and in a large number of Indian recipes made out of gram (chickpea) flour (Mathur *et al*., 1998). It is commonly believed that the recipes become tastier with the blending of gram flour with grass pea flour. It is also preferred for its good straw quality. Farmers in the region feed their animals on paddy straw and the grass pea straw, which being rich in nutritive value, serves as a good supplement to nutritionally poor paddy straw, since under rainfed situation growing of other quality fodder is not feasible (Arora *et al.,* 1996).

2. DIVERSITY IN CULTIVATED GRASS PEA

There are two cultivated forms of grass pea grown in the region. The bold seeded type, popularly known as *lakh*, is cultivated as a post rainy season (*rabi*) crop in un-bunded vertisols (locally called *bharri*) left fallow during rainy season. The other type, popularly known as *lakhadi*, is small seeded and is largely sown as a relay crop (*utera*) in standing paddy fields. This classification is arbitrarily based on seed size and its genetics is not properly understood. The karyotypic, protein profile and peroxidase and esterase isozyme studies did not reveal any clear differences among genotypes belonging to these two broad categories.

3. GENETIC RESOURCES OF GRASS PEA

Grass pea is grown as a fodder as well as grain purpose used for human consumption and livestock feed. The initial efforts for the systematic collection of grass pea germplasm in India was started during the year 1967 when jointly the Pulses Improvement Project of USAID, New Delhi; Nutritional Research Laboratory, Hyderabad and Directorate of Agriculture and Directorate of Health, Government of Madhya Pradesh surveyed the seven district of Madhya Pradesh. About 600 collections were made during this period and also analysed for BOAA. In the year 1969 under a PL 480 Project at IARI, New Delhi some more grass pea germplasm were collected from Bihar, eastern Uttar Pradesh, West Bengal, Gujarat and Haryana through the courtesy of the Division of Plant Introduction, IARI, New Delhi (Arora *et al*., 1996). Later during 1975 to 1977, special efforts were made by IARI scientist to collect germplasm from tribal district of Bihar. In the year 1992, all the collected germplasm at IARI was transferred to Kanpur and later to Raipur where the coordinated programme was operated. Further, the collection was continued under a research project entitled 'Genetic improvement of grass pea' initiated in 1988 at the Division of Genetics, IARI, New Delhi and the germplasms were collected from Raipur district of Madhya Pradesh, Bihar and Maharashtra, and introduced from the foreign countries *viz.,* Afghanistan, Bangladesh, Canada, Cyprus, Ethiopia, France, Germany, Syria and USSR through courtesy of NBPGR, Pusa Campus, New Delhi.

4. EVALUATION AND CHARACTERIZATION

The accessions collected were evaluated and characterized for phenological, morphological, agronomical and quality traits. For the estimation of toxin content (ODAP), a well equipped laboratory had also been established in IGKV, Raipur. Considerable variability was observed for all the traits and is being utilized for its improvement in breeding programme in relation to quality of seed *i.e.* low toxin and grain yield. The information generated after the evaluation and characterization of germplasm was documented for 1963 accessions in form of catalogue and published in 2008 (Pandey *et al.*, 2008).

Enormous variation in grass pea seed ODAP content was observed by evaluating diverse genotypes. The range of ODAP content varied across studies. Results have included ranges of 102.6 mg/100g to 1254 mg/100g in 32 grass pea samples (Khandare *et al.*, 2014); 0.06-0.71% among 1963 accessions (Pandey *et al.*, 2008); 0.1-2.6% among 576 accessions (Nagarajan *et al.*, 1968); 0.1-0.3% among 1500 accessions (Jeswani *et al.*, 1970); 0.10-0.78% across 643 accessions (Somayajulu *et al.*, 1975); 0.2-2.0% across 100 accessions (Leakey, 1979), and 0.128-0.872% across 1187 accessions (Pandey *et al.*, 1997). Notably, grass pea germplasm from the Indian subcontinent contained higher ODAP (0.7-2.4%) than local germplasm (0.02-1.20%) from the Near East (Abd-El-Moneim *et al.*, 2000).

5. OUT-CROSSING IN GRASS PEA

The floral biology of grass pea favours self-pollination but some extent of out-crossing is also reported (Mehta and Santha, 1996), which is dependent on environmental or genetical factors. Rahman *et al.* (1995) reported out-crossing ranging from 9.8 to 27.8% with four flower colours. Considering the extent of variation in out-crossing in grass pea, there is a need to standardize the regeneration technique and provide protocols for seed regeneration for the *ex-situ* gene banks. Estimation of out-crossing rate in the locations where the grass pea accession are maintained and regenerated like in Chhattisgarh and Maharashtra state, is important.

6. HEALTH POTENTIAL OF GRASS PEA

The major health concern associated with grass pea consumption is the neurotoxin ODAP, which is also known as β-N-oxalyl-amino-L-alanine (BOAA). Irreparable loss of motor function may result from prolonged consumption of grass pea grains. Instances of lathyrism have been reported from various parts of India. It was observed that lathyrism could affect anyone consuming a diet consisting of more than 25% grass pea for 3–4 months. In view of these findings, the sale or storage of grass *pea* has been banned in all states in India except for Chhattisgarh, Maharashtra and West Bengal under rule 44-A of the Prevention of Food Adulteration Act, 1954 (Dixit *et al.*, 2016).

In India, grass pea cultivation is concentrated mainly in the Chhattisgarh region, where limited cases of human lathyrism are known. In contrast, a higher incidence of human lathyrism has been reported in Rewa division of Madhya Pradesh state, occurring when grass pea constituted more than 2/3 of the diet for prolonged periods (3–6 months). A survey of the socioeconomic conditions of *grass pea* growing farmers and their culinary practices was conducted in two villages near Raipur. In these villages, the consumption was related to the size of the farm holdings, with non-farm holding families having greater consumption of *grass pea.*

7. NUTRITIONAL VALUE

The nutritional value of grass pea is determined by its content of biologically available nutrients and the effects of its anti-nutrients. The seeds of grass pea contains protein 28.0%, fat 1.0%, carbohydrate 61% and other major essential minerals like iron (6.3 mg/100 g of seeds), zinc (328 mg/kg of dry matter), manganese (134 mg/kg of dry matter), cupper (81 mg/kg of dry matter), along with major amino acids *viz.*, glutamic acid (16%), aspartic acid (13.3%) and lysine (6.4%) which may provide nutritional security to the low income people in the society (Heuze *et al.*, 2016). The seeds of grass pea were found to be deficient in methionine, cysteine, lysine, isoleucine, vitamins C, D, E and B1, lipids, sodium chloride, cobalt, flourine, iodine, phosphorus and sulphur (Table 1). The chemical analysis for grass pea seed indicated a content of protein, starch, fat, minerals, metabolisable energy and digestibility varying with species (Enneking, 2011).

Table 1. Nutritive value of grass pea seed

Components	**Content/100 g seeds**
Protein (g)	28
Fat (g)	1.0
Total carbohydrate (g)	61
Calcium (mg)	90
Phosphorous (mg)	317
Iron (mg)	6.3
Potassium (mg)	644
Magnesium (mg)	92
Thiamin (mg)	0.39
Riboflavin (mg)	0.17
Niacin (mg)	0.17

8. MAJOR PRODUCTION CONSTRAINTS

The productivity of grass pea in this region is quite low. The main reasons are:

(i) **Inadequate plant stand:** The *utera* system of cultivation, evolved over years as an insurance against aberrant weather conditions, results in poor plant stand, although very high seed rate (75-80 kg/ha) is used. It is because the moisture status in the field is not uniform and the harvested paddy is left in the field for several days for drying. The poor seed quality is another factor responsible for inadequate plant stand.

(ii) **Lack of suitable varieties:** The farmers are growing their traditional varieties, which have evolved over the years to suit the poor growing environment. The breeders have been trying to select varieties from local landraces and systematic introduction and introgression of diverse germplasm have been undertaken. Previously, the varietal improvement could not progress because of the restrictions imposed on the release of new varieties regarding the BOAA (ODAP) content. The recent improvement in technique requiring low sample size is likely to help in the development of varieties having high yield and low ODAP content. Low ODAP containing lines have been developed by Indira Gandhi Agricultural University, Raipur by conventional breeding method and at Indian Agricultural Research Institute, New Delhi using tissues culture technique. These lines are currently under evaluation.

(iii) **Losses due to insect-pests:** Thrips are the major pest limiting grass pea production. There is no known source of resistance. The newly bred low ODAP containing lines are extremely susceptible to thrips.

(iv) **Losses due to diseases:** Powdery mildew causes extensive damage to grass pea. The available germplasm does not have resistant donors. The downy mildew becomes a problem only if water stagnation occurs due to winter rains.

(v) **Losses due to weeds:** Since the grass pea seeds are broadcasted in standing paddy fields, weeds are a serious problem. Hand weeding, although effective, is very expensive.

(vi) **Moisture stress:** Although, grass pea is drought resistant and most of the germplasm has typical drought resistance characteristics like low leaf area index (LAI), less chlorophyll content in order to increase the short wave radiation reflectivity (albedo) etc., still the crop suffers moisture stress and is benefitted, if winter rains are received.

9. CULTIVATION PRACTICES

Grass pea is known as hardy crop and thus raised under harsh conditions. Generally, it is grown under three farming system.

(i) **Sole crop in *kharif* (rainy season) fallow:** In the rainfed areas where there is scarcity of water for winter crops and the soils are *versitols*, farmers usually leave the field fallow in rainy days and cultivate grass pea or chickpea during winter.

(ii) **Relay or *utera* system:** This is the most prevalent system in rice growing areas particularly in Chhattisgarh, Vidarbha region of Maharashtra, parts of Orissa and West Bengal. This system is preferred due to its easier cultivation without much efforts but the productivity is not much. Farmers broadcast the grass pea seeds in standing crop of rice, nearly 20-30 days before its harvest and harvest the crop after three month of sowing. Under such situation, farmers give more emphasis for fodder yield and consider the grain yield as bonus.

(iii) **Mixed cropping:** In the rainfed areas of Rewa, Jabalpur, Hoshangabad, Bhopal and Indore division of Madhya Pradesh and in certain areas of Uttar Pradesh, grass pea is grown as mixed crop with wheat, chickpea, barley and linseed.

Grass pea as sole crop

Grass pea as relay crop with *kharif* rice

10. SOCIO-ECONOMIC IMPACT OF GRASS PEA

Grass pea effectively withstands un-favorable conditions including excessive moisture at sowing, which is often followed by moisture stress at advanced growth stages. In fact, grass pea is preferred for cultivation in such areas owing to its hardy nature coupled with its marginal costs of cultivation. In early 1990s, the socioeconomic impact of grass pea consumption was assessed in a random sample of 100 farmers from Raipur, Bilaspur and Bastar. This study revealed that almost 60% of the rice growers included grass pea in their cropping system. Most of the farmers practiced subsistence agriculture with smaller land holdings (of below 5 ha). However, its consumption among non-farmers did not exceed 3% of total food intake. The most common use of grass pea was to prepare *dal*, and nearly 25% of consumers adopted conventional measures to detoxify grass pea grains before consumption. Considerable awareness was found among rural people about the toxic effects of grass pea consumption. Another study conducted in Gondia district in Maharashtra showed that nearly 60% of the population consumed grass pea as a part of their diet; however, the quantity of grass pea consumed per day was reported to be less than 25 g (Khandare *et al.*, 2014). The ODAP content in grass pea grain samples collected from Maharashtra and Chhatisgarh is given in table 2.

Table 2. β-ODAP content in grass pea samples of Maharashtra and Chhattisgarh districts

Village	Disitrict	β-ODAP (g/100g)
Bora	Gondia	1.254 ± 0.528
Menda	Gondia	0.102 ± 0.248
Malgaon	Gondia	0.413 ± 0.415
Bhanpur	Gondia	0.994 ± 0.219
Malapari	Gondia	0.895 ± 0.197
Pindikepar	Gondia	0.938 ± 0.127
Beradipar	Gondia	1.034 ± 0.311
Gurde	Gondia	1.010
—	Bilaspur	0.630 ± 0.148
—	Durg	0.650 ± 0.137
—	Raipur	0.650 ± 0.137

(Source: Khandare *et al.*, 2014; Khandare *et al.*, 2018)

11. VARIETAL IMPROVEMENT

In the third phase (1990s), several varieties and lines were developed that combined low ODAP with high yield potential and resistance to a variety of biotic and abiotic stresses. For example, Bio R 202, Bio L-203, Bio L 212, Bio R 231, and Bio L 208 had enhanced yield and high harvest index. Bio L 212 was identified and released as 'Ratan' in 1997 for cultivation in the North East Plain Zone (NEPZ) and Central Zone (CZ) in India. Later, two varieties were developed, Prateek (LS 157-14) and Mahateora (RLS 4595), that had very low ODAP content (<0.1%) and yielded up to 1.5 t/ha. Bio L 212 x JRL 2, known as 'Mahateora' with low ODAP content (0.07-0.08%) is found suitable for rainfed and *utera* cultivation and as irrigated crop in *rabi* late sowing in entire Chhattisgarh and Madhya Pradesh under medium (*Dorsa*) to heavy (*Kanhar*) soils. It is of medium duration (90-100 days), non-shattering, non-lodging, highly nutritious, protein rich, green and dry fodder for cattle's and tolerant to moisture stress. Another variety LS 8246 x A 60, known as 'Prateek' has low ODAP (0.076%) content with highly rich in nutritious protein (25.83%), medium duration (110-115 days), bold seeded and high *dal* recovery (78.6%). The details of grass pea varieties are given in Table 3. At present also, the National Bureau of Plant Genetic Resources (NBPGR) and the Indira Gandhi Krishi Vishwavidhyalaya (IGKV), Raipur are involved in the conservation of genetic resources and development of high yielding and low toxic varieties.

Table 3. Recommended varieties for central region along with its characteristics

Variety	Source	Release/ Notification Year	Area of adoption (Zone/State)	Ave. Yield (q/ha)	Days to Maturity	Special characteristics
Ratan (Bio L-212)	IARI	1997	NEPZ (East Uttar Pradesh, Bihar, West Bengal)	15.0	108-116	Tolerant to stress, low ODAP, bold seed, purple flowered
Prateek (LS 157-14)	IGKV, Raipur	2001	Madhya Pradesh, Chhattisgarh	6-9 (under *Utera*) 11-15 (sole crop)	110-115	Tolerant to downy mildew & moderately resistant to powdery mildew (PM)
Mahateora (RLS 4595)	IGKV	2007	Chhattisgarh	15	94	Tolerant to nematode & thirps, moderately resistant to PM, Pink flowered

12. CONCLUSION

Grass pea being a climate smart crop needs attention for development and production of low or minimal ODAP content varieties. Vigorous screening of grass pea germplasms is essentially required to get new material. The biosynthetic pathway of β-ODAP needs to be understood thoroughly. New genomic tools such as RNAi and gene editing tools like CRISPER-CAS9 need to be studied to eliminate the toxicity in grass pea. Being the poor man's crop, with less input, efforts are to be made to develop varieties with increased yield and protein contents but with low ODAP. Grass pea being rich in nutrition needs more concerted efforts for safe use for both fodders for animals and/or human consumption. Moreover, a high variability found in the primary gene pool within the grass pea accessions allows the improvement of yield, nutritional quality and adaptability of grass pea itself. The change in the crossing behaviour is also observed which needs strict attention by the breeders to work upon. Being a legume, growing grass pea in rotation with cereal crops like rice would have beneficial effects on soil health.

13. WAY FORWARD

- There is an urgent need for the exploration of untouched areas and conservation of germplasm. Attention is required for their characterization and to identify climate smart/resilience germplasm. Priority should be given to increase awareness on the importance and contribution of grass pea genetic resources to food and nutritional security and challenges and opportunities in integrating genetic resources into national breeding programmes.
- The crop is grown in marginal land by poor farmers with poor management without applying any chemical to control insect-pests and diseases. Therefore, development of varieties resistant to prevalent pests and diseases has become utmost essential. Rigorous screening of the germplasm is also required to identify the donors for specific character. Wild species having genes for biotic stress should be incorporated in the programme on interspecific hybridization.
- The evaluation of collected germplasm for various traits particularly those influencing value addition is the need of the day. This would include basic studies pertaining to genetic potentials of different species for the production of biomass/grain/fodder/dual purpose/straw feed, ornamental purposes, disease and pest resistance and low neurotoxin content.
- The productivity of grass pea is low due to following of traditional cultivation practices. There is an urgent need of development and popularization of agro-techniques for cultivation of grass pea under different agro-ecoregions.
- A socio-economic study is needed to determine the trend on grass pea consumption pattern in different parts of the country. There is also need to work out the safe limit in human daily diet.
- International network on grass pea research should also be strengthened for genetic enhancement and development of suitable varieties. Information on the biosynthesis of ODAP content is essential to know the transmission of this compound to seed.
- Research should also be conducted using modern tools and techniques of biotechnology for developing varieties with novel traits. Elimination of ODAP through biotechnological techniques would be of great significance. The molecular markers detect the diversity and variation among and within species directly at the DNA level and independently of environmental factors. They can be used to determine number, position, and individual effects of genes/quantitative trait loci (QTLs) that control interesting traits, such as disease or pest resistance, reduced β-ODAP concentration, increased protein content and other characteristics of agronomic importance, *via*, for instance, genetic mapping and QTL analysis.
- Recently biosynthesis and pathway of β-ODAP in grass pea is under study in India. The RNAi mechanism needs to be studied where this can inhibit production of β-ODAP in the cultivar.

REFERENCES

Abd-El-Moneim, A.M., Van-Dorrestein, B., Baum, M. and Mulugeta, W. (2000) Improving the nutritional quality and yield potential of grass pea (*Lathyrus sativus* L.). *Food and Nutrition Bulletin* 21, 493–496.

Anonymous. (2018) Annual report of CG government. Area, Production and Productivity of Agricultural rabi crops in Chhattisgarh. Department of Agriculture, Chhattisgarh State.

Arora, R.K., Mathur, P.N., Riley, K.W. and Adham, Y. (Eds.). (1996) Lathyrus Genetic Resources in Asia: Proceedings of a Regional Workshop, 27-29 December 1995, Indira Gandhi Agricultural University, Raipur, India.

Asthana, A.N. (1996) Grass pea cultivation in problem areas: present approaches. Arora RK, Mathur PN, Riley KW and Adham Y (Eds.). *Lathyrus* Genetic Resources in Asia: Proceedings of a Regional Workshop, December 27–29, 1995, Indira Gandhi Agricultural University, Raipur, India. pp. 43-48.

Campbell, C.G. (1997) Grass pea. *Lathyrus sativus* L. Promoting the conservation and use of underutilized and neglected crops. Institute of Plant Genetics and Crop Plant Research, Gatersleben/International Plant Genetic Resources Institute, Rome, Italy. Pp. 33.

Chowdhury, S.D., Sultana, Z., Ahammed, M., Chowdhury, B.L., Das, S.C. and Roy, B.C. (2005) The Nutritional Value of *Khesari* (*Lathyrus sativus*) for Growing and Laying Pullets. *The Journal of Poultry Science* 42, 308-320.

Dixit, G.P., Parihar, A.K., Bohra, A. and Singh, N.P. (2016) Achievements and prospects of grass pea (*Lathyrus sativus* L.) improvement for sustainable food production. *The Crop Journal* 4(5), 407-416.

Enneking, D. (2011) The nutritive value of grass pea (*Lathyrus sativus*) and allied species, their toxicity to animals and the role of malnutrition in neurolathyrism. *Food and Chemical Toxicology* 49, 694–70.

Geda, A.K. (2012) Antinutritional factots and their possible detoxification in Rabi pulses for safe human food and animal feed. Model training course on Production Techniques in Rabi Pulses, 09-16 January, 2012. IGKV, Raipur, India. pp. 84-90.

Hao, X., Yang, T., Liu, R., Hu, J., Yao, Y., Burlyaeva, M., Wang, Y., Ren, G., Zhang, H., Wang, D., Chang, J. and Zong, X. (2017) An RNA sequencing transcriptome analysis of grass pea (*Lathyrus sativus* L.) and development of SSR and KASP markers. *Frontier in Plant Science* 8, 1873.

Heuze, V., Tran, G., Hassoun, P., Lessire, M. and Lebas, F. (2016) Grass pea *(Lathyrus sativus)*. Feedipedia, a programme by INRA, CIRAD, AFZ and FAO. *15, 36.*

Jeswani, L.M., Lal, B.M. and Prakash, S. (1970) Studies on the development of low neurotoxin (beta-N-oxaylamino alanine) lines in *Khesari* (*L. sativus* L.). *Current Science* 39, 518–519.

Khandare, A.L., Kumar, R.H., Meshram, I.I., Arlappa, N., Laxmaiah, A., Venkaiah, K., Rao, A.P., Validandi, V. and Toteja, G.S. (2018) Current scenario of consumption of *Lathyrus sativus* and lathyrism in three districts of Chhattisgarh State, India. *Toxicon* 150, 228-234.

Khandare, A.L., Babu, J.J., Ankulu, M., Aparna, N., Shirfule, A. and Rao, G.S. (2014) Grass pea consumption & present scenario of neurolathyrism in Maharashtra state of India. *Indian Journal of Medical Research* 140, 96-101.

Lambein, F., Travella, S., Kuo, Y.H., Montagu, M.V. and Heijde, M. (2019) Grass pea (*Lathyrus sativus* L.): orphan crop, nutraceutical or just plainfood. *Planta* 250, 821–838.

Leakey, C. (1979) *Khesari dal*-the poisonous pea. *Appropriate Technology* 6, 15–16.

Mathur, P.N., Rao, V.R. and Arora, R.K. (Eds.). (1998) *Lathyrus* Genetic Resources Network: Proceedings of a IPGRI-ICARDA-ICAR Regional Working Group Meeting, 8-10 December 1997, National Bureau of Plant Genetic Resources, New Delhi. IPGRI Office for South Asia, New Delhi, India.

Mehta, S.L. and Santha, I.M. (1996) Plant Biotechnology for development of non-toxic strains of *Lathyrus sativus*. Arora RK, Mathur PN, Riley KW and Adham Y (Eds.). *Lathyrus* Genetic Resources in Asia: Proceedings of a Regional Workshop, December 27–29, 1995, Indira Gandhi Agricultural University, Raipur, India, pp. 129-138.

Nagarajan, V. and Gopalan, C. (1968) Variation in the neurotoxin (beta-N oxalylamino alanine) content in *Lathyrus sativus* samples from Madhya Pradesh. *Indian Journal of Medical Research* 56, 95–99.

Pandey, R.L., Kashyap, O.P., Sharma, R.N., Nanda, H.C., Geda, A.K. and Nair, S. (2008) Catalogue on Grass Pea (*Lathyrus sativus* L.) Germplasm, Indira Gandhi Krishi Vishwavidyalaya, Raipur, India.

Pandey, R.L., Sharma, R.N. and Chitale, M.W. (1997) Status of *Lathyrus* genetic resources in India, in: P.N. Mathur, V.R. Rao, R.K. Arora (Eds.), *Lathyrus* Genetic Resources Network: Proceedings of a IPGRI-ICARDA-ICAR Regional Working Group Meeting, December 8–10, National Bureau of Plant Genetic Resources, New Delhi 1998. pp. 7–14.

Rahman, M.M., Kumar, J., Rahaman, M.A. and Afzal, A.M. (1995) Natural outcrossing in *Lathyrus sativus* L.. *Indian Journal of Genetics and Plant Breeding* 55, 204-207.

Singh, I.P. and Chandel, K.P.S. (1996) *Lathyrus* germplasm resources at NBPGR, India Introduction and Evaluation. Arora RK, Mathur PN, Riley KW and Adham Y (Eds.). *Lathyrus* Genetic Resources in Asia: Proceedings of a Regional Workshop, December 27–29, 1995, Indira Gandhi Agricultural University, Raipur, India (1996). pp. 53-57.

Somayajulu, P.I.N., Barat, G.K., Prakash, S., Mishra, B.K., Shrivastava, V.C. (1975) Breeding of low toxin containing varieties of *Lathyrus sativus*. *Proceedings of the Nutrition Society* of *India* 19, 35–39.

Tiwari, A.K. and Shivhare, A.K. (2017) Pulses in India: Retrospect & Prospects. Report, Govt. of India, Ministry of Agriculture and Farmers Welfare, Directorate of Pulses Development, Bhopal (MP).

CHAPTER 15

Technological interventions for enhancing pulses production under rice fallows in India

Narendra Kumar*, C.P. Nath, C.S. Praharaj, K.K. Hazra and Asik Dutta
ICAR-Indian Institute of Pulses Research, Kanpur – 208024, Uttar Pradesh
*Corresponding author email: nkumar.icar@gmail.com

Abstract

Rice is the most important staple food crop grown mainly during rainy season throughout the country in an area of about 40 M ha out of which 11.7 M ha remains fallow during succeeding winter/rabi season due to many several production related constraints. The major constraints of these areas are lack of irrigation facilities and severe soil moisture stress or drought in season crops. But, the great opportunities exist in these areas for cultivation of short duration, drought tolerant and low inputs requiring crops like pulses by following of improved resource conservation and production technologies. Thus, these areas offer scope for area expansion of pulses and crop intensification. Cultivation of pulses in these areas can help to generate additional employment and income of resource poor farmers of this region. Importantly, cultivation of pulses in rainfed rice fallow can mitigate the negative impact of continuous following of monocropping rice system and provide a sustainable production base.

***Keywords*:** Abiotic stress, Foliar nutrition, Lifesaving irrigation, Relay cropping, Rice ratoons, Seed priming, Soil moisture conservation

1. INTRODUCTION

Rice (*Oryza sativa* L.) is a major rainy season crop of Southeast Asia and contributes significantly to the food basket of this region. It is a most important staple food crop of this region. Due to favourable climatic conditions and wider adaptability, rice is grown throughout country during rainy season in an area of 39.63 M ha (avg. 2013-14 to 2017-18 of rainy season) with production of 93.55 Mt and productivity of 236 kg/ha (DES, 2020). But, about 11.695 M ha area of *kharif* rice remains fallow during succeeding winter season (Gumma *et al.*, 2016) due to many production and socio-economic related constraints. Lack of irrigation facilities and severe drought during winter crop growing season are most important constraints among them. In addition, poor soil structures and fertility, fast receding of residual soil moisture, terminal heat stress, stray cattle, diseases and pests, non-availability of suitable technology and inputs, etc. are also creating hindrance in taking winter crops (Kumar *et al.*, 2016). This area is popularly known as rice fallow area (RIFA), a lowland rainfed agro-ecology, is a point of attention of the researchers and policy makers for sustainable cropping intensification through introduction of crops like pulses and oilseeds in fallow winter season. But, the cropping intensification of these areas still remained a great challenge.

In India, RIFA is mostly confined to eastern and central parts of the country (81.5%) in states of Assam, Bihar, Chhattisgarh, Jharkhand, Madhya Pradesh, West Bengal, Odisha and NEH states (Subbarao *et al.*, 2001). The remaining area lies in states like Tamil Nadu, Karnataka and Andhra Pradesh. The details of RIFA in different states and districts of the country are given in Table 1 and 2, respectively. The details of constraints and the production technologies for pulses cultivation in RIFA is this chapter.

Table 1. Area under rice fallow area (RIFA) in different states of India

State	Kharif rice area (M ha)		Rice fallow area (M ha)	RIFA as % of kharif area	% of total RIFA of country*
	2001	2018-19*	2001		
Andhra Pradesh	2.66	1.56	0.31	11.5	2.6
Assam	2.23	2.02	0.54	24.1	4.6
Bihar & Jharkhand	5.97	4.63	2.20	36.8	18.8
Gujarat	0.47	0.81	0.08	17.7	0.7
Karnataka	0.98	0.99	0.18	18.5	1.5
Madhya Pradesh & Chhattisgarh	5.60	5.98	4.38	78.3	37.5
Maharashtra	1.76	1.42	0.63	35.7	5.4
Odisha	3.88	3.59	1.22	31.4	10.4
Tamil Nadu	1.70	1.57	0.02	1.2	0.2
Uttar Pradesh	6.26	5.72	0.35	5.6	3.0
West Bengal	4.62	4.23	1.72	37.2	14.7
Total (All States)	**40.18**	**39.96**	**11.65**	**29.0**	100

Source: Subbarao *et al* (2001); *Authors inputs

Table 2. Major districts of different states under rice fallow area (RIFA) in India

State	Major districts
Andhra Pradesh	Krishna, Guntur, East Godavari, West Godavari, Srikakullam, Nellore and Prakasham
Assam	Lakhimpur, Jorhat, Sibsagar, Dibrugarh, Golaghat, Karbi, Nagaon and Maringon
Bihar	Kishanganj, Sahibganj, Gaya, Aurangabad, Katihar, Mokama, Bhagalpur and Nalanda
Chhattisgarh	Surguja, Jashur, Raigarh, Durg, Bilaspur and Bastar
Jharkhand	Ranchi, PurbiSingbhum, Pashchim Singbhum, Hazaribagh, Gumala, Sahibganj, Deogarh, Palamau, Dumka and Dhanbad
Maharashtra	Dhule, Amravati, Nagpur, Wardah, Bhandara, Chandrapur and Nanded
Madhya Pradesh	Shahdo, Seoni, Balaghat, Damoh, Mandla, Rewa, Betul and Sidhi

Odisha	Mayurbhanj, Balasore, Bhadrak, Sundergarh, Baragarh, Bolangir, Keonjhar, Ganjam, Nawrangpur, Khordha, Jajapur, Dhenkanal, Sonpur, Koraput, Kalahandi, Sambalpur, Cuttak and Puri
West Bengal	Purulia, Bankura, Birbhum, Bardhaman, Medinapur, Murshidabad, South 24-Parganas, Maldah, West Dinajpur, Jalpaiguri and Coochbihar
Uttar Pradesh	Gonda, Siddarthnagar, Lakhimpur, Kheri, Pilibhit, Etawah, Mirzapur, Sonbhadra and Chandauli
Karnataka	Shimoga and Belgaum
Tamil Nadu	Salem, Namakkal, Tiruchirappali, Cuddalore, Ramnathpuram, Madurai, Villupuram, Thanjavur, Tiruvarur and Nagapattinam

Source: NAAS (2013) and authors inputs

2. UTILIZATION OF RICE FALLOW

RIFA is widely distributed in different rainfed agro-ecologies of the country. Based on soil and agro-climatic conditions, rice fallow can be broadly classified into three sub-groups i.e., (i) Eastern and Northeast region, (ii) Central India and (iii) Coastal Peninisula region. The climatic and edaphic factors of these RIFA in the country are diverse and unique for location. Eastern and Northeast region includes Eastern Uttar Pradesh, Bihar, Jharkhand, Odisha, West Bengal, Assam and north-eastern states where lentil and lathyrus are traditionally grown under RIFA as relay cropping (*paira*). In some parts of Odisha, mungbean and urdbean are taken due to their climatic conditions and ecology. Present study showed that pea and lentil are performing well under NEH states and chickpea can be taken in Bihar, West Bengal and some parts of Odisha. Central India covers Chhattisgarh, Madhya Pradesh and Maharashtra where lathyrus and lentil are traditionally broadcasted as a *paira/relay* crop. Chickpea can be also grown successfully in this situation. Coastal Peninisula region comprising of coastal areas of Andhra Pradesh, Tamil Nadu and Karnataka is suitable for growing of urdbean and mungbean under *paira*/relay cropping system after rice.

The RIFA of eastern region has alluvial and calcareous soil which is deficit in organic carbon, phosphorus, zinc and has excessive soil moisture content after rice harvest. Acidic soils with Mo deficiency also observed in some of the parts of this region. In RIFA of central India, soils are generally clay (*Vertisol*), very hard and develop deep cracks when dried. The soils of this region are also poor in organic matter and plant nutrients along with severe moisture stress towards reproductive stage. However, RIFA of southern peninsula has deltaic alluvial, coastal alluvial, laterite and loamy with pH between 5.0-8.0. The deltaic alluvial soils are very fertile and enriched with potassium. The excessive soil moisture during sowing of pulses and soil moisture stress at reproductive stages is the characteristics of RIFA in this region. Soil types greatly influence the soil moisture depletion pattern in RIFA. Even soil moisture depletion pattern of similar type of soils differ according location as faster depletion observed in *Vertisol* of southern India than *Vertisol* of central India (Fig 1).

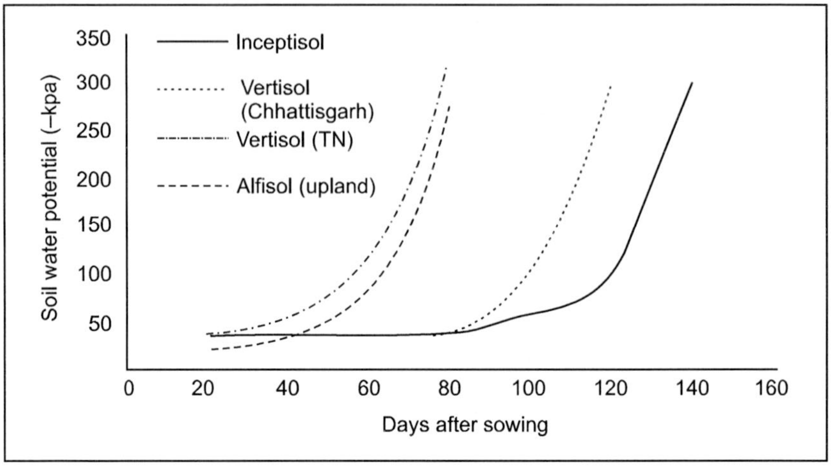

Fig 1. Drying pattern in different soil types in RIFAs

A detailed SWOT analysis is being done for promotion of pulses in RIFA (Table 3). It shows that great strength and opportunities exist in RIFA for successful cultivation of pulses either as rice+pulse relay/utera cropping or rice-pulse cropping systems with location specific improved technological interventions. Till 1960s, RIFA states contributed significantly (about half) to the total pulses production of the country. But, sharp decline in pulses area and production in RIFA was observed with time. At present, about 0.5 M ha RIFA is utilized for pulses cultivation. Looking to the importance of these areas for horizontal expansion, a target of 4.5 M ha additional RIFA area is fixed to bring under pulses cultivation through technological and policy backup that can contributes 3-4 Mt of pulses to meet out the country demand.

Table 3. SWOT analysis of rice fallow area (RIFA) of the country

Description	Characteristics
Strength	• Availability of large area (11.7 M ha) under rice fallow in diverse agro-ecological regions • Availability of early maturing varieties of rice and pulses suitable for rice fallow situation (System approach) • On an average, monsoon rainfall is good and available soil moisture is sufficient for seed germination followed by 1 or 2 winter rainfall • Technical and economic feasibility of pulses cultivation
Weaknesses	• Very low extent of cultivation • Delayed sowing of rice and lack of initiative to introduce early maturing rice variety • Uncertain winter rainfall • Lack of appropriate varieties of pulse crops suitable for diverse agro ecological regions of rice fallow • Use of poor quality seed with low germination (local seed)

	• Higher incidence of insect-pests and diseases in pulses • Lack of irrigation facilities • Non practice of foliar application of 2% urea/DAP • Terminal drought and heat stress during the reproductive and grain filling stage • Lack of efficient machines for tillage, sowing and weeding for pulses • Weak extension system for effective transfer of improved technologies • Poor understanding the ecology of rice fallow
Opportunities	• Availability of pulses for cultivation on residual soil moisture • Pulses are low input requiring crops • Resource conservation technology is available for both the crops • Pulses can intercrop with competitive crops like oilseeds, sorghum and maize • Income augmentation • Employment generation
Threats	• Low and instable yield • Production risks due to uncertain rainfall and high incidence of insect-pests and diseases • Timely non-availability of key inputs (fertilizer, seeds, pesticides etc.) • Low or no input application

Source: Kumar *et al* (2020)

3. PULSES: CANDIDATE CROPS FOR RICE FALLOW

Pulses, belonging to the family Fabaceae, are a wonderful gift of nature to mankind. They provide not only nutritious food, feed, and fodder but also help in conserving the natural resources and maintain ecological balance (Kumar *et al.*, 2018b). Pulses are endowed with the unique gift of nature to fix atmospheric nitrogen through their root nodules in association with *Rhizobium* bacteria besides addition of large quantity of organic matter to the soil. Pulses, in general, fix 40-150 kg of nitrogen which not only reduce the N-demand of pulse and succeeding crops, but also help in cutting industrial production of GHGs. In addition, the deep root systems and leaf falls add huge quantity of organic matter to soil. Their unique ability to get established even with surface seeding as in case of *utera* or relay cropping make them most suitable candidate for cultivation under RIFA. Furthermore, their inherent properties like, low input requirements, short duration and ability to withstand drought besides soil fertility restoration through BNF, narrow C:N ratio enriched crop residues etc are adding to their suitability under RIFA. Now pulses became the first choice of farmers for cultivation in RIFA due to the recent development of short duration and multiple disease resistant varieties of pulse crops.

The continuous practice of monoculture of rice in RIFA led to deterioration in soil physical, chemical and biological properties. Under these situations, introduction of pulses in RIFA for crop diversification and intensification can reverse the process and improve the overall soil health besides enhancing the microbial activities in soil by improving the population of bacteria, actinomycetes and fungi. Also integration of pulses in rice monocropping system helps in breaking of pest cycle, thereby decreasing the diseases and pest incidence, and hence less use of pesticide.

4. PRODUCTION CONSTRAINTS IN RICE FALLOW

A number of factors area associated in poor utilization and pulses productivity in RIFA. Some of the major production constraints associated in pulses production in RIFA are discussed here.

4.1 Abiotic/climatic constraints

Abiotic constraints related to climate like soil moisture deficit stress or drought and heat hampered the pulses production in different agro-ecologies of RIFA. Among abiotic stresses, drought and heat are the most important yield limiting factors accounting 50% of chickpea yield loss due to drought and 15-20% yield loss due to heat stress (Gunes *et al.*, 2008; Varshney *et al.*, 2013).

4.1.1 Soil moisture or drought stress

Winter season pulses in RIFA are grown with the residual soil moisture. After harvest of rice soil moisture content gradually declines causing mid and terminal drought during the flowering stages and early pod filling stage which adversely affects the productivity of pulses in rice fallows and sometimes causes 50% reduction in seed yield. Further, lesser amount of rains received during winter seasonand hence it further adds to the problem (Kumar *et al.*, 2018).

4.1.2 Heat stress

Winter or *rabi* season pulses in general mature during February-March in southern India and March end- April in eastern and central India. The major constraint during maturing of these crops is high temperature. High temperature exposure (30-35°C)during the reproductive phase adversely affects pollen viability, fertilization, pod set and seed development which resulted in abscission of flowers and pods and substantial losses in grain yield. The exposure of chickpea to ≥35°C at flowering resulted in drastic reduction in chickpea yield (Wang *et al.*, 2006). The optimum average day/night temperature of 5–25°C/8–10°C required at reproductive stage for lentil and the temperature >32°C during flowering and pod filling stage causes damage to reproductive organs which resulted in flower drop, pollen sterility, pod abortion and reduction in yield of lentil (Kumar *et al.*, 2016c). In a study in chickpea showed 10-15% decrease in yield for every 1°C increase in temperature above the optimum (Upadhaya *et al.*, 2011). In a similar kind of study Kalra *et al* (2008) reported decrease in chickpea yields by 53 kg/ha with a 1°C increase in seasonal temperature. Dubey *et al* (2011) showed that with every 0.1°C temperature rise combined with 31% reduction in seasonal rainfall resulted in 38.5 kg/ha reduction in chickpea yields. These results have shown that drought and heat are the major factors that affect pulses production.

4.2 Soil impediments

Puddling is main practice for growing rice in the Indian continent. The repeated ploughing in presence of water resulted in disruption of the soil structure and thus clay particles settle down at top which makes an impervious layer. The use of tractor driven machineries like rotavator further intensified the problem. The impervious layer helps to hold the irrigation water for longer period which is good for rice growth and development. But, this layer is responsible for poor root growth and nodulation in succeeding winter season pulse crops and hence poor yields of pulses in RIFA (Nadarajan and Kumar, 2018). In addition, the poor physical conditions of soil due to puddling for rice cultivation limit the nutrients mobilization. The anaerobic condition during rice cultivation reduced the microbial population and hence reduced nodulation and biological N_2 fixation observed in pulses under RIFA. Thus, problem of nutrients stress has been observed in many parts of RIFA in the country.

4.3 Soil reaction

Soil acidity is one of the major constraints in RIFA of Eastern and NEH region. About 70% RIFA soil in Odisha is acidic in nature (Jagadev *et al.*, 2016) and the figure will be much higherin NEH. In acid soils have Al and Mn, and low pH, P and Ca that adversely affect the growth and N-fixation by root nodules (Rai, 1991). The poor nodulation and root development lead to poor plant growth and yield of pulses in acid soils. Similar is true in case of soil with high pH (>7.5).

4.4 Delay planting

Sowing at optimum window period plays an important role in achieving good yield of any crop (Kumar *et al.*, 2008). In general, long duration rice varieties (150-165 days) are used by farmers in RIFA. Sometimes rice crop is also transplanted late as a common practice followed by farmers to grow rice nursery with onset of monsoon and then transplanting in 2nd fortnight of July which led to late harvest of rice crop. In both the situations, the sowing of winter pulses delayed under RIFA which causes loss of soil moisture even during initial stage for crop establishment and growth. Sowing of pulses beyond November causes significant yield loss (Singh *et al.*, 2011). Roy *et al* (2009) and Sen *et al* (2016) reported that the optimum time of sowing of lentil in West Bengal is firstfortnight of November.

4.5 Non-availability of suitable varieties and quality seed

Till now breeding programme of either rice or pulses are not designed to develop varieties suitable for RIFA. Situation specific rice cultivars (early or medium maturity) and early or extra-early cultivars of pulses with initial high rate of growth have been found to be suitable for RIFA. Kumar *et al* (2020a) reported that early maturing rice cultivar followed by early and high biomass variety of chickpea found suitable in RIFA. Similarly, non-availability of quality seed on time is another problem which sometimes led to failure of crop.

4.6 Poor plant stand/planting technique

Maintaining optimum plant population is the pre-requisite to get good yield of any crop. The following of traditional sowing practices like broadcasting seed and *utera* or relay cultivation are other reasons which limit the proper germination and plant stand. Poor plant population in case of *utera* cultivation is mainly due to soil compactness poor soil-seed contact, higher soil moisture and seedling damage during rice harvest, especially when combine harvesters are used. The seedling mortality observed in the range of 10-15 per cent due to movement of wheels of combine harvesterin the field (Fig 2). However, in case of pulses sown after rice harvest under zero tillage is often affected due to improper seed dropping in presence of stubble and fast drying of surface soil.

Fig 2. Pulses seedling damage following rice harvest by combine harvester

4.7 No- or minimum use of fertilizers

In general, farmers do not apply fertilizers and other inputs for taking pulses under RIFA. They considered as bonus yield of pulses without using any inputs, especially under *utera* or relay cropping in which pulses seed is broadcasted in standing rice field. The other reason is difficulty in application of fertilizers inputs in case of surface seeding under relay cropping. The fast drying of soil surface after rice harvest also prohibit the application of fertilizer inputs. The monocropping of pulses in RIFA also led to deficiency of certain nutrients in soil.

4.8 Rice ratooning

Re-growth of rice stubble or ratooning is a major event observed in RIFA. The re-growth of rice stubble extracts limited soil moisture and nutrients which develop competition for resources with pulse crops during initial growth. In an estimate, it was observed that rice ratoons deplete the soil moisture up to 25% (Kumar *et al.*, 2018).

4.9 Weed menace

Weed is a serious problem in winter season pulses grown in RIFA. Weed plants compete with the pulse crops for scarce resources of RIFA as soil moisture and nutrients which lead to substantial loss in crop yield (Kumar *et al.*, 2020). In case of *utera* or relay cropping, weed problems are more serious because of no tillage operation and use of pre-emergence herbicide. Manual weeding is also difficult because of fast drying of soil surface (hard surface) and presence of rice stubble. In many regions, a parasitic weed like cuscuta infestation is also reported in mungbean and urdbean (Satyanarayana *et al.*, 1997).In a survey of RIFA in Andhra Pradesh reported that rice fallow blackgram infested with a total of 45 weed species belonging to 23 families, of these seven monocots, 33 dicots and five sedges (Rao and Kiran, 2014). Ramesh and Rathika (2015) reported 63% increase in blackgram yield under efficient weed management through post-emergence herbicide in RIFA.

4.10 Diseases & insect-pests

Many diseases are prevalent in pulses under different agro-ecologies of RIFA. Powdery mildew is one of the important diseases followed by mungbean yellow mosaic virus (MYMV) of mungbean and urdbean grown in southern states and in Odisha. However, rust and *Fusarium* wilt are commonly observed in lentil in central and eastern India. Similarly in chickpea, dry root rot and wilt in central zone, and *Botrytis* grey mold and collar rot in eastern plains cause severe losses. The major diseases in pulse crop observed in RIFA are given in Table 4.

In India, more than 250 insect species are reported which affect the pulses. About one dozen are considered as serious pest that causes severe yield loss. Among them, pod borer (*Helicoverpa armigera)* is most harmful especially in chickpea, pea and lathyrus. Aphids and white flies are important insect-pests of urdbean, mungbean and lentil in RIFA.

Table 4. Important diseasesrecorded in pulses grown in RIFA

Crop	Season	Diseases
Chickpea	Timely sown	Fusarium wilt, root rot, chickpea stunt, Botrytis gray mould
	Late sown	Fusarium wilt
Mungbean	Rabi/ RIFA	MYMV, Powdery mildew, Rust
Urdbean	RIFA	MYMV, Ascochyta blight, anthracnose
Lentil	Rabi/ RIFA	Fusarium wilt, Root rot, rust
Lathyrus	Rabi/ RIFA	Downy mildew, Rust
Pea	Rabi/ RIFA	Powdery mildew, Rust, Ascochyta blight, Fusarium wilt
MYMV- Mungbean yellow mosaic virus		

4.11 Socio-economic constraints

Lack of knowledge, non-availability of improved seed, poor technical guidance were few socio economic institutional constraints while seed storage, poor irrigation and poor marketing were socio economic infrastructural constraints in pulses production (Subbarao *et al.*, 2001; Pande *et al.*, 2003). The poor extension system is not effective in faster dissemination of the improved technologies and recent information to the farmers. Non-availability of required inputs like quality seed, fertilizers and plant protection chemicals on time are the major hindrances in the successful cultivation of pulses in RIFA. Social practice of community grazing systems and tray cattle are other reasons for keeping land fallow after rice harvest in these regions.

5. PRODUCTION TECHNOLOGIES OF PULSES FOR RAINFED RICE FALLOW

In RIFA, yields of rabi pulses are low due to poor management practices and the reasons explained above. To overcome the constraints and to increase the pulses productivity in rainfed RIFA, researchers have suggested certain strategies which are compiled in Table 5 and the details of technologies explained below.

Table 5. Technological interventions for improving productivity of pulses in RIFA

Issues	Technological intervention
Lack of suitable cultivars	Early and extra early varieties with higher yield potential under rainfed RIFA need to be developed
Poor plant population	Sowing method, seed rate, seed priming, seeding machines for RIFA
Weed menace	System based weed management, post-emergence herbicides identification, herbicides to contains rice ratoons, rice cultivation techniques, rice residue retention
Nutrient management	System based nutrient management, use of ZT ferti-seed drill, seed priming/pelleting of micro-nutrients, foliar nutrition, use of bio-fertilizers
Soil moisture management	In-situ soil moisture conservation, rice residue retention, water harvesting in farm ponds for lifesaving irrigation
Terminal heat stress	Timely planting, selection of early maturing and heat tolerant varieties, residue mulching
Non-availability of quality seed	Promotion of formal and informal seed production and supply systems
Lack of mechanization	Development of pulses sowing and rice harvesting machineries for RIFA
Disease and pest management	Use of disease resistance varieties of pulses as per location, development of IPM modules
Poor extension machineries	Innovative extension methods for fast dissemination of improved technologies to farmers, farmers participatory research, use of modern ICTs

Source: NAAS (2013) and authors inputs

5.1 Soil moisture conservation

Following of soil moisture conservation is first and foremost important practice for successful cultivation of pulses in rainfed RIFA. The effective management of in-situ soil moisture through following of resource conservation practices can help in mitigating the terminal drought and heat stress in pulses (Kumar *et al.*, 2016a). Thus, resource conservation technologies (RCTs) that helps in maintaining soil moisture for longer period by preventing transpiration loss of soil water and improve soil health (SOC, chemical and bio-physical properties) could be a strategic approach to increase yield of pulses in RIFA. Besides supplementing fertilizers, retention of rice residue in ZT improves soil properties and thereby increasing productivity and nutrients use efficiency (Kumar *et al.*, 2014b).

Singh *et al* (2017) reported higher soil moisture conservation under retention of 30 cm rice stubble in rice+lathyrus relay cropping in comparison of farmers practice of retaining 15 cm stubble under rainfed RIFA of Eastern Plateau of India. However, from rainfed RIFA of Eastern India, retention of 20 cm rice stubble in rice+lentil relay cropping system resulted in higher soil moisture storage for an extended period of crop growth that further enhanced nodulation, BNF, plant physiological parameters in lentil (RLWC, LAI and chlorophyll content) and grain yield (11 % higher under 20 cm stubble over 10 cm stubble). Similar results were also reported with retention of 30 cm rice stubble in rice+urdbean relay cropping in black cotton soil of rainfed RIFA in Sothern Peninsular India (Singh *et al.*, 2017).

Sowing of pulses immediately after harvest of rice crop is essential to utilize residual soil moisture in RIFA (Kumar *et al.*, 2014a). Thus, the following of minimum and no-tillage prevents moisture loss due to tillage operation and time, and advances the sowing time of pulses by at least a week. Kar and Kumar (2009) reported that in rice fallows of eastern region, reduced tillage (RT) can increase the pulses (lathyrus, urdbean, field pea and mungbean) yield by 33–44% over conventional tillage (CT). Further, they reported higher soil moisture conservation under reduced tillage over no-tillage.The higher yield of pulses under reduced tillage under rainfed eastern India was also reported by Mahata *et al* (1992) and Ghosh *et al.* (2010). Kumar *et al* (2012) reported higher soil moisture and chickpea yield in RIFA under zero-tillage and rice residue mulch. In a multi-location field experiment at Kanpur (Uttar Pradesh), Kalyani (West Bengal), Raipur (Chhattisgarh), Barapani (Meghalaya) and Aduthurai (Tamil Nadu) revealed that rice residue/ stubble (20-30 cm) retention and zero tillage maintained higher soil moisture for longer period of crop growth which resulted in higher yield of pulse crops in different agro-ecologies of RIFA (Singh *et al.*, 2017). Bandyopadhyay *et al* (2016) reported 19 and 14% more yield and 25 and 15% more water use efficiency (WUE) in lentil under zero-tillage and residue mulching over ZT-stubble and zero-tillage in RIFA of Eastern India.In NEH region, no-till cultivation along with residue retention (5 t/ha) or 40 cm stubble gave higher yield of lentil under RIFA (Das *et al.*, 2013). Mishra *et al* (2016) reported that retaining 30% rice residues on soil surface and ZT sowing with Happy Seeder increased yields of succeeding lentil and chickpea by 3.1 and 11.7%, respectively. Further, relay cropping performed better than ZT (with or without mulch), and produced the maximum seed yield due to advantage of early sowing and better utilization of residual soil moistures.

5.2 Crop and variety selection

Selection of pulse crop is decided by growing period, climatic condition, soil type and local food habit. However, variety selection is depends on duration (early maturing), disease & insect-pest resistance and resistance to abiotic stresses. Sometimes, local situations like time of rice harvest and soil moisture decide the crop selection such as in Bolangir, Keonjhar, Sundargarh, Khurda, Boudh, Jharsuguda, Nayagarh, Angul, Kalahandi, Nuapada, Mayurbhanj, Koraput, Bargarh, Deogarh districts of Odisha, if rice crop is harvested late (December) then mungbean and urdbean taken and if crop harvested early in the month of October or November and soil moisture is proper then lathyrus, lentil and chickpea are taken in RIFA. Based on the above limiting factors, mungbean and urdbean are grown in RIFA in Southern Peninsular region (Tamil Nadu, Karnataka and Andhra Pradesh) and lathyrus, lentil, chickpea and pea are taken in Central, Eastern and NEH regions. Based on the local food habit, urdbean is preferred over mungbean in Sothern Peninsular region. Similarly, small seeded lentil is preferred in Eastern India and chickpea in central India. Some parts of Chhattisgarh, Jharkhand, Bihar and West Bengal lathyrus is preferred crop of RIFA due to their hardiness against abiotic and biotic stresses and use of green leaves and pods for vegetable purpose. Since RIFA is rainfed, hence varieties with early crop vigour are more suitable than medium and late vigour.

The development of first powdery mildew resistance and high yielding variety of urdbean LBG 17 has revolutionised the cultivation of RIFA in Southern Peninsula. Similarly, development of mungbean yellow mosaic virus (MYMV) resistance variety 'LBG 752' has further increased its adoption in RIFA in this region. Some of the urdbean varieties developed for RIFA in this region are LBG-402, LBG-611, LBG-22, LBG-648, LBG-685, LBG-645, LBG-709 and LBG-752 for timely sowing (mid- November to mid-December) and LBG-22, LBG-645, LBG-685 and LBG-752 are for late planting (second fortnight of December). The recommended varieties of mungbean for normal planting are LGG-460, LGG-410, LGG-450, LGG-407 andIM 96-3 (NAAS, 2013).

In RIFA of Eastern India, small seeded and rust resistance varieties of lentil WBL 77, KLS 218, PL 8, NM 1, IPL 220 and DPL15 are recommended. In a2 years of studyin West Bengal,lentil varieties L 4710 and IPL 534 were recorded better yield than other tested varieties (Ghosh *et al.*, 2019). Similarly chickpea varieties like Pusa372, PG 186 and Udai are recommended for this region. However, small seeded chickpea varieties like JSC 55, JSC 56, JG 14,Vijay, JG 315, JAKI 9218 and SAKI 9516 are recommended for cultivation under RIFA in central India. Kumar *et al.* (2014) reported higher yield of chickpea varieties JAKI 9218 (early high biomass) over DCP 92-3 (medium high biomass). Low ODAP (neurotoxin) containing varieties of lathyrus Ratan, Mahateora and Prateek are recommended for cultivation under RIFA in Central and Eastern India (NAAS, 2013). Short duration (about 100 days) varieties of pea with erect growth habit like Prakash and Vikash are found more suitable than other varieties. Das *et al* (2017) from a study in NEH region reported Arkel, VL-42, MUD P 15, IPFD 4-6, IPFD 1-01 and IPFD 99-13 were suitable pea varieties in RIFA.

Similar to pulses, selection of rice varieties is also important. Short or medium duration high yielding varieties of rice are recommended under RIFA in Central and Eastern India, whereas, long duration varieties in Southern India. The main reason of selection of long duration rice varieties in southern India is higher tillering and biomass production which helps in conserving soil moisture for succeeding winter pulse crop. Long duration varieties of rice are also recommended in lowland areas in Eastern India where excessive soil moisture remains till November-December. However, early/medium high yielding rice varieties and early maturing with early high biomass producing pulse varieties are found suitable combinations for most of the RIFA.

5.3 Planting technique & plant population management

Maintaining optimum plant population is foremost important for obtaining higher yield in rainfed RIFA. In general, 25% higher seed rate is recommended in RIFA for maintaining proper plant population. Broadcasting of pulses seed at 1-2 week before rice harvest is a common traditional practice in rice+pulse relay cropping in different agro-ecologies of RIFA in the country. However, young seedling damage is observed during harvest of rice either manually or by using combine harvester. In case of combine harvesting, seedlings damage by mainly due to movement of combine harvester wheels. This problem can be overcomes by two ways, i) broadcasting of seed at 4-5 days before rice harvest and ii) sowing of pulses just after harvest of rice by using ZT-seed drill.

In rice-pulse system in RIFA, sowing of pulses just after rice harvest by following of conservation tillage (ZT+residue retention as 20 cm stubble or mulch) observed to be beneficial than sowing under ZT or conventional tillage (Kumar *et al.*, 2020a). Mishra *et al* (2016) reported higher yield of pulses under ZT+mulch over ZT alone. Kumar *et al* (2013) reported higher yield of chickpea when sowing was done by dibbling method under zero tillage and mulching.

5.4 Seed priming

Seed priming is one of the low-cost technologies to obtain higher yield of crops under rainfed agro-ecosystems. In this process, seeds are soaked (6-8 hours) in water or nutrient solution before sowing which improves/fasten the germination and seedling vigour. Solaimalai and Subburamu (2004) reported seed priming with KH_2PO_4,/Na_2HPO_4/water improves seed germination, seedling vigor and early root growth which resulted in better crop establishment and drought tolerance, and finally higher crop yield. Bhowmick *et al* (2014) from a trial at Murshidabad, West Bengal reported seed priming of lathyrus with 2% KH_2PO_4 recorded higher seed yield under relay cropping in RIFA. Similar results were also recorded in urdbean under RIFA in Tamil Nadu (Singh *et al.*, 2017).

5.5 Rice cultivation practices

The cultivation practices followed in rice has direct effect on succeeding winter season pulses. The traditional method of puddling for taking transplanted rice is beneficial for rice yield, but the disturbed soil structure has negative effect on pulses establishment and root/ nodulation growth. However, the intact soil structure under direct seeded rice (DSR) has favourable effect of succeeding pulse crops. Kumar *et al.* (2018a) reported significantly higher yield of chickpea and lentil under ZT-DSR than that of unpuddled transplanted rice (UPTR) and puddle transplanted rice (PTR). In a study at Raipur, Chhattisgarh and Kalyani, West Bengal has shown that winter season pulses performed better under PTR, while at Kanpur, Uttar Pradesh higher yield of pulse crop was recorded under ZT-DSR.

5.6 Nutrient management

No or less use of fertilizer nutrients in pulses is one of the major constraints in poorproductivity of pulses grown in rainfed RIFA. Further, due to monoculture of rice in RIFA, deficiency of several major and micro-nutrients has been observed which causes yield loss of pulses. Thus, location specific soil test based nutrient management strategies need to be followed. Pulses, in general, need good amount of P for root growth that supports nodulation and N-fixation. Sulphur is also required by pulses for protein synthesis. Therefore, system based P& S management strategies need to be developed. Venkatesh *et al* (2019) reported combined application of fertilizer P and FYM had a strong positive impact on soil available-P, soil biochemical properties, P acquisition and crop productivity. Bandyopadhyay *et al* (2016a) reported that application of 10 tonnes/ha FYM along with recommended fertilizers to kharif rice crop increased the yield of lentil.

Micronutrients (Zn, Mo, Fe etc) deficiencies are also becoming common in RIFA soils. Mo deficiency is more commonly observed in acid soils which can be overcome either by liming or seed treatment with Mo solution. Foliar application of micronutrients also found effective under rainfed conditions of RIFA. Seed pelleting with micronutrients can be also recommended.

Soil moisture deficit stress is commonly observed at flowering and pod development stages in pulses under RIFA that restrict the nutrients absorption and movement inside plants. Under such situation, foliar nutrition with 2% urea/DAP and micronutrients (Fe, Zn, Mo and B) may alleviate the soil moisture stress up to some extent. The study at Kanpur revealed that foliar application of 2% urea combined with micronutrients at flowering and early pod development stages increased the pulses yield significantly under RIFA. Sarkar and Malik (2001) reported that foliar spray of KNO_3 and $Ca(NO_3)_2$ at0.5% significantly improved the lathyrus yield in RIFA of eastern India. Similarly, foliar application of diammonium phosphate (DAP) or urea in pre-flowering stage enhances productivity of pulses (Layek *et al.*, 2014).

Biofertilizers is emerging as an economically attractive and ecologically sound means of fertilization especially under rainfed pulses. Besides improving soil health, biofertilizer also reduce the amount of chemical fertilizer. Pulses fix atmospheric-N in symbiotic association with root nodulating *Rhizobium*. Therefore, pulses seed inoculation with *Rhizobium* and PGPRs are an effective and economical approach of N-management in pulse crops in RIFA.

5.7 Lifesaving irrigation

Soil moisture deficit stress is most commonly observed at different crop stages in variable intensities in RIFA which affect pulses yield to a great extent i.e., sometimes complete crop failure. Under such situation, application of life saving irrigation at critical crop growth stages will help the crop plants to complete the life cycle and thus, reasonable yields can be expected. Therefore, water harvesting ponds need to be constructed at farm or community level for collecting of excessive rainfall runoff water during rainy season for providing irrigation in winter season pulses during water deficit situation. The stored water can be economically used through micro-irrigation (sprinkler/drip). The land used for construction of pond can be compensated by increased yields (20-30%).

5.8 Weed management

One of the key concerns for successful cultivation of pulses in RIFA is weed menace. Weeds compete with crop plants in RIFA for limited resources like soil moisture and nutrients (Kumar *et al.*, 2016b). In general, winter pulses are poor competitor of weeds. However, application of pre-emergence herbicide like pendimethalin is not possible in case of rice + pulse relay cropping system. The limitation of effective weed management under such situation is mainly due to lack of good post-emergence herbicide and higher cost of manual weeding. The early post-emergence application of quizalofop-ethyl can control grassy weeds in winter pulses. However, imazethapyr 100 g/ha can be used as post-emergence herbicide in urdbean and mungbea for effective management of all kinds of weeds. Whereas in case of rice-pulse system, application of pre-emergence herbicide pendimethalin 1.0 kg/ha followed by quialofop-ethyl as early post-emergence can be recommended for effective weed control. Glyphosate 1.0 kg/ha either before or after sowing of pulses under ZT can kill all kind of existing weeds present after rice harvest including ratooning of rice stubble.

Re-growth or ratooing of rice stubble is major problem in almost all RIFAs. Ratooning starts just after harvest of rice and within a week, new narrow leaves emerged out from the apparently dry rice stubbles. The new leaves emerged from rice stubbles utilize soil moisture and nutrients. This may cause soil moisture loss up to 25% apart from considerable uptake of plant nutrients. In case of rice + pulse relay cropping, application of quizalofop-ethyl or imazethapyr can be used to contain the rice ratoons. However, in case of rice-pulse system, non-selective herbicide glyphosate 1.0 kg/ha applied either before or after sowing of pulses under zero tillage or application of post-emergence quizalofop-ethyl. Besides herbicide option, some of the rice varieties like, IET 4786 with no or minimal ratooning habit could also be viable option to contain rationing in rice under RIFAs.

5.9 Pest management

The common diseases of pulses are mentioned in previous section (Table 3). Location specific problem based integrated pest management (IPM) strategies need to followed for effective and economical management of diseases and insect-pests in pulses under rainfed RIFA. The IPM module should include use of disease resistant varieties, seed treatment with fungicide and bio-control agent *Trichoderma*, use of plant based pesticides and chemical pesticides. The development of first powdery mildew resistance varieties LBG 17 with high yield potential (1.5 t/ha) has drastically increased the area of urdbean under RIFA in southern peninsula (Satyanarayana *et al*., 1997). Similarly, rust resistant and small seeded lentil varieties WBL 77, IPL 220, KLS 218, NM 1 and DPL15 have been found promising in eastern and NEH regions. The development of low ODAP content varieties of lathyrus viz., Ratan, Parteek and Mahateora have increased its cultivation under RIFA in central and eastern India.

To control the seed borne diseases, seed should be treated with *Trichoderma*+carboxin or alternately carbendazim + thiram for root rot, color rot and wilt. Sucking pest of urdbean, mungbean and lentil can be managed by application of systemic insecticides like imidacloprid and to control the podborer bird perches, spray of nuclear polyhedrosis virus (NPV), chemical pesticides at economic threshold level (ETL) can be used.

6. CONCLUSION

To meet the vegetable protein requirement of burgeoning population, country needs 39.0 Mt pulses by 2050. The larger area (11.7 M ha) exist in RIFA provides an opportunities for horizontal area expansion of pulses in the country. Pulses, being hardy and low inputs requiring crop, most suitable candidate crops in winter fallow under rainfed RIFA. The major constraints exist in RIFA are soil moisture deficit stress (drought) and lack of irrigation facilities. But, these can be utilized for cultivation of winter pulses by following of improved production technology. The main technological interventions required in RIFA are soil moisture conservation, early maturing varieties with resistant to multiple diseases, life saving irrigation, seed priming, foliar nutrition, use of biofertilizers, biopesticides, etc (Fig 3). The strengthening of extension system and policy support along with technological back-up are needed for sensitization of farmers for cultivation of pulses in RIFA. The country will achieve self sufficiency in pulses production andnutritional security, if one-third area of RIFA (4.0 M ha) is utilized for pulses cultivation.

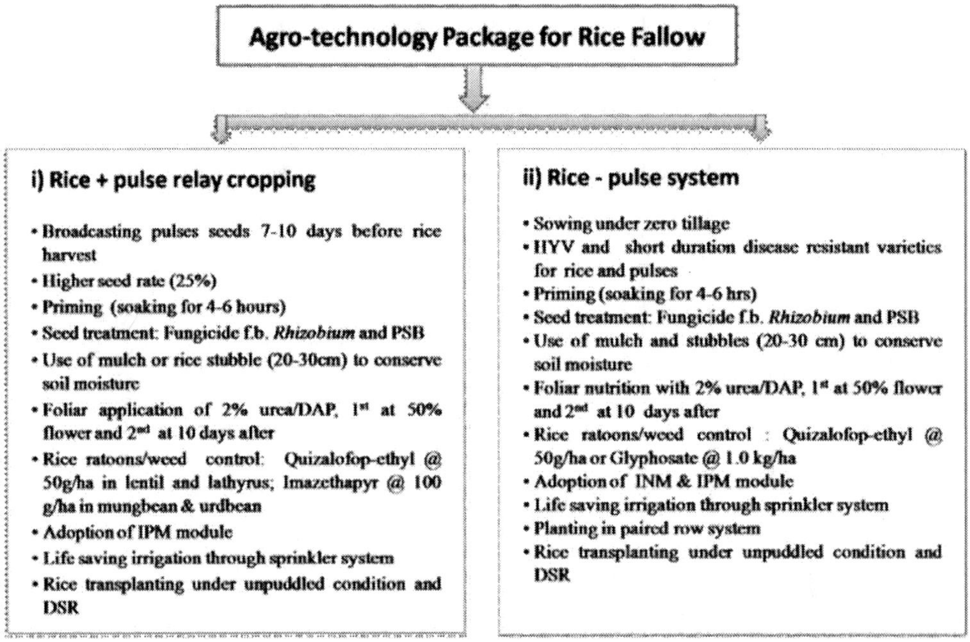

Fig. 3. Package and practices for pulses cultivation in RIFA

7. WAY FORWARD

The concerted research, extension and policy interventions are needed for utilization of potential of RIFA for pulses cultivation. The following areas need to be addressed in future:

(i) Quantification of residual soil moisture and drying pattern of soil profile moisture is required for estimation of available growing period in RIFA under different agro-ecological regions of the country.

(ii) Need to assess the changes in soil bio-physical properties due to rice cultivation practices and their effect on pulses performance (seed germination, seedling vigour, root growth, nodulation, etc).

(iii) Production technologies need to be developed for optimum plant population management, especially under rice+pulse relay cropping.

(iv) Location and situation specific short duration and multiple biotic and abiotic stresses resistant pulses varieties need to be developed for rainfed RIFA.

(v) Mapping of RIFA is required on the basis of plant nutrients deficiencies in soils to develop nutrient management strategies.

(vi) System based complete package and practices (rice and pulses) need to be developed for efficient utilization of locally available resources.

(vii) Based on prevailing diseases and insect-pests, IPM modules should be developed.

(viii) Poor mechanization is bottleneck in maintaining proper plant population. Therefore, location specific machineries need to be developed for sowing in present of rice stubble or residue in RIFA.

(ix) Extension systems need to be strengthen for fast and effective dissemination of improved production technologies among poor farmers of RIFA.

(x) Policy interventions are required for timely availability of quality seeds and other inputs, construction of community pond for runoff storage, measures to protect crops stray cattle or wild animals, rural credit facilities, etc.

REFERENCES

Bandyopadhyay, P.K., Singh, K.C., Mondal, K., Nath, R., Kumar, N. and Singh, S.S. (2016a) Effect of balanced fertilization in puddled rice on the Productivity of lentil in rice- fallow system under zero tillage. *Bangladesh Agronomy Journal* 19(1), 67-79.

Bandyopadhyaya, P.K., Singh, K.C., Mondal, K., Nath, R., Ghosh, P.K., Kumar, N., Basu, P.S. and S.S. Singh. (2016) Effects of stubble length of rice in mitigating soil moisture stress and on yield of lentil (*Lens culinaris* Medik) in rice-lentil relay crop. *Agricultural Water Management* 173, 91–102.

Bhowmick, M.K., Dhara, M.C., Duary, B., Biswas, P.K. and Bhattacharyya, P. (2014) Improvement of lathyrus productivity through seed priming and foliar nutrition under rice–*utera* system. *Journal of Crop and Weed* 10, 277–80.

Das, A., Chowdhury, S., Layek, J., Ramkrushna, G.I., Panwar, A.S., Ngachan, S.V. and Buragohain, J. (2017) Agro-physical assessment of different pea (*Pisum sativum*) cultivars in lowland rice (*Oryza sativa*) fallow under no–till system for enhancing cropping intensity and productivity in mid hills of northeast India.*Indian Journal of Agricultural Sciences* 87, 1612–8.

Das, A., Ramkrushna, G.I., Nagchan, S.V. and Munda, G.C. (2013) Resource conservation technologies in pulse-based cropping system in NEH region. (In) *Resource Conservation Technology in Pulses*, pp 43–57. Ghosh P K, Kumar N, Venkatesh M S, Hazra K K and Nadarajan N (Eds). Scientific Publishers, Jodhpur, Rajasthan, India.

DES. (2020) Agricultural Statistics at a Glance 2019. Directorate of Economics & Statistics, Department of Agriculture and Cooperation and Farmers Welfare, Ministry of Agriculture and Farmers Welfare, Government of India. Pp. 315.

Dubey, S.K., Sah, U. and Singh, S.K. (2011) Impact of climate change in pulse productivity and adaptation strategies as practiced by the pulse growers of Bundelkhand region of Utter Pradesh. *Journal of Food Legume* 24, 230–234.

Ghosh, P.K., Das, A., Saha, R., Enboklang, K., Tripathi, A.K., Munda, G.C. and Ngachan, S.V. (2010) Conservation agriculture towards achieving food security in North East India. *Current Science* 99, 915–21.

Ghosh, A.,Reja, M.H, Nalia, A., Mukherjee, B., Nath, R. and Sarker, A. (2019) Evaluation of extra early lentil varieties in rice-fallow areas of West Bengal. *The Pharma Innovation Journal* 8(4), 312-314.

Gumma, M.K., Thenkabail, P.S., Teluguntla, P., Rao, M.N., Mohammed, I.A. and Whitbread, A.M. (2016) Mapping rice fallow cropland areas for short-season grain legumes intensification in South Asia using MODIS 250 m time-series data. *International Journal of Digital Earth* 9(10), 981-1003.

Gunes, A., Inal, A., Adak, M.S., Bagci, E.G., Cicek, N. and Araslan, F. (2008) Effect of drought stress implemented at pre- or post-anthesis stage on some physiological parameters as screening criteria in chickpea cultivars. *Journal of Plant Physiology* 55(1), 59-67.

Jagadev, P.N., Garnayak, L.M., Paikaray, R.K., Sahu, S, Rath, B.S. and Sahoo, S.C. (2016) OUAT strategies for pulse production in rice fallows of Odisha.Orissa University of Agriculture and Technology Bhubaneswar 751003, Odisha. 32 pages.

Kalra, N., Chakraborty, D., Sharma, A., Rai, H.K., Jolly, M., Chander, S., Kumar, P.R., Bhadraray, S., Barman, D., Mittal, R.B., Lal, M. and Sehgal, M. (2008) Effect of temperature on yield of some winter crops in northwest India. *Current Science* 94, 82–88.

Kar, G. and Kumar, A. (2009) Evaluation of post-rainy season crops with residual soil moisture and different tillage methods in rice–fallow of eastern India. *Agricultural Water Management* 96, 931–8.

Kumar, N., Ghosh, P.K., Singh, M.K., Hazra, K.K. and Venkatesh, M.S. (2013) Boost rice-fallows chickpea production system in India through suitable soil moisture conservation practices. Proceedings of the 100th Session of the Indian Science Congress: Section –Agriculture and Forestry Sciences; 100th Indian Science Congress 3-7 January, 2013, Kolkata. pp. 223.

Kumar, N., Nath, C.P., Hazra, K.K. and Sharma, A.R. (2016b) Efficient weed management in pulses for higher productivity and profitability. *Indian Journal of Agronomy* 61 (4th IAC Special Issue), S93-105.

Kumar, N., Singh, S.S., Ghosh, P.K., Praharaj, C.S., Basu, P.S., Hazra, K.K., Senthilkumar, M. and Singh, M.K. (2016a) Mitigating abiotic stresses in pulses under rice fallows in India. Extended Summaries Vol. 1: 4th International Agronomy Congress, Sec: Abiotic and Biotic (Weeds) Stress Management, Nov. 22–26, 2016, New Delhi, India. Pp. 370-371.

Kumar, N., Singh, M.K., Ghosh, P.K. and Hazra, K.K. (2012) Soil moisture conservation in chickpea through tillage and mulching in rice fallows. Extended Summaries: 3rd International Agronomy Congress on "Agriculture Diversification, Climate Change Management and Livelihoods", New Delhi, November 26-30, 2012. Vol. 3: pp 916-817.

Kumar, N., Singh, S.S., Ghosh, P.K., Hazra, K.K., Venkatesh, M.S., Praharaj, C.S., Singh, M.K., SenthilKumar, M., Basu, P.S., Yadav, A., Yadav, S.L., Singh, S. and Singh, N.P. (2020a) Improving chickpea productivity in rice-fallow of Indo-Gangetic Plain with soil moisture conservation and cultivar selection.*Journal of Food Legumes* 33(1), 28-35.

Kumar, N., Singh, S.S., Ghosh, P.K., Basu, P.S., Singh, M.K., Venkatesh, M.S., Hazra, K.K., Praharaj, C.S., SenthilKumar, M., Yadav, S.K., Singh, S. and Yadav, A. (2014) Enhancing chickpea (*Cicer arietinum*) productivity through conservation practices under rainfed rice-fallow regions of India. "Extended Summaries of Voluntary Papers" of National Symposium on "Agricultural Diversification for Sustainable livelihood and Environmental Security" November 18-20, 2014, Ludhiana, Punjab. Pp. 734-735.

Kumar, N., Hazra, K.K., Nath, C.P., Praharaj, C.S. and Singh, U. (2018b) Grain Legumes for Resource Conservation and Agricultural Sustainability in South Asia. In: Meena R., Das A., Yadav G., Lal R. (eds) Legumes for Soil Health and Sustainable Management. Springer, Singapore. PP. 77-107.

Kumar, N., Singh, M.K. and Singh, S. (2014a) Advances in resource conservation technology in pulse production system. In- Ghosh PK, Narendra Kumar, Venkatesh MS, Hazra KK and Nadarajan N (Ed.) Resource Conservation Technology in Pulses. Scientific Publisher, Jodhpur. Pp. 90-102.

Kumar, N., Singh, M.K. and Singh, S. (2014b) Residue management in pulse based cropping system under resource conservation technologies. In- Ghosh PK, Narendra Kumar, Venkatesh MS, Hazra KK and Nadarajan N (Ed.) Resource Conservation Technology in Pulses. Scientific Publisher, Jodhpur. Pp. 419-428.

Kumar, R. Mishra, J.S., Upadhyay, P.K. and Hans, H. (2018a) Rice fallows in the eastern India: Problems and prospects. *Indian Journal of Agricultural Sciences* 89 (4), 567–77.

Kumar, J., Kant, R., Kumar, S., Basu, P.S., Sarker, A. and Singh, N.P. (2016c) Heat tolerance in lentil under field conditions. *Legume Genomes Genet.* 7, 1–11.

Kumar, N., Gopinath, K.A., Srivastva, A.K. and Mahajan, V. (2008) Performance of pigeon pea (*Cajanus cajan* L. Millsp.) at different sowing dates in mid-hills of Indian Himalaya. *Archives of Agronomy and Soil Science* 54(5), 507-514.

Kumar, N., Singh, S.S., Ghosh, P.K., Singh, N.P., Agrawal, P.K., Hazra, K.K., Praharaj, C.S., Yadav, A., Yadav, S.L. and Singh, S. (2020) Issues and Strategies for Promotion of Pulses in Untapped Rice-fallow in India: A review. *Journal of Food Legumes* 33(3): 139-150.

Kumar, N., Yadav, A., Singh, S. and Yadav, S.L. (2018) Growing Pulses in Rice Fallow: Ensuring Nutritional Security in India. In Anup Das *et al* (eds). Conservation Agriculture for Advancing Food Security in Changing Climate. Today & Tomorrow's Printers and Publishers, New Delhi. Vol. 1 (2018): 107-122.

Kumar, N., Hazra, K.K., Singh, S. and Nadarajan, N. (2016) Constraints and prospects of growing pulses in rice fallows of India. *Indian Farming* 66(6), 13-16.

Layek, J., Chowdhary, S., Ramkrushna, G.I. and Das, A. (2014) Evaluation of different lentil cultivars in lowland rice fallow under no–till system for enhancing cropping intensity and productivity. *Indian Journal of Hill Farming* 27(2), 4–9.

Mahata, K.R., Sen, H.S. and Pradhan, S.K. (1992) Tillage effects on growth and yield of blackgram and cowpea after wet season rice on an alluvial sandy clay loam in eastern India. *Field Crops Research* 11, 55–68.

Mishra, J.S., Kumar, R., Kumar, R., Rao, K.K., Singh, S.K., Idris, M., Jha, B.K., Naik, S.K., Mali, S.S. and Bhatt, B.P. (2016) Evaluation of pulses and oilseed under different crop establishment methods in rice-fallows of Eastern India. Extended Summaries Vol.2.4th International Agronomy Congress, Nov.22–26, 2016, New Delhi, India. pp 1272–4.

NAAS. (2013) Improving productivity of rice fallows. Policy Paper No. 64, National Academy of Agricultural Sciences, New Delhi, 16 p.

Nadarajan, N. and Kumar, N. (2018) Role of Pulses in Conservation Agriculture. In: Singh V.K. and Gangwar B. (Eds.) System Based Conservation Agriculture, Westville Publishing House, New Delhi. pp 134-154.

Pande, S., Bourai, V.A., Neupane, R.K. and Joshi, P.K. (2003) Chickpea Production Constraints and Promotion of integrated Pest Management in Nepal. On –farm IPM of Chickpea in Nepal-1. Information bulletin no. 64. Patancheru, 502 324, Andhra Pradesh, India. International Crops Research Institutes for the Semi-Arid Tropics (CRISTAT), Department for International Development (DFID). pp 4-8. ISBN 92-9066-462-2.

Rai, R. (1991) Effects of soil acidity factors on interaction of chickpea (*Cicer arietinum* L.) genotypes and Rhizobium strains: Symbiotic N-fixation, grain quality and grain yield in acid soils. In: Wright R.J., Baligar V.C., Murrmann R.P. (eds) Plant-Soil Interactions at Low pH. Developments in Plant and Soil Sciences, vol 45. Springer, Dordrecht. https://doi.org/10.1007/978-94-011-3438-5_70.

Ramesh, T. and Rathika, S. (2015) Weed Management in Rice Fallow Black Gram through Post-Emergence Herbicides. *Madras Agricultural Journal* 102(10-12), 313-316.

Rao, A.S. and Kiran, G.G.S. (2014) Studies on composition of weed flora in rice fallow blackgram in Krishna zone of Andhra Pradesh. *Journal of Research ANGRAU* 42(3&4), 18-20.

Roy, A., Aich, S.S., Bhowmick, M.K. and Biswas, P.K. (2009) Response of lentil varieties to sowing time in the plains of West Bengal. *Journal of Crop and Weed* 5(2), 92-94.

Sarkar, R.K. and Malik, G.C. (2001) Effect of foliar spray of potassium nitrate and calcium nitrate on grass pea (*Lathyrus sativus* L.) grown in rice fallows. *Lathyrus Lathyrism Newsletter* 2, 47–53.

Satyanarayana, A., Seenaiah, P, SudhakaraBabu, K. and Prasada Rao, M.P. (1997) Extending pulses area and production in rice fallows. In Asthana, A.N. and Ali, Masood (Eds) Recent Advances in Pulses Research, pp. 569–558.Indian Institute of Pulses Research (ICAR), Kanpur, Uttar Pradesh, India.

Sen, S., Ghosh, M., Mazumdar, D., Saha, B. and Dolui, S. (2016) Effect of sowing date and variety on phenology and yieldof lentil during *rabi* season. *Journal of Crop and Weed*12(1), 135-138.

Singh, S,S,, Kumar, N., Praharaj, C.S. and Singh, N.P. (2017). Agro-technologies for enhancing pulses production in rice fallows. ICAR-Indian Institute of Pulses Research, Kanpur - 208 024 (Uttar Pradesh), India.36 pages.

Singh, T.P., Deshmukh, P.S. and Nagar, R.V.S. (2011) Effect of sowing time of chickpea on its yield and plant growth in North-western parts of India. *Bhartiya Vaigyanik Evam Prodhogik Anushandhan Patrika* 19(1), 31-35.

Solaimalai, A. and Subburamu, K. (2004) Seed hardening for field crops–A review. *Agricultural Reviews* 25, 129–40.

Subbarao, G.V., Kumar Rao, J.V.D.K., Kumar, J., Johansen, C., Deb, U.K., Ahmed, I., Krishna Rao, M.V., Venkataratnam, L., Hebbar, K.R., Sai, M.V.S.R., and Harris, D. (2001) Spatial distribution and quantification of rice-fallows in South Asia – potential for legumes. International Crops Research Institute for the Semi-Arid Tropics, Patancheru, India.

Upadhaya, H.D., Dronavalli, N.,Gowda, C.L.L. and Singh, S. (2011) Identification and evaluation of chickpea germplasam for tolerance to heat stress. *Crop Science* 51, 2079–2094.

Varshney, R., Thudi, M., Nayak, S., Gaur, P., Kashiwagi, J., Krishnamurthy, L., Jaganathan, D., Koppolu, J., Bohra, A., Tripathi, S., Rathore, A., Jukanti, A.K., Jayalaxmi, V., Vemula, A., Singh S.J., Yasin, M., Sheshshayee, M.S. and Viswanatha, K.P. (2013) Genetic dissection of drought tolerance in chickpea (*Cicer arietinum* L.). *Theoretical and Applied Genetics* 127, 1-18.

Venkatesh, M.S., Hazra, K.K., Ghosh, P.K. and Singh, M. (2019) Integrated phosphorus management in maize–chickpea cropping system on alkaline Fluvisol. *Nutrient Cycling in Agroecosystems*113, 141–156

Wang, J., Gan, Y.T., Clarke, F. and McDonald, C.L. (2006) Response of chickpea yield to high temperature stress during reproductive development. *Crop Science* 46, 2171–2178.

CHAPTER 16

Role of pulse crop green manuring on soil health and agricultural sustainability

M.A. Ansari[1]*, Anup Das[2], M.H. Ansari[3], S.K. Sharma[1], S.S. Roy[1] and Narendra Kumar[4]

1. *ICAR Research Complex for NEH Region, Manipur Centre, Lamphelpat, Imphal- 795004*
2. *ICAR Research Complex for NEH Region, Tripura Centre, Lembucherra- 799 210*
3. *Guest Teacher, Faculty of Agricultural Science, Aligarh Muslim University, Aligarh*
4. *ICAR-Indian Institute of Pulses Research, Kanpur-208 024, Uttar Pradesh*

*Corresponding author email: merajiari@gmail.com

Abstract

Pulses have symbiotic relationship with terrestrial pool and considered as the architect of soil fertility. Pulses fix atmospheric nitrogen; solubilize phosphates and add the essential nutrients into the soil. At the same time, pulses especially green manure pulses playing important role in reducing the burden of synthetic fertilizer application in agriculture and ultimately reducing the risk of soil and water pollution. Reduction of water pollution due to synthetic fertilizers improves the aquatic and terrestrial biodiversity and combating and building resilience to climate change. It is fact that organic manure application either by conventional mulching or green manuring has declined over the years due to various operational constraints. Legumes which were cultivated on large areas during the 1960s and 1970s have now been virtually eliminated from cereal-based systems, and all this has led to serious consequences on soil fertility. Despite their great potential for making significant N contributions and improving productivity, the adoption of legumes in many parts of South Asia and Africa is poor due to wide range of physical and socio-economic variables. Therefore, green manuring act as the restoration factory to maintain the soil fertility for sustainable agriculture. Green manure crops protect bare soil against erosion and improve physico-chemical and biological properties of soil. Therefore, the issue of soil health and agricultural sustainability can be mitigated to a great extent by growing different green manuring crops, which will improve the organic matter and micronutrients status of the soil and also go a long way with maintain soil health and sustainability.

Keywords: Agricultural sustainability, Green manuring, Pulses, Soil health

1. INTRODUCTION

Green manuring (GM) is gaining popularity as an approach that improves soil productivity and agricultural sustainability. Legumes/pulses are most popular for green manuring, though non-legumes are also used as GM crops. Green manuring is the ploughing under or soil incorporation of green manure crop, while they are green or soon after they start flowering and biomass is still tender. Green manures are mostly leguminous crops that are grown for their leafy materials needed for soil nutrient enrichment and conservation. Dual purpose legume crops grown as catch crops or intercrops like vegetable cowpea (*Vigna unguiculata*), greengram (*Vigna radiata*), blackgram (*Vigna mungo*), velvet bean (*Mucuna* spp) and vegetable ricebean (*Vigna umbellata*) not only provides economic produce but also generates N rich stover/haulms for incorporation in soil which are a viable alternative for effecting N economy, addition of other essential nutrients in soil and enhancing crop productivity and sustainability (Sharma and Behera, 2009; Ansari *et al.*, 2015). It is fact that pulses are the architect of the soil fertility and have symbiotic relationship with terrestrial pool. They fix atmospheric nitrogen; solubilize phosphates and add the essential nutrients in to the soil. Thus, pulses especially green manure pulses playing important role in reducing the burden of synthetic fertilizer application in agriculture and ultimately reducing the risk of soil and water pollution. Reduction of water pollution due to synthetic fertilizers improves the aquatic and terrestrial biodiversity and combating and building resilience to climate change. Biological nitrogen fixation is particularly important for global agricultural productivity and might be considered as one of the most important biological processes on the planet. It provides 100 million metric tonnes of N which leads to an annual saving of around USD10 billion in N fertilizers (Graham, 2008; Howieson *et al.*, 2008). Furthermore, the reduced need for (or use of) synthetic fertilizers indirectly reduces the amount of greenhouse gases released into the atmosphere. Incorporation of pulses GM into soil also promotes soil carbon sequestration and, ultimately, reduces soil erosion when grown as intercrop in farming systems and/or used as cover crops. Many studies have shown the great potential of green manure for supplying nutrients to crops (Adediran *et al.*, 2004; Sharma and Behera, 2009; Ansari *et al.*, 2015) and the improve soil physical, biological and chemical properties (Adediran *et al.*, 2004; Sharma and Behera, 2009; Das *et al.*, 2018). Organic matter is the basic components for building soil fertility and practices for increasing organic matter in soil always favors the sustainable productivity (Katyal *et al.* 2001; Behera *et al.* 2007). Incorporation of plant residues/pulses green manure is a useful ways to sustain and enrich in organic matter content and thereby enhance the biological activity, improve physical properties and increase nutrient availability (Min *et al.*, 2003; Sultani *et al.*, 2007; Yao *et al.*, 2006; Salazar *et al.*, 2011; Yuan *et al.*, 2012).

It is fact that organic manure application either by conventional mulching or green manuring has declined over the years due to various operational constraints. Legumes which were cultivated on large areas during the 1960s and 1970s have now been virtually eliminated from cereal-based systems, and all this has led to serious consequences on soil fertility. Despite their great potential for making significant N contributions and improving productivity, the adoption of legumes in many parts of South Asia and Africa is poor due to wide range of physical and socio-economic variables (Shah *et al.* 2003; Chikowo *et al.* 2006; Ojiem *et al.* 2007; Sharma and Behera, 2009). Retention of legume residues improves the N economy of the cropping system and enhances the crop productivity through the additional N and many other potential benefits such as reduce weed infestation (Ansari *et al.*, 2017a; 18) lower pests and disease incidence (Chalk 1998; Shah *et al.* 2003; Kirkegaard *et al.* 2008). It is not only desirable but quite possible to reduce the reliance on synthetic N fertilizers and move towards greater use of legumes to supply N for crop production. In fact, legume-based systems are likely to be more sustainable than cereal-based or fertilizer-based systems. Hence, comprehensive studies on role of green manuring on improving soil heath and sustainability are compiled in this chapter and suggested a low-cost eco-friendly technology for ensuring sustainable productivity.

2. GREEN MANURING

Green manuring is defined as incorporation of plant material into the soil while green or at maturity. For soil improvement, a green manure crop is any crop grown for the purpose of being turned under while green or soon after maturity for soil improvement (Soil Science Society of America, 1997). It is obtained in two ways: by growing green manure crops or by collecting green leaf (leaf, stem along with twigs) from plants grown in wastelands, field bunds and forest or brought from outside as cuttings of trees and shrubs. The latter practice is called green leaf manuring (Singh *et al.*, 1991). The term green fallow has been coined to describe a green-manure farming system that is typically used as partial fallow replacement in a wheat-fallow rotation (Pikul *et al.*, 1997). In this system, a legume is seeded early in the fallow year, grown to about full bloom, and killed by chemicals or tillage. An important aspect of this green fallow system is to balance water use for N_2-fixation with the water and N requirements of the subsequent wheat crop (Pikul *et al.*, 1997). Green manure crop is ready for incorporation into soil in 45-50 days after sowing and helps improves the production and productivity of the subsequent crops. Actually this period will be a good investment for the next two seasons of crops. In olden days the biomass was generated as 'off-farm' and 'on-farm'. The most popular legume green manure/dual purpose crops are Sesbania spp, cowpea, greengram, mungbean, ricebean etc.

2.1 Off-farm green manure

As an off-farm, the foliages from variety of species of the shrub and herb type of weeds that grow along the roadside, riverside and lake bunds are harvested and brought-in farm. The commonly used weeds are as follows: *Pungamia pinnata, Cassia auriculata, Calatropis gigantea, Ipomoea* sps, *Vitex negundo, Eichhornia* etc.

2.2 On-farm green manure

2.2.1 Tree green manure

Biomass from the farm can be generated from the legume or non-legume trees/shrubs that are grown along the boundaries of the farm and along the main bunds of the fields at a regular interval. While preparing the main fields for the next crop, the foliage from this tress are lopped and chopped into small pieces and then incorporated by hoeing in the garden lands and by puddling in the wet lands. The trees that can be grown for this purpose are: *Azadiracta indica, Pungamia pinnata, Glyricidia sps, Thespesia populina, Cassia seamia* etc.

2.2.2 Live fence and hedge rows

Some shrub species can be grown along the fence as live fence or as hedge rows along the pathways and waste patches. These life fences and the hedge rows can be trimmed-off whenever needed and used. The suitable shrubs are: *Vitex negundo, Nerrium thevitifolia, Adathoda vasica, Datura stramonium, Artemisia nilagirica* etc.

The non-legume supplies a large amount of energy (carbohydrate) material readily, but the bacteria responsible for the decay of this material must have access to N. If the N carried in the green manure crop isn't sufficient (that is, a C: N greater than 30:1, or less than 1.5%), the bacteria will draw on the available soil N and the newly grown crop will show a nitrogen deficiency symptom for some time.

2.3 Characteristics of legume green manure crops

- Short duration, fast growing, high nutrient accumulation ability
- Produces abundant and succulent shoots (foliages)
- Have a high rate of nitrogen fixation
- Have high water-use efficiency when used in drier regions
- Little water is required, while still producing substantial quantities of top-growth
- Wide ecological adaptability
- Timely release of nutrients
- Photoperiod insensitivity
- High seed production
- High seed viability
- Ease in incorporation
- Ability to cross-inoculate or responsive to inoculation
- Pest and disease resistant
- High N sinks in underground plant parts.

3. SIGNIFICANCE OF GREEN MANURING

3.1 Nitrogen fixation/sparing by legumes crops

About 21 Mt of atmospheric nitrogen is fixed by the legumes and 5-7 Mt nitrogen is returned in to the soil by pulses (Foyer *et al.*, 2016). Long term sustainable agriculture system demands must rely on the use and effective management of in-situ/ex-situ available resources. Most of the legumes/pulses play a significant role to fix the atmospheric nitrogen, which offer an economically feasible and ecologically sound means of reducing external nitrogen inputs dependency and improving the soil quality (Das *et al.*, 2018a; Kumar *et al.*, 2019). Biological nitrogen fixation can be a major source of N in agriculture when symbiotic N_2-fixing systems are used; the amount of N input fixed by legume crops are given in Table 1

Table 1. Estimates of N amount derived from symbiotic N_2 fixation for commonly grown food legumes in tropical and sub tropical systems

Common name	Location	Treatment variable	Scientific name	N fixed (kg N/ha)	Source
Cowpea	Brazil	Site/season	*Vigna unguiculata*	9-51	Boddey *et al.* (1990)
	Indonesia	Rotation		12-22	Sisworo *et al.* (1990)
	Kenya	Phosphorous		24-39	Ssali and Keya (1984)
Mungbean	Australia	--	*Vigna radiata*	34	Unkovich *et al.* (2010)
Pea	Australia	--	*Pisum sativum*	105	Unkovich *et al.* (2010)
Pigeonpea	India	season	*Cajanus cajan*	68-88	Kumar Rao *et al.* (1987)
Soybean	Brazil	Site/season	*Glycine max*	85-154	Boddey *et al.* (1990)
	Hawaii	Temperature		117-237	George *et al.* (1988)
	Indonesia	Rotation		26-33	Sisworo *et al.* (1990)
	Thailand	Cultivar		17-450	Rennie *et al.* (1988)
	Australia	--		180	Unkovich *et al.* (2010)
Lupine	Australia	--	*Lupinus albus*	130	Unkovich *et al.* (2010)
Groundnut	India	Cultivar	*Arachis hypogaea*	109-152	Giller *et al.* (1987)
	Brazil	Inoculation		68-116	Boddey *et al.* (1990)
Chickpea	Australia	--	*Cicer arietinum*	70	Unkovich *et al.* (2010)
Fababean	Australia	--	*Vicia faba*	110	Unkovich *et al.* (2010)
Lentil	Australia	--	*Lens culinaris*	58	Unkovich *et al.* (2010)

Source: Peoples and Craswell, 1992; Drew *et al.*, 2014

Pulses plays important role in nitrogen sparing/companion effect in either of vertical intensification (intercropping)/sequential cropping with cereals. Cereal + legume intercropping provides a great scope for minimizing the adverse impact of moisture and nutrient stress in addition to improving system productivity and soil health (Layek *et al.*, 2018). Stagnari *et al.*, (2017) reported that the nitrogen uptake of various crops increases between 23–59% after rotations with field pea and lupin. The N economy due to inclusion of pulses in sequential cropping is given below in the Table 2.

Table 2. N economy due to inclusion of pulses in sequential cropping

Preceding legume	Following cereal	Fertlizers N equivalent (kg N/ha)	Reference
Chickpea	Maize	60-70	Subbarao (1988)
	Pearl millet	40	Lee and Wani (1989)
Pigeonpea	Wheat	40	
	Maize	20-49	
	Pearl millet	30	
Lentil	Pearl millet	40	
	Maize	18-30	
Peas	Pearl millet	40	
	Maize	20-32	
Mungbean	Pearl millet	30	
Lathyrus	Maize	36-48	
Cowpea	Pearl millet	60	
Pigeonpea	Sorghum	51	Ali (1984-87)
Mungbean	Rice	40	
Chickpea	Rice	40	
Rajmash	Rice	40	
Fodder cowpea	Rice	40	

Source: Das *et al.*, 2018b

3.2 Nutrient content and accumulation by incorporation of green manure crops into soil

The green manure crops are rich source of nutrients (primary, secondary and micronutrients). Leguminous crop residues return up to 5 times more nitrogen into soil than non leguminous crop residues due to high concentration of N. The C: N ratio of legume green manure crops varied from crop to crop (Cowpea: 13.9, Soybean: 17.9, *Sesbania*: 11.8, *Gliricidia*: 13.6, *Leaucaena*: 12.4 etc.) (Clement *et al.*, 1998; Dinesh and Dubey, 1998). Nutrient contents (%) of some commonly used green manure crops and crop residues in South and South East Asia are given in Table 3.

Table 3. Nutrient content in residues of pulse green manure crops

Common name	Scientific name	N (%)	P (%)	K (%)	Source
Dhaincha	*Sesbania sp.*	2.51	0.40	0.76	Timsina (2018a & b); BARC (2012)
Cowpea	*Vigna unguiculata*	0.70	0.15	0.95	
Mungbean	*Vigna radiata*	0.80	0.20	0.95	
Blackgram	*Vigna mungo*	0.80	0.20	0.95	

Pea	*Pisum sativum*	2.09-2.89	0.12-0.20	1.50-2.17	Wutke *et al.* (2009); Valadares *et al.* (2016)
Vetch	*Vicia sativa*	0.1-0.4	2.1-2.6	0.9-1.1	
Pigeonpea	*Cajanus cajan*	1.3-3.4	0.1-0.3	0.5-2.8	
Lab lab	*Dolichos lab lab*	1.4-5.0	0.1-1.2	0.5-2.8	
Leucaena	*Leucaena leucocephala*	3.2-4.4	0.2-0.3	1.0-1.9	
Velvet bean	*Mucuna nívea*	1.6-2.7	0.2-0.6	1.0-1.5	
Soybean	*Glycine max*	0.4-4.0	0.2-0.3	1.1-1.8	
Grasspea	*Lathyrus sativus*	2.2-3.3	0.1-0.3	2.9-3.0	
Lupine	*Lupinus albus*	1.2-2.0	0.1-0.3	1.0-2.7	
Groundnut	*Arachis hypogaea*	1.76	0.27	2.68	Mubarak *et al.* (2002)

The most frequently cited reasons (Fox *et al.*, 1990; Hatch *et al.*, 1991) for greater N mineralization in soils under legume or grass legume mixture have been more easily decomposable material, low C/N and lignin/N ratios, low (lignin + polyphenol)/N ratio, and higher litter contribution from legumes compared with grasses (Gil and Fick, 2001). Becker *et al* (1994) identified the lignin to N (L/N) ratio as a significant factor controlling N release in green manure crops. Carbon to N ratio of green manure or crop residue incorporated into the soil play an important role in the release or immobilization of soil N because plant tissue is a primary source and sink for C and N. When plant residues having C/N ratio greater than 20 are incorporated into the soil, available soil N is immobilized during the first few weeks of decomposition (Doran and Smith, 1991; Dinnes *et al.*, 2002). Grant *et al.* (2002) reported that nitrogen concentration in the crop residue would determine the net balance between mineralization and immobilization. If the N concentration in the residue is below approximately 20 to 24 g N/kg, immobilization will exceed mineralization, and the decomposition residues will tie up N rather than release (Goos, 1995). Legume residues contain considerable amount of N and have a relatively low C/N residue, leading to more rapid release of N than lower N containing cereal residue (Janzen and Kucey, 1988). Average the total fresh biomass accumulated through various green manure crops varied from 20.33 t/ha (greengram) to *Sesbania rostrata* (29.33 t/ha) and dry biomass varied from 2.16 to 5.12 t/ha (Irin *et al.*, 2019; Pooniya *et al.*, 2012; Singh and Shivay, 2014). Pooniya *et al.* (2012) reported that, summer green manure crops accumulated varying amount of nitrogen from crop to crop. *Sesbania aculeata* accumulated 177.3 to 183.7 kg N/ha followed by cowpea (137.5 to 146.7 kg N/ha) and mungbean (121.8 to 126.8 kg N/ha). Similarly, they also reported that the phosphorus (21.7 to 23.5 kg/ha) and potassium (257.3 to 278.3 kg/ha) are also enriched in soil by legumes. The growth duration for incorporation of green manure crops and N accumulation are given in Figure 1.

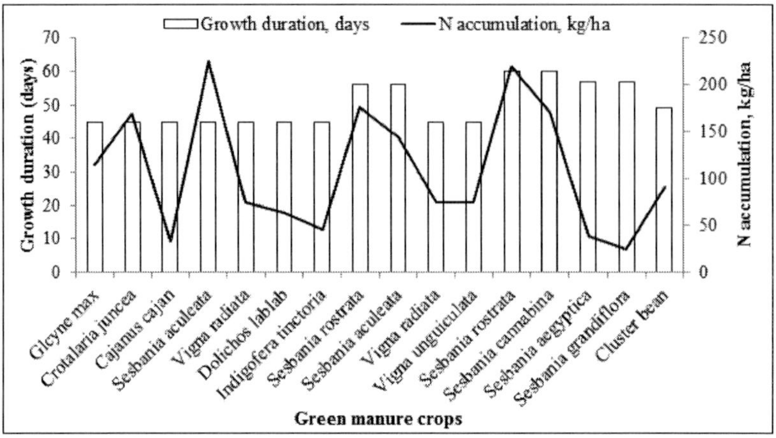

Fig. 1. Growth duration for incorporation of green manure crops and N accumulation (Source: Fageria, 2007)

Fig. 2. Green manuring of greengram, cowpea and sesbania, respectively in maize/groundnut sole and their intercrop at ICAR Manipur Centre, Imphal (Source: Ansari *et al.*, 2017b)

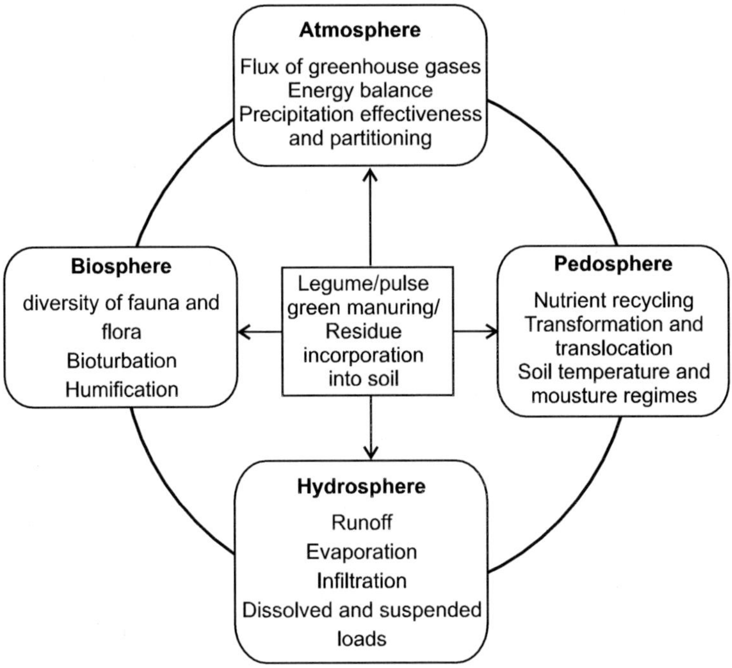

Fig. 3. Significance of legume/pulse green manuring to maintain balance among atmosphere, pedosphere, hydrosphere and biosphere

4. ROLE OF GREEN MANURING IN SOIL HEALTH IMPROVEMENT AND AGRICULTURAL SUSTAINABILITY

Growing of legumes (improving nitrogen and phosphorus availability); green manure crops (improve physical, chemical and biological soil fertility); cover crops (preventing soil erosion and soil organic carbon); and nutrient catch crops (keeping nutrients available for subsequent crops) can help to improve the sustainability of the cropping system, i.e. to maintain the natural resources and the carrying capacity of the cropping system (Pooniya and Shivay, 2009; Das *et al.*, 2016). Green manure crop provide soil cover and reduces water evaporation and soil temperature, and increases water infiltration. It also provides protection from erosion. Green manure crops act as cover crop and reduce weed infestation. Incorporation of green manure biomass enriches in nutrients and it adds biomass to soil in order to accumulate soil organic matter, add and recycle nutrients and increase soil health. It improves the soil structure, water holding capacity and infiltration as well as biological soil penetration. Green manure crops improved the soil physical, chemical and biological properties as reported by many researchers.

4.1 Improvement of soil physical properties

Continuous/intensive crop cultivation decreases the soil organic carbon and adversely affects the soil health. Reductions in soil organic carbon increase the soil compaction/ density of the soil (Unger and Kaspar, 1994). Bulk density is inversely related to total porosity, which provides a measure of the porous space left in the soil for air and water movement (Min *et al.*, 2003). Lower bulk density implies greater pore space and improved aeration, developing a suitable environment for soil biological activity (Min *et al.*, 2003). Higher bulk density and compaction obstructs the internal soil drainage system due to blockage of soil pores (Akram and Kemper, 1979) and ultimately reduced the infiltration and lead to the surface soil erosion and environmental degradation (Gimenez *et al.*, 1992). Green manuring had significant positive influence on soil physical properties like aggregate stability, soil porosity, water infiltration rate, optimization of soil temperature etc. Green manuring crops, like *Sesbania* specifically influence soil structural properties by enmeshing soil primary particles and micro aggregates into macro aggregation through direct physical action of roots, and production of cementing agents from enhanced microbial activities (Sultani *et al.*, 2007). Organic matter is the primary stabilizing agent for aggregates in soils. Specifically, the decomposition products of plant and animal residues are responsible for aggregate stabilization. These include microbial gums and mucilages, low molecular weight fulvic-acid molecules, and linear organic polymers like fats and waxes (Allison, 1973). It was reported that *Sesbania* produced greater number of macro and large mesopores about 41% increased over control followed by cluster bean (29%) and rice bean (16%). Incorporation of green manure crops into the soil improved the soil physical conditions and it may promote root growth and increased use of soil water and resource use efficiency (Anderson *et al.*, 1997). In another study, Chikowo *et al.* (2004) reported that incorporation of woody legumes into the soil reduces bulk density and increases soil granulation and porosity. Penetration resistance of soil was found to vary directly with density and inversely with soil moisture content. Green manure crops significantly reduce the penetration resistance due to improvement in soil physical quality. Cover crops also facilitate to maintain soil humidity through shading and control of the thermal regime (lowers temperature, therefore reduces evaporation of water from the soil and increases water infiltration).

4.2 Improvement of soil biological properties

Pulses/legumes green manures incorporation stimulates the soil microbial growth and activity that decompose the fresh material and subsequently mineralization of plant nutrients, and therefore increases soil biological properties. The decomposed incorporated green manure crops releases plant nutrients and made available to the succeeding crop. This condition also favours the greater biological activity of the soil's flora and fauna (improves the activity of soil organisms like Rhizobia, Mycorrhizae, improves nodulation of legumes, increases the quantity of earthworms, etc.).

The activity of soil microorganisms is positively correlated to the enzymatic activities. Soil organic matter decomposition is mediated by microorganisms through enzymes that catalyze innumerable reactions necessary for the life processes of microorganisms in soils, decomposition of organic residues, nutrient cycling, and formation of organic matter and soil structure (Dick, 1994). These enzymes are constantly synthesized and can be accumulated, inactivated and/or decomposed in soil, with a great impact on nutrient recycling (Dick, 1997). Sürücü *et al* (2014) reported that the urease and dehydrogenase enzymatic activities were significantly higher in the green manuring system compared to the conventional system. Dehydrogenase soil enzyme is the most important and extensively used indicators of overall soil microbial activity because it occurs intracellular in all living microbial cells and plays a significant role in the biological oxidation of soil organic matter (Yao *et al.*, 2006; Salazar *et al.*, 2011; Yuan *et al.*, 2012). Piotrowskaa and Wilczewski (2012) reported higher enzymatic activity in catch crop treatment as compared with the control probably resulted from the input of the catch crop biomass, which can stimulate the soil microbiological biomass and enzymatic activity through the modification of the physical properties of the soil and the addition of readily available C and N sources. Based on a long term study in Entisol, significant improvement in soil properties under pulse-based system in terms of higher concentration of SOC, MBC, and organic and total soluble N than non-pulse-based systems have been reported (Nath *et al.*, 2019). Legumes affects soil biological attributes related to SOC cycling, microbial biomass C, nutrient buffering and enzyme activities in sustainable food production system under rainfed conditions in different parts of the world (Meena, *et al.* 2017; Das *et al.*, 2018b)

4.3 Improvement of soil chemical properties

Leguminous green manure with a low C/N ratio often results in high and rapid N mineralization, while rice straw (high C/N ratio) usually results in low N mineralization and a slow N release (Li *et al.*, 2015; Zhou *et al.*, 2019). Many researcher reported that the soil organic C did not change significantly (P=0.05) in short-term, with the addition or incorporation of green manure indicating that soil organic matter is not sensitive to short-term changes of soil quality with different soil or crop management practices (Liu et 0al., 2013). Usually, soil organic C increases in medium- to long-term as reported in previous studies (Huang *et al.*, 2010). In contrary of above finding, soil microbial biomass carbon (SMBC) is a sensitive indicator of soil quality and responds quickly to changes in soil management and improved significantly by using of legumes as green manure (Shah *et al.*, 2010). Hargrove (1986) reported that legume cover crops optimize the soil pH, improves distribution of potassium (K+) to the soil surface from deeper in the soil profile, and lower C/N ratio in soil organic matter. Furthermore, legume green manure crops improved uptake of soil NO_3, reduced risk of leaching and runoff (Shipley *et al.*, 1992) and enhanced N availability to succeeding crop and thus reduced need for N fertilizer (Stute and Posner, 1993). The legume green manure crops promote mycorrizae on the roots of succeeding crops, increasing soil phosphorus (P) and micronutrient availability. Furthermore, legume green manuring can improve P uptake of succeeding crops via converting unavailable native and residual fertilizer P to more available chemical forms (Cavigelli and Thien, 2003). Some researcher also reported that the legume green manure crops in high P fixation capacity soils, P availability may enhance by organic compounds released during decomposition process by blocking P absorption sites (Easterwood and Sartain, 1990) or via anion exchange (Kafkafi *et al.*, 1988).

4.4 Reduction in weed growth and pest infestation

Excellent weed suppression has been shown with under seeded biennial sweet clover (*Meliloutus offcianalis* L. Lam.) (Moyer *et al.*, 1997). Similarly, the weed suppression effect of perennial alfalfa (*Medicago sativa* L.) has been shown to last for three years for wild oat and other, but not all, weed species (Entz *et al.*, 1995; Ominski *et al.*, 1999). Brown manuring with *Sesbania* is another technique to reduce weed problems in rice (Ansari *et al*., 2017; 2018). They have reported that the *Sesbania* green manuring were significantly reduced density and dry weight of *Echinochloa spp., L. chinensis, C. benghalensis, Eclipta alba, Cyprus spp.* and other weeds as compared to control in direct seeded rice. Talebbeigi and Ghadiri (2012) suggested that cowpea living mulch is a good candidate for use as the summer companion with maize. Cowpea living mulch suppressed weeds and can reduce weed growth. Likewise, control of weeds through cowpea living mulch may ultimately result in reduction in herbicide inputs. Green manure has also potential effects on soil borne diseases. Incorporation of the above-ground biomass of green manure crops, significant amounts of carbon, nutrients and secondary metabolites are added to the soil. The amounts of readily useable carbon in the form of organic amendments (fresh or dried plant material) added to the soil stimulates the general soil microbial activity (Stark *et al*., 2008; Michel and Lazzeri, 2011). Such increases in soil microbial activity can sometimes be correlated with a decrease in the number of soil-borne pathogens e.g., *Verticillium dahliae* (Michel and Lazzeri, 2011). In another hand, the incorporation of fresh organic matter can occasionally also lead to a temporarily increase of certain soil-borne diseases (Hoitink and Boehm, 1999). Plants containing essential oils are another group of green manure crops that can also be used for the control of soil-borne pathogens (Gwinn *et al*., 2010).

4.5 Increase in crop productivity and profitability

Dual purpose legumes green manure or pulse green manuring improves soil health along with enhancement in system productivity and net returns due to additional yield with adjustment in cropping pattern (Ansari *et al*., 2017c). Ali *et al* (2012) reported that the green manuring of *Sesbania rostrata* and legume crops (mungbean, cowpeas and lentil) produced significantly higher grain yield of rice and wheat than the other crops. They have found that the maximum paddy yield of 3.73 t/ha was produced by rice – wheat – sesbania cropping system followed by 3.57, 3.52, 3.40 and 3.39 t/ha produced by rice – wheat – mungbean, rice – berseem, rice – wheat – cowpea and rice – lentil cropping systems, respectively and these were statistically at par with each other. Pooniya and Shivay (2012) found that the residue incorporation of *Sesbania aculeata* summer green-manuring crop increased the growth and yield attributes and yields of basmati rice compared with the remaining green-manuring crop. In another study, Ansari *et al.* (2018) reported that the *Sesbania* brown manuring on an average increased the yield attributes of direct seeded rice like number of panicle (8.1%), length of panicle (7.3%) and number of grains per panicle (1.8%) over control. Higher growth and yield attributes under *Sesbania* brown manuring led to the 17.25% higher grain yield as compared to without *Sesbania* brown manuring. Consequently, the production efficiency was significantly higher under DSR with *Sesbania* green manuring (28.99 kg/ha/day) as compared to without green manuring (23.99 kg/ha/day).

4.6 Increase in energy and carbon use efficiency

Green-manure crops are being increasingly used in agricultural systems to recycle nutrients and energy as well as improve soil conditions for plant growth. Chemical fertilizers lead to emission of GHGs into the atmosphere with strong adverse effects on the environment.

Legume green manure crops fixed the atmospheric nitrogen and reduce the fertilizer requirements specially N for succeeding crops. Lal *et al.* (2019) reported that among the all the agricultural inputs, fertilizer consumed highest energy followed by diesel in rice-maize cropping system. They have also found various inputs included in the cultivation, carbon foot print were highest for fertilizer application followed by N_2O emission. Hence, legume green manuring plays important role in reduction of GHG emission and energy through addition of nitrogen into soil. Hence, it is important to reduce the emission of GHGs from farming and related activities to reduce the rate of climate change (Liu *et al.*, 2016; Meena and Meena, 2017). However, the emission intensity can be substantially reduced by including N_2-fixing pulse crops in a crop rotation. The inclusion of pulses in the rotation allows the system to rely on the symbiotic N_2 fixation from the atmosphere, which significantly decreases the use of synthetic N fertilizer, thus lowering the carbon footprint.

5. CONCLUSION

A primary focus of agriculture should be to increase productivity, agricultural sustainability and nutritional value to the human diet through the adoption of sustainable agricultural practices. Inclusion of pulse /legume green manuring or incorporation of their residues in to soil has great potential to improve the soil health by improving soil physical, chemical and biological properties. On the hand, green manuring with legume would substantially reduce burden on inorganic fertilizers, thus contribute to reduction of carbon foot print and GHGs emission.

REFERENCES

Adediran, J.A., Akande, M.O. and Oluwatoyinbo, F.I. (2004) Effect of mucuna intercropped with maize on soil fertility and yield of maize. *Ghana Journal of Agricultural Science* 37, 15-22.

Akram, M. and Kemper, W.D. (1979) Infiltration of soils as affected by the pressure and water content at the time of compaction. *Soil Science Society of America Journal* 43, 1080–1086.

Ali, M. (1984-1987) *Annual Report, IIPR, Kanpur*.

Ali, R.I., Awan, T.H., Ahmad, M., Saleem, M.U. and Akhtar, M. (2012) Diversification of rice-based cropping systems to improve soil Fertility, sustainable productivity and economics. *The Journal of Animal & Plant Sciences* 22(1), 108-112.

Allison, F.E. (1973) Soil organic matter and its role in crop production. Elsevier Scientific Publishing Co., New York.

Anderson, I.C., Buxton, D.R., Karlen, D.L. and Cambardella, C. (1997) Cropping system effects on nitrogen removal, soil nitrogen, aggregate stability, and subsequent corn grain yield. *Agronomy Journal* 89, 881–886.

Ansari, M.A., Baishya, L.K., Singh, D., Roy, S.S., Prakash, N., Ansari, M.H. and Lal, B. (2017b) Carbon sequestration in terrestrial pool: mitigation strategy to climate change. *Indian Farming* 67 (06): 50-53.

Ansari, M.A., Prakash, N., Reeta Devi, N. and Meitei, C.B. (2015) Biodynamic management in cropping systems for improving eco-physiological attributes, crop productivity and soil organic carbon dynamics under hill regions of Manipur. National Seminar on advances of life science, Manipur University, March 23-24, 2015. pp: 99-100.

Ansari, M.A., Saraswat, P.K., Roy, S.S., Sharma, S.K., Punitha, P., Ansari, M.H., Prakash, N., Mishra, R.K., Lal, N. and Ramakrishna, Y. (2017c) Significance and strategies of legume production for achieving nutritional security in North East Indian Himalayan Region. *Journal of Food Legumes* 30(3), 56-63.

Ansari, M.H., Ansari, M.A., Yadav, R.A., Siddiqui, M.Z. and Khan, N. (2018) Weed control and productivity studies in direct seeded (*Oryza sativa* L.) through sesbania brown. Bangladesh Journal of Botany 47(2), 227-235.

Ansari, M.H., Yadav, R.A., Siddiqui, M.Z., Ansari, M.A., Khan, N., Mishra, D. and Husain, K. (2017a) Efficacy of crop establishment techniques and weed control measures on weed dynamics, weed control efficiency and productivity in rice (*Oryza sativa*). *Indian Journal of Agricultural Sciences* 87(8), 1084–8.

BARC. (2012) Fertilizer recommendation guide-2012. Farm gate, Dhaka-1215; BARC: Dhaka, Bangladesh, 2012.

Becker, M., Ladha, J.K., Simpson, I.C. and Ottow, J.C.G. (1994) Parameters affecting residue N mineralization in flooded soils. *Soil Science Society of America Journal* 58, 1666–1671.

Behera, U.K., Sharma, A.R., Pandey, H.N. (2007) Sustaining productivity of wheat–soybean cropping system through integrated nutrient management practices on the Vertisols of Central India. *Plant and Soil* 297, 185–199.

Boddey, R.M., Urquiaga, S., Suhet, A.R., Peres, J.R. and Neves, M.C.P. (1990) Quantification of the contribution of N2 fixation to field-grown grain legumes: A strategy for the practical application of the '-'N isotope dilution technique. *Soil Biology and Biochemistry* 22, 649-655.

Cavigelli, M.A. and Thien, S.J. (2003) Phosphorus bioavailability following incorporation of green manure crops. *Soil Science Society of America Journal* 67, 1186–1194.

Chalk, P.M. (1998) Dynamics of biologically fixed N in legume–cereal rotations: a review. *Australian Journal of Agricultural Research* 49, 303–316.

Chikowo, R., Mapfumo, P., Leffelaar, P.A. and Giller, K.E. (2006) Integrating legumes to improve N cycling on small holder farms in sub-humid Zimbabwe: resource quality, biophysical and environmental limitations. *Nutrient Cycling in Agroecosystems* 76, 219–231.

Clement, A., Ladha, J.K. and Chalifour, F.P. (1998) Nitrogen dynamics of various green manure species and the relationship to lowland rice production. *Agronomy Journal* 90, 149–154.

Das, A., Babu, S., Yadav, G.S., Ansari, M.A., Singh, R., Baishya, L.K., Rajkhowa, D.J. and Ngachan, S.V. (2016) Status and strategies for pulses production for food and nutritional security in North-Eastern region of India. *Indian Journal of Agronomy* 61(Special issue), 43-57.

Das, A., Devi, M.T., Babu, S., Ansari, M.A., Layek, J., Bhowmick, S.N., Yadav, G.S. and Singh, R. (2018) Cereal-Legume Cropping System in Indian Himalayan Region for Food and Environmental Sustainability. (in) Legumes for Soil Health and Sustainable

Management. R.S. Meena *et al.* (eds.). Springer Nature Singapore Pte Ltd. https://doi.org/10.1007/978-981-13-0253-42.

Dick, R.P., Rasmussen, P.E. and Kerle, E.A. (1988) Influence of long-term residue management on soil enzyme activities in relation to soil chemical properties of a wheat-fallow system. *Biology and Fertility of Soils* 6, 159-164.

Dinesh, R. and Dubey, R.P. (1998) Nitrogen mineralization rates and kinetics in soils freshly amended with green manures. *Journal of Agronomy and Crop Science* 181, 49–53.

Dinnes, D.L., Karlen, D.L., Jaynes, D.B., Kaspar, T.C., Hatfield, J.L., Colvin, T.S. and Cambardella, C.A. (2002) Nitrogen management strategies to reduce nitrate leaching in tile-drained Midwestern soils. *Agronomy Journal* 94, 153–171.

Doran, J.W. and Smith, M.S. (1991) Role of cover crops in nitrogen cycling. In Cover crops for clean water, Proceedings of International Conference, ed. W. L. Hargrove, 85–90. Jackson, TN. 9–11 Apr. 1991. Soil and Water Conservation Society, Ankeny, IA.

Drew, E., Herridge, D., Ross, B., Graham, O., Rosalind, D., Matthew,D., Ron, Y., Greg, G., Elizabeth, H., Lori, P., Nikki, S., John, H. and Neil, B. 2014. Inoculating legumes: a practical guide. https://www.researchgate.net/publication/257799935.

Easterwood, G.W. and Sartain, J.B. (1990) Clover residue effectiveness in reducing orthophosphate sorption on ferric hydroxide coated soil. *Soil Science Society of America Journal* 54, 1345–1350.

Foyer, C.H., Lam, H.M., Nguyen, H.T., Siddique, K.H.M., Varshney, R.K., Colmer, T.D., *et al.* (2016) Neglecting legumes has compromised human health and sustainable food production. *Nature Plants* 2(8), 16112. doi: 10.1038/ nplants.2016.112.

George, T., Singleton, P.W. and Bohlool, B.B. (1988) Yield, soil nitrogen uptake, and N2 fixation by soybean from four maturity groups grown at three elevations. Agronomy Journal 80, 563-567.

Gil, J.L., and Fick, W.H. (2001) Soil nitrogen mineralization in mixtures of eastern gamagrass with alfalfa and red clover. *Agronomy Journal* 93, 902– 910.

Giller, K.E., Nambiar, P.T.C., Srinivasa Rao, B., Dart, P.J. and Day, M. (1987) A comparison of nitrogen fixation in genotypes of groundnut (Arachis hypogaea L.) using 15Nisotope dilution. *Biology and Fertility of Soils* 5, 23-25.

Gimenez, D.C., Dirksen, R., Miedema, L.A.A,, Eppink, J. and Schoonderbeek, D. (1992) Surface sealing and hydraulic conductance under varying intensity rains. *Soil Science Society of America Journal* 56, 234– 242.

Graham, P.H. (2008) Ecology of the root-nodule bacteria of legumes. In M.J. Dilworth, E.K. James, J.I. Sprent & W.E. Newton, eds. Nitrogen-fixing leguminous symbioses, pp. 23–58. Dordrecht, the Netherlands, Springer.

Gwinn, K.D., Ownley, B.H., Greene, S.E., Clark, M.M., Taylor, C.L., Springfield, T.N., Trently, D.J., Green, J.F., Reed, A. and Hamilton, S.L. (2010) Role of essential oils in control of Rhizoctonia dampingoff in tomato with bioactive monarda herbage. *Phytopathology* 100, 493-501.

Hargrove, W.L. (1986) Winter legumes as nitrogen sources for no-tillage grain sorghum. *Agronomy Journal* 78, 70–74.

Hoitink, H.A.J. and Boehm, M.J. (1999) Biocontrol within the context of soil microbial communities: A substrate-dependent phenomenon. *Annual Review of Phytopathology* 37, 427-446.

Howieson, J.G., Yates, R.J., Foster, K.J., Real, D. and Besier, R.B. (2008) Prospects for the future use of legumes. In Dilworth MJ, James EK, Sprent JI and Newton WE, eds. Nitrogen-fixing leguminous symbioses, pp. 363–393. Dordrecht, the Netherlands, Springer.

Huang, S. Sun, Y., Rui, W., Liu, W. and Zhang, W. (2010) Long-term effect of no-tillage on soil organic carbon fractions in a continuous maize cropping system of Northeast China. *Pedosphere* 20, 285-292.

Irin, I.J., Biswas, P.K., Ullah, M.J., Roy, T.S. and Khan, M.A. (2019) Influence of green manuring crops on dry matter Production and soil health improvement. *Bangladesh Agronomy Journal* 22 (1): 39-45.

Kafkafi U, Yosef BB, Rosenberg R and Sposito G. (1988). Phosphorus ad- sorption by kaolinite and montmorrillonite: II. Organic anion competition. *Soil Science Society of America Journal* 52, 1585–1589.

Katyal, J.C., Rao, N.H., Reddy, M.N. (2001) Critical aspects of organic matter management in the tropics: the example of India. *Nutrient Cycling in Agroecosystems* 61, 77–88.

Kirkegaard, J., Christen, O., Krupinsky, J. and Layzell, D. (2008) Break crop benefits in temperate wheat production. *Field Crops Research* 107, 185–195.

Kumar, K. and Goh, K.M. (2000) Crop residues and management practices: effects on soil quality, soil nitrogen dynamics, crop yield, and nitrogen recovery. *Advances in Agronomy* 68, 197–319.

Kumar, N., Nath, C.P., Hazra, K.K., Das, K., Venkatesh, M.K., Singh, S.S., Prahraj, C.S. and Singh, N.P. (2019) Impact of zero-till residue management and crop diversification with legumes on soil aggregation and carbon sequestration. *Soil and Tillage Research* 189, 158-167.

Kumar Rao, J.V.D.K., Thompson, J.A., Sastry, P.V.S.S., Giller, K.E. and Day, J.M. (1987) Measurement of N2 fixation in field-grown pigeonpea [*Cajanus cajan* (L.) Millsp.] using 15N-labelled fertilizer. *Plant and Soil* 101, 107-113.

Lal, B., Gautam, P., Nayak, A.K., Panda, B.B., Bihari, P., Tripathi, R., Shahid, M., Guru, P.K., Chatterjee, D., Kumar, U. and Meena, B.P. (2018) Energy and carbon budgeting of tillage for environmentally clean and resilient soil health of rice-maize cropping system. *Journal of Cleaner Production.* https://doi.org/10.1016/j.jclepro.2019.04.041.

Layek, J., Das, A., Mitran, T., Nath, C.P., Meena, R.S., Yadav, G.S., Shivakumar, B.G., Kumar, S. and Lal, R. (2018) Cereal + Legume Intercropping: An Option for Improving Productivity and Sustaining Soil Health. (In) Legumes for Soil Health and Sustainable Management (R.S. Meena *et al.* (eds.), https://doi.org/10.1007/978-981-13-0253-4_11.

Lee, K.K. and Wani, S.P. (1989) Proc. Colloquium on Soil Fertility and Fertilizer Management in Semi-Arid and Tropical India. IFDC Muscle Sholas, AL 89- 108. Subbarao, N.S. 1988. Biological N Fixation: Recent Developments. Oxford and IBH: pp. 1-19.

Li, F., Wang, Z., Dai, J., Li, Q., Wang, X., Xue, C., Liu, H. and He, G. (2015) Fate of nitrogen from green manure, straw, and fertilizer applied to wheat under different summer fallow management strategies in dryland. *Biology and Fertility of Soils* 51, 769–780.

Liu, E., Yan, C., Mei, X., Zhang, Y. and Fan, T. (2013) Long-term effect of manure and fertilizer on soil organic carbon pools in dryland farming in northwest china. *PLoS ONE* 8,e56536.

Liu, Q., Liu, B., Ambus, P., Zhang, Y., Hansen, V., Lin, Z., Shen, D., Liu, G., Bei, Q., Zhu, J. and Wang, X. (2016) Carbon footprint of rice production under biochar amendmentea case study in a Chinese rice cropping system. *Gcb Bioenergy* 8(1), 148e159. Lu, X., Liao, Y., 2016.

Meena, H. and Meena, R.S. (2017) Assessment of sowing environments and bioregulators as adaptation choice for clusterbean productivity in response to current climatic scenario. *Bangladesh Journal of Botany* 46(1), 241e244. Meena, R.S., Yadav, R.S., 2014.

Michel, V.V., Hartman, G.L. and Midmore, D.J. (1996) Effect of previous crop on soil populations of Burkhoderia solanacearum, bacterial wilt, and yield of tomatoes in Taiwan. *Plant Disease* 80, 1367- 1372.

Min, D.H., Islam, K.R., Vough, L.R. and Weil, R.R. (2003) Dairy manure effects on soil quality properties and carbon sequestration in alfalfa-orchard-grass systems. *Communications in Soil Science and Plant Analysis* 34, 781-799.

Mubarak, A.R., Rosenani, A.B., Anuar, A.R. and Zauyah, S. (2002) Decomposition and nutrient release of maize stover and groundnut haulm under tropical field conditions of Malaysia. *Communications in Soil Science and Plant Analysis* 33(3-4), 609-622.

Fageria, N.K. (2007) Green Manuring in Crop Production. *Journal of Plant Nutrition* 30 (5), 691-719.

Ojiem, J.O., de Ridder, N., Vanlauwe, B. and Giller, K.E. (2006) Socio-ecological niche: a conceptual framework for integration of legumes in smallholder farming systems. *International Journal of Agricultural Sustainability* 4, 79–93.

Palm, C.A., Giller, K.E., Mafongoya, P.L. and Swift, M.J. (2001) Management of organic matter in the tropics: translating theory into practice. *Nutrient Cycling in Agroecosystems* 61, 63–75.

Pikul, J.L.Jr., Aase, J.K. and Cochran, V.L. (1997) Lentil green manure as fallow replacement in the semiarid northern Great Plains. *Agronomy Journal* 89, 867–874.

Piotrowskaa, A. and Wilczewski, E. (2012) Effects of catch crops cultivated for green manure and mineral nitrogen fertilizationon soil enzyme activities and chemical properties. *Geoderma*. doi:10.1016/j.geoderma.2012.04.018.

Pooniya, V., Shivay, Y.S., Rana, A., Nain, L. and Radha, P. (2012) Enhancing soil nutrient dynamics and productivity of Basmati rice through residue incorporation and zinc fertilization. *European Journal of Agronomy*. doi: https://10.1016/j.eja.2012.03.004.

Rennie, R.J., Rennie, D.A., Siripaibool, C., Chaiwanakupt, P., Boonkerd, N. and Snitwongse, P. (1988) N2 fixation in Thai soybeans: Effects of tillage and inoculation on 15 N-determined N_2 fixation in recommended cultivars and advanced breeding lines. *Plant and Soil* 112, 183-193.

Salazar, S., Sanchez, L., Alvarez, J., Valverde, A., Galindo, P., Igual, J., Peix, A. and Santa-Regina, I. (2011) Correlation among soil enzyme activities under different forest system management practices. *Ecological Engineering* 37, pp. 1123- 1131.

Shah, Z., Ahmad, S.R. and Rahman, H.U. (2010) Soil microbial biomass and activities as influenced by green manure legumes and N fertilizer in rice-wheat system. *Pakistan Journal of Botany* 42, 2589-2598.

Shah, Z., Shah, S.H., Peoples, M.B., Schwenke, G.D. and Herridge, D.F. (2003) Crop residue and fertilizer N effects on nitrogen fixation and yields of legume–cereal rotations and soil organic fertility. *Field Crops Research* 83, 1–11.

Sharma, A.R. and Behera, U.K. (2009) Nitrogen contribution through Sesbania green manure and dual-purpose legumes in maize–wheat cropping system: agronomic and economic considerations. *Plant and Soil* 325, 289–304.

Shipley, P.R., Meisinger, J.J. and Decker, A.M. (1992) Conserving residual corn fertilizer nitrogen with winter cover crops. *Agronomy Journal* 84, 869–876.

Singh, A. and Shivay, Y.S. (2014) Enhancement of growth parameters and productivity of basmati rice through summer green manuring and zinc fertilization. *International Journal of Bio-resource and Stress Management* 5(4), 486-494.

Singh, Y., Khind, C.S. and Singh, B. (1991) Efficient management of leguminous green manures in wetland rice. *Advances in Agronomy* 45, 135–189.

Sisworo, W.H., Mitrosuhardjo, M.M., Rasjid, H. and Myers, R.J.K. (1990) The relative roles of N fixation, fertilizer, crop residues and soil in suplying N in multiple cropping systems in a humid, tropical upland cropping system. *Plant and Soil* 121, 73-82.

Soil Science Society of America. (1997) Glossary of soil science terms. Madison, Wisconsin: Soil Science Society of America.

Ssali, H. and Keya, S.O. (1984) Phosphorus and cultivar effects on nodulation, growth, dinitrogen fixation and yield of cowpea (*Vigna unguiculata*). *The East African Agricultural and Forestry Journal* 45, 188-193.

Stagnari, F., Maggio, A., Galieni, A. and Pisante, M. (2017) Multiple benefits of legumes for agriculture sustainability: an overview. Chem. Biol. Technol. In Agric. 4(2), 2. doi: 10.1186/s40538-016-0085-1.

Stark, C.H., Condron, L.M., O'Callaghan, M., Stewart, A. and Di, H.J. (2008) Differences in soil enzyme activities, microbial community structure and short-term nitrogen mineralization resulting from farm management history and organic matter amendments. *Soil Biology & Biochemistry* 40, 1352- 1363.

Stute, J.K. and Posner, J.L. (1993) Legume covers option for grain rotations in Wisconsin. *Agronomy Journal* 85, 1128–1132.

Subbarao, N.S. (1988) Biological Nitrogen Fixation: Recent Developments. Oxford and IBH: pp. 1-19

Sultani, M.I., Gill, M.A., Anwar, M.M. and Athar, M. (2007) Evaluation of soil physical properties as influenced by various green manuring legumes and phosphorus fertilization under rain fed conditions. *International Journal of Environmental Science and Technology* 4(1), 109-118.

Sürücü, A., Özyazici, M.A., Bayrakli, B. and Kizilkaya, R. (2014) Effects of green manuring on soil enzyme activity. *Fresenius Environmental Bulletin* 23(9), 2126-2132.

Talebbeigi, R.M. and Ghadiri, H. (2012) Effects of Cowpea Living Mulch on Weed Control and Maize Yield. *Journal of Biological and Environmental Sciences* 6(17), 189-193.

Timsina, J. (2018a) Can organic materials supply enough nutrients to achieve food security? *Journal of Agriculture and Forestry University* 2, 9–21.

Timsina, J. (2018b) Can organic sources of nutrients increase crop yields to meet global food demand? *Agronomy* 8, 214; doi:10.3390/agronomy8100214.

Unger, P.W. and Kaspar, T.C. (1994) Soil compaction and root growth: A review. *Agronomy Journal* 86, 759–766.

Unkovich, M.J., Baldock, J. and Peoples, M.B. (2010) Prospects and problems of simple linear models for estimating symbiotic N_2 fixation by crop and pasture legumes. *Plant and Soil* 329, 75-89.

Valadares, R.V., Avila-Silva, L.D., Teixeira, R.D., Sousa, R.N.D. and Vergütz, L. (2016) Green Manures and Crop Residues as Source of Nutrients in Tropical Environment. http://dx.doi.org/10.5772/62981.

Vijay, P. and Shivay, Y.S. (2012) Summer green-manuring crops and zinc fertilization on productivity and economics of basmati rice (*Oryza sativa* L.) *Archives of Agronomy and Soil Science* 58:(6), 593-616.

Wutke, E.B., Trani, P.E., Ambrosano, E.J., Drugowich, M.I. and Adubação verde no Estado de São Paulo. Campinas: Coordenadoria de Assistência Técnica Integral-CATI; 2009. 89 p.

Yao, X.H., Huang, M., Lu, Z.H. and Yuan, H.P. (2006) Influence of acetamiprid on soil enzymatic activities and respiration. *European Journal of Soil Biology* 42, 120–126.

Yuan, B. and Yue, D. (2012) Soil microbial and enzymatic activities across a chronosequence of Chinese pine plantation development on the Loess Plateau of China. *Pedosphere* 22, 1-12.

Zhou, G., Cao, W., Bai, J., Xu, C., Zeng, N., Gao, S. and Rees, R.M. (2019) Non-additive responses of soil C and N to rice straw and hairy vetch (*Vicia villosa* Roth L.) mixtures in a paddy soil. *Plant and Soil* 436(1-2), 229-244.

CHAPTER 17

Mechanization in pulses production systems in India: status and way forward

M.K. Singh

ICAR- Indian Institute of Sugarcane Research, Lucknow – 226 002, Uttar Pradesh

*Corresponding author email: mksinghars@gmail.com

Abstract

Mechanization of agriculture is essential to enhance productivity and profitability, besides reduction in human drudgery and cost of cultivation. Efficient machineries help in timeliness in agricultural operations and increasing the utilization efficiency of other inputs. Pulses being largely grown under rainfed with minimum inputs are poorly mechanized even though machineries are available to perform different agricultural operations.Till now, most of the operations of pulses cultivation are carried out manually, except tillage. Considering the poor economical conditions of farmers and small land holdings, custom hiring facilities need to be developed to facilitate mechanization in pulses production systems. This chapter includes details of suitable implements available to perform different farm operations such as tillage, sowing, interculture, harvesting and threshing in pulse crops.

Keywords: Conservation tillage, Harvester, Interculture, Land levelling, Planter, Raised bed, Thresher

1. INTRODUCTION

The low productivity of pulses is attributed to inadequate inputs, untimely field operations, lack of irrigation (major area under rainfed conditions) and inefficient crop production technologies. For profitable pulses production, the farm mechanization is the need of hour to improve the land and labour productivity. There is a strong correlation exist between efficient farm mechanization and crop productivity. The rising wage rates and non-availability of manpower during peak hours further necessitates the mechanization. The factors that justify the strengthening of mechanization are numerous. The timeliness of operations and increasing precision input application e.g. water, fertilizer, seed, pesticide, energy and other inputs with minimum cost demand for more use of farm machinery. The various operations for which efficient tools and equipments required are: soil preparation and fertilization, seeding and planting, weeding and interculture, harvesting and handling, milling, grading and storage. These farm operations need a high degree of precision to increase the efficiency of the inputs and reduce the losses. For example, planting of the seeds at proper depth and uniform application of given dose of fertilizer in large areas can be possible with the use of proper mechanical devices. However, when such operations are performed through indigenous methods, their efficiency is reduced.

Mechanization also imparts capacity to the farmers to carry out farm operations, with ease and freedom from drudgery. The time taken to perform sequence of operations is a factor determining the per unit production cost. Effective engineering interventions have the potential to result in further useful technology packages for post harvest loss minimization. The primary processing of agro produce in production catchments, cold chain activities enhance employment and income generation opportunities. In small and marginal farms, except for tillage, other operations such as sowing, weeding, harvesting and threshing are normally manually performed.

2. LAND LEVELLING

Land levelling operations are done by tractor drawn levellers and laser land levellers. Land leveling is necessary for good agronomic, soil and crop management practices. It saves irrigation water, facilitates field operations and increases yield and quality of the produce. Leveled land also helps in smooth operations of various farm machineries during their field operations. Studies have revealed that a significant (20-25%) amount of water is lost during its application at the farm due to unevenness of the fields. Laser land leveling technology involves the process of smoothening the land surface within +/- 2cm of its average micro-elevation using laser guided drag scrapper. The main components of laser guided land leveler (Fig. 1) are Laser transmitter, Laser receiver mounted on electric/ manual mast and one receiver is used for mapping, control box, electric/ manual mast fitted on the leveler, external hydraulic system of leveler and drag scraper. More than 14 manufacturers from Punjab, Haryana, New Delhi and Uttar Pradesh manufacture about 4000-5000 units per year. These units are being used on custom hiring basis to generate additional benefits for farmer.

Fig. 1. Laser land leveler

3. TILLAGE MACHINERY

The soil needs to be prepared before sowing and/or planting, usually by some form of tillage to kill the weeds in the seedbed that would compete with crop for water and nutrients. Generally, tillage methods can be divided into three major categories, depending on the amount of crop residue they leave on the surface.

Conventional tillage: The standard tillage practice is use of the mould board plough or disc plough for primary tillage followed by several secondary tillage operations e.g. harrow and cultivator. The traditional animal drawn country plough has low output (30-40 h/ha) and unflattenned land for sowing.

Reduced tillage: It is a practice of minimizing soil disturbance due to tillage operation. In this practice, the off-season and primary tillage operations are escaped and tillage is done only for seedbed preparation. This is usually done with cultivator and rotavator. Generally, in this practice leaves 15% to 30% crop residue coverage on the soil surface.

Conservation tillage: It leaves at least 30% residue coverage on the soil surface. Conservation tillage methods include no-till, where no tillage is done at all and seeds are placed directly into the previous season's crop residue; strip-till, in which only the narrow strip of land needed for the crop row is tilled; ridge till; and mulch till. In no-till systems, the herbicide is applied directly on last season's crop residue to kill weeds. In the other methods, some soil preparation takes place before the herbicide is applied.

4. COMBINATION TILLAGE IMPLEMENTS

The full utilization of power source is crucial during soil tillage operations for low production cost of any crop. Conventionally the primary and secondary tillage operations consume double time and fuel with a very less power utilization. To overcome the power non-utilization, tractor drawn combination tillage implements (Plough–Harrow and Cultivator-Harrow, etc.) have been developed for seedbed preparation in one pass of the tractor (Fig. 2).

Fig. 2. (a) Culti-harrow (b) Powered disc harrow

5. SOWING AND PLANTING MACHINERY

5.1 Drills

For precise application of seed and fertilizer, mechanically metered seed drill and seed-cum-fertilizer drill are the implements used to sow the crops in closely spaced rows. Drills are commonly used for cereal crops. Now-a-days combination of seed and fertilizer placement equipment has gained popularity.Grain drills are typically equipped with shovel to open a small furrow in the soil, a metering system to deliver a measured, controlled amount of seed to drop tubes which guide the seed to the furrow. There are means (drag chains or *pata*) of closing the furrow with soil to cover the seeds. Zero-till drill and strip-till drill have also been developed to reduce energy inputs in crop production for conservation agriculture.

5.2 Planters

These are the implements used to plant row crops (typically in row spacings ranging from 10 to 40 inches). Planters open a furrow, meter seeds one-at-a-time, drop seeds into the furrow and cover the seed. Some planters can cut through residues and till a small strip of soil in each row at the time of planting. Planters can also be equipped to apply fertilizer, pesticides, and herbicides during planting. Planters come in different sizes where rows spacing can be adjusted. Inclined plate planter and pneumatic planters have been developed for precision sowing.Inclined Plate Planter developed by AICRP on FIM (PAU Ludhiana centre) and CIAE Bhopal is a multi-crop planter (Fig. 3) used for planting bold and small seeds at uniform spacing. It is presently being manufactured by 5 private manufacturers who have sold more than 100,000 units till date. It has direct impact on increasing productivity of crops by maintaining recommended plant population in field achieved through uniform planting of seeds.

Fig. 3. CIAE 6-Row Inclined Plate Planter

5.3 Seeder for companion cropping

Pulses are also raised as companion cropping with other crops e.g. sugarcane. Deep Furrow Sugarcane Cutter Planter-cum-Multi Crop Raised Bed Seeder is a multitasking machine which performs sowing of pulses/wheat on raised beds along with simultaneous planting of sugarcane in furrows (Fig. 4). The planter makes two furrows at a spacing of 75 cm and two raised beds (one full raised bed + two half raised beds) in a single pass. It consisted of a frame, two deep furrowers and raised bed maker, power transmission unit, whole cane seed trays for each row, sett-cutting unit, fertilizer-metering unit, chemical/insecticide application unit, soil covering and tamping unit and seeder for sowing of intercrop on raised beds. Its actual field capacity is 0.20 ha/h. Cost of planting operation is reduced by 60% and labour by 90% with its utilization. This machine is very useful to the areas where intercropping of sugarcane is practiced and hence is helpful for more production of pulses in the country.

Fig. 4. IISR Deep furrow sugarcane planter-cum-raised bed multi-crop seeder

5.4 Raised bed technology

The concept of raised bed planting is very advantageous in water logged and limited water area. The system of planting crops on raised bed alters crop geometry and land configuration, imposes effective control over irrigation and drainage. Now-a-days raised bed planters are available with adjustable rows and planting spacing, and simultaneous application of fertilizers (Fig. 5). There are several advantages associated with raised bed planting system as:

- Irrigation water can be efficiently applied. On an average it saves 30% irrigation water than flat bed methods and improves crop yields by more than 15%.
- Better upland crop production is possible in the wet monsoon because of better drainage.
- Inputs use efficiency (fertilizer and seeds) can be increased due to better placement.
- Bed planting facilitates irrigation before sowing and thus provides an opportunity for weed control prior to planting.
- Weeds between the beds (in furrows) can be controlled mechanically during early crop growth stages.

The recent efforts are being made to promote growing of crops on Permanent Raised Beds. By definition, a Permanent Raised Bed implies that the bed stays in place for several seasons, in comparison with being ploughed down and reconstructed every year as with more intensive tillage systems.

Fig. 5. Raised bed planter

6. WEEDING AND INTERCULTURE EQUIPMENT

Weeding is an important but equally labour intensive agricultural unit operation in pulses production. There is an increasing interest in the use of mechanical intra-row weeders because of concern over environmental degradation and a growing demand for organically produced food. Weeding is usually done manually by *khurpi* or sickle by small farmers or by blade harrow. Use of long handle wheel hoe and peg type weeders are being accepted as they reduce drudgery and weeding time to 25-110 hours from 300-700 hours inconventional practice (Fig. 6).

Fig. 6. Wheel hoe weeders

Animal drawn weeder and cultivator are also used for control of weeds. Self propelled and power operated weeders are being increasingly accepted on limited scale (Fig. 7). The power tiller of 5-8 hp are being extensively used to perform weeding/ interculture operations in pigeonpea, chickpea and other wide spaced pulses without damaging the plants. A depth control wheel is also provided for maintaing uniform depth of operation. The mechanical vibration is limiting factor as it significantly accelerates fatigue and affects sensitivity and reaction rates of the operator.

Fig. 7. Self propelled rotary weeder

7. PLANT PROTECTION EQUIPMENT

Many types of sprayers and dusters are used for applying insecticides, pesticides, herbicides, and fungicides. Different designs of low cost hand operated sprayers and dusters are available for application of plant protection chemicals. Low volume and ultra-low volume (ULV) sprayers, which require comparatively smaller quantity of water, are also in use.

8. HARVESTING

Timely harvest of the crop is important for quality produce and reduced the losses. There are two different methods of harvesting.

8.1 Hand/manual harvesting

In India most of the pulses, whether rainfed or irrigated, is harvested by human labour with simple farming implements like sickle. On an average, it takes about 80-100 man-hours per hectare to cut the plants by sickle. Self-sharpening serrated sickle is finding adoption. With serrated blade, this predominantly follows the friction and shear principles to cut the plants. The cutting force was drastically reduced compared to traditional sickle which uses impact principle.

8.2 Mechanical harvesting

Walk behind and self-propelled reaper harvesters, which facilitate quick harvesting, are also being popularized. Mechanized harvesting of pulses is usually done with combine-harvesters designed for wheat but adapted for pulses crops. However, it be used only in large fields and that too which has been levelled before sowing and then planted with varieties which are erect in nature and reach maturity simultaneously. The capacity of these machines generally varies from 0.9– 1.1 h/ha. Mechanized harvesting in case of pulse crops is minimal due to unavailability of mechanical harvesters at affordable price. The research and development in this segment needs a holistic approach. As the biological scientists are gearing up to develop plant types/ varieties amenable to mechanical harvesting, it is necessary that development/identification of a mechanical harvester suitable for different pulses is given due consideration to coincide with the advent of such plant types.

8.3 Pigeonpea harvesting

It is estimated that harvesting of crops consumes about the 25-30 per cent of the total labour requirementsof the crop production system. The harvesting of pigeonpea requiredon an average about 160 man hours per hectare. The pigeonpea plants are harvested by cutting the stem at the base and after making bundles placed to dry. The pods and grain are separated by beating the dry plants with sticks or by using threshers. In view to mechanize the harvesting of pigeonpea crop, a front mounted tractor drawn pigeonpea harvester was developed at PDKV Akola (Fig. 8). The machine was PTO driven consisting of cutting unit, conveying unit, gear box, propeller shaft, hydraulic motors, etc. The harvesting of pigeonpea is two stage processes. Holding the plant stem and striking the knife on stem for cutting. The developed equipment maximum cutting efficiency and field efficiency were 87.50% and 73.33% with 2.4 and 3.0 km/h speed of operation, respectively. The cost of operation of tractor front mounted pigeonpea harvester was 25.41% less when compared with manual harvesting.

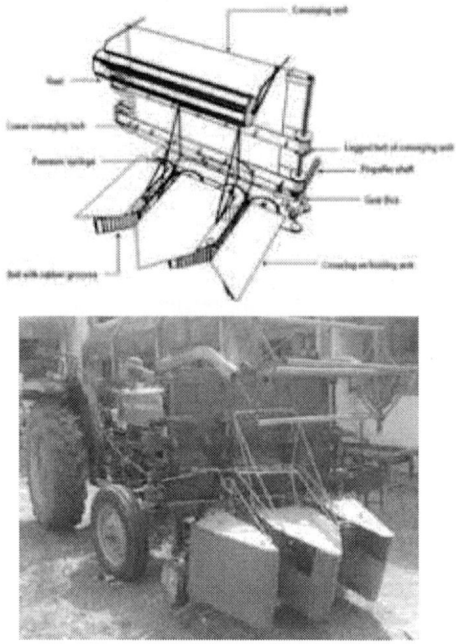

Fig. 8. Pigeonpea Harvester (PDKV, Akola)

8.4 Bengalgram harvesting

Generally harvesting of chickpea is done manually. An attempt has been made to develop a tractor drawn chickpea harvester at RARS, Nandyal, Andhra Pradesh (Fig. 9). When the tractor moves forward, a V-shaped blade which is mounted in the front portion of the tractor penetrates in to the soil and uproots the plants. Guides are provided on either side of the V-shape blade to avoid the trampling of the uprooted plants. The uprooted plants are thrown between the tyres and are collected. With this equipment, 10-12 acres can be harvested per day. Though now-a-days combine harvesters with suitable adjustments are being used for bengalgram harvesting but there is a need to develop suitable tractor operated equipment that can perform both harvesting and threshing simultaneously in a single pass.

Fig. 9. Bengalgram Harvester (RARS, Nandyal)

9. THRESHING

Traditional threshing by animal treading has been almost fully replaced by power threshers operated by 5-15 hp engine or electric motor. Multi-crop Thresher developed by PAU, Ludhiana and CIAE, Bhopal (Fig. 10) is suitable for threshing multiple crops viz. wheat, maize, sorghum, gram, soybean, pigeonpea and sunflower is very popular among farmers. The original design and its variants are being manufactured by more than 50 manufacturers across India. More than 70,000 to 80,000 units are being manufactured every year. Equipped with a rotating threshing drum (with beaters or teeth) and a stationary counter-thresher, these machines often have devices to shake out the straw and to clean and bag the grains. The use of motorized threshers may require two or three workers. Yields depend on the type of machine, the nature and maturity of the grains, the skill of the workers and organization of the work.

Fig. 10. CIAE High Capacity Thresher

A specific 10-hp high capacity pigeonpea thresher was designed and developed at CIAE, Bhopal. By this thresher, farmers may retain the threshed stalks of pigeonpeas for domestic use. The threshing efficiency, cleaning efficiency, total grain loss, feed rate, output capacity and germination percentage were found to be 96.54%, 91.99%, 10.122%, 1243.17 kg/h, 263.88 kg/h and 91%, respectively, at the optimum cylinder speed (200 rpm) and grain moisture content (7.7%). Its unit cost of operation was the lowest compared to other multicrop threshers.

9.1 Pigeonpea stripping & threshing

Being woody structure of plant makes pigeonpea problematic for threshing. Conventionally pods are separated manually by flail wooden stick followed by animal trampling or tractor treading. Seed is separated from threshed mass by winnowing. But this process is very time and labour intensive. Furthermore, it induces injury as well as considerable losses in terms of un-threshed materiel, injured seed and splited kernels. In view of this, a system of stripping and threshing has been developed. Stripping operation is carried out by modified Paddy thresher (Fig. 11). The stripped pods are threshed with developed Pulse thresher at optimized operational parameters for pigeonpea (Fig. 12). Both the machines can be operated at field itself as they are using power source as diesel engine or tractor. This feature reduced the bulk handling of material problems. The harvested material of pigeonpea comes around 250 m^3/ha. Furthermore, this system of stripping and threshing leave intact the plant part, which is required by farmer for their domestic use. Total threshing operation is completed with only 50% of labour required in conventional methods and higher seed recovery.

Fig. 11. A view of stripper for pigeonpea (a) IARI Karnal (b) IIPR Kanpur

Fig. 12. A view of threshing of pigeonpea

10. CONCLUSION

Farm mechanization is essentially a judicious mix of resources, implements, machines, and power sources. The present trend is towards use of high capacity and energy efficient machinery on custom hiring to reduce the cost of operation in major production hubs. The custom hiring system for farm implements requires promotion in rural areas. The farm machinery bank may be established for machines being manufactured elsewhere in the country to supply in low mechanised region on custom hiring basis. Various initiatives like National Food Security Mission, Rashtriya Kriski Vikas Yojana and Sub-Mission on agricultural mechanization have been started to increase the farm mechanization level of the country. Precision agriculture using GIS/GPS techniques for region specific crop planning, controlled precision application of inputs (seeds, fertilisers, chemicals, water, etc), conservation agriculture for carbon sequestration, multi-functional farm equipment to conserve energy and to reduce turnaround time, farm machinery management, application of dronesin agriculture, occupational health hazards andsafety on the farms, application of sensors, microprocessor and computer in agriculture are some ofthe areas that need more attention in future. In future, agriculture is expected to be dominated by precision and cloud data and supported by advanced infrastructure like smart tractors, unmanned aerial vehicles and wireless technology.

REFERENCES

Anonymous (2016) Proc. of conference on 'Innovations in Agricultural Mechanization-Development of Linkage Among R&D Institutes-Industry-Farmers' during July 7-8, 2016. http://farmech.gov.in/revised/Conference%20Doc.pdf

Kern, M.J. (2016) Digital agriculture: The future is now. AgriMech, 1(6), 16-19.

Mehta, C.R., Chandel, N.S., Senthilkumar, T. and Singh, K.K. (2014) Trends of Agricultural Mechanization in India. CSAM Policy Brief, June 2014.

Mehta, C.R., Chandel, N.S. and Senthilkumar, T. (2014) Status, challenges and strategies for farm mechanization in India. *Agricultural Mechanisation in Asia, America and Latin America (AMA)* 45(4), 43-50.

Pandey, M.M. (2009) Country Report India -Indian Agriculture an Introduction. Central InstituteofAgricultural Engineering Bhopal, India. Presented in Fourth Session of the Technical Committee of APCAEM 10-12 February 2009, Chiang Rai, Thailand 8.

Singh, G. (2006) Estimation of a mechanisation index andits impact on production and economic factors-a case studyin India. *Biosystems Engineering* 93(1), 99-106.

Singh, G. and Chandra, H. (2002) Production and economic factors growth in Indian Agriculture. Central Institute of Agricultural Engineering. Tech. Bull. No. CIAE/200/91.

Singh, R.S., Singh, S. and Singh, S.P. (2015) Farm Power and Machinery Availability on Indian Farms. *Agricultural Engineering Today* 39(1), 45-56.

Singh, S. (2007) Farm machinery - Principles and applications. Directorate of Information and Publications on Agriculture, Indian Council of Agricultural Research, New Delhi.

Singh, S.P., Solanki, R.C., Singh, M.K. and Singh, K. (2016) Development of tractor operated bund former-cum-packer for increasing resource productivity. *Indian Journal of Agricultural Sciences* 86(9), 1121-6

Singh, S.P., Singh, M.K. and Solanki, R.C. (2016) Design and development of four wheel weeder for wide-row crops. *Indian Journal of Agricultural Sciences* 86(1), 42–9.